GLADYS PROTHEROE - FOOTBALL GENIUS
by SIMON CHEETHAM

Juma

First published in 1994 by
Juma
Trafalgar Works
44 Wellington Street
Sheffield S1 4HD
Tel. 0114 272 0915
Fax. 0114 278 6550

ISBN 1 872204 10 4

Wolverhampton Wanderers FC
(1986) Limited

Molineux Stadium, Waterloo Road,
Wolverhampton WV1 4QR
Telephone: (0902) 655000
Ticket Office: (0902) 653653
Facsimile: (0902) 687006

Our ref : GT \ DMW

16 September 1994

Gladys Protheroe

Dear Gladys

What with Botham, Venables and Clough bringing out autobiographies this month, it really will make a pleasant change to read something worth while when your book makes the shops in October.

I do of course look forward to receiving a copy, which I hope will be of no cost to me. I am now a grandfather, and I am finding that having a grandchild is much more expensive than having children of your own.

It really was nice to hear from you again Glad (I hope the informality does not offend you) and perhaps this letter could be used as a foreword to your book because it obviously shows what an intimate relationship we have had over so many years.

I am not into handshakes any more – I've lost faith in them.

Best wishes

Yours sincerely

GRAHAM TAYLOR
MANAGER

President: Sir Jack Hayward OBE **Chairman:** Jonathan Hayward,
Directors: Jack Harris, Billy Wright CBE, John Harris, Nic Stones, Keith Pearson ACIS,
Company Secretary: Keith Pearson ACIS **Team Manager:** Graham Taylor
Director of Marketing & Public Affairs: David Clayton **Commercial Manager:** Gary Leaver

VAT Reg. No. 431 4856 56
Company Registered Number: 1989823 England

" We're Gladys' Boys "

We're Gladys' Boys, Strike Up The Band,
We're Gladys' Boys,
We're The Best In The Land.

From Coast To Coast, They Know Our Name,
We're The Champions Of This Great Old Game.
Three Cheers For Gladys Protheroe,
We'll Follow Her Wherever She Goes,
Hip, Hip For Good Old Glad,
So Play Up Lads For Good Old Glad.

Anon.

CHAPTER ONE 'JUST A GIRL'.

When, on January 16th. 1907, Jenny Simpson gave birth to a tiny baby girl, who could have guessed the influence that infant would have on the greatest game on Earth, The Beautiful Game? The bonny cherub was christened Gladys by her mother and her father, Alf 'Stubby' Simpson, a hard-working, honest professional footballer who had loyally served Burslem Port Vale and Leicester Fosse before ending his playing days as a tough tackling full back at Vicarage Road, Watford.

Alf Simpson never achieved great success in his playing career, although he was respected and trusted by his fellow professionals, and his robust, hard but fair style won him many plaudits from the terraces. Simpson played in the days when the clubs treated their players poorly, paying them a pittance, while the grounds and stadia were overflowing with spectators. But although Simpson was never a wealthy man, he always made certain his wife and new family were provided for. Like many fellow players, Simpson's career was interrupted by the Great War, and after returning to these shores having fought for King and Country in a conflict where he had lost many team mates, Alf tried to pick up the threads.

The years in the trenches had taken their toll, and it was obvious to everyone at Vicarage Road that Simpson had lost a yard or two, and would not be able to hold his own in the cut and thrust of The Football League. As it happened, Watford's full time groundsman had been mysteriously involved with some kind of Prohibition incident while visiting friends in Chicago, so when Watford manager Harold Bell offered Alf the opportunity to take over the responsibilities of the Vicarage Road pitch, Alf jumped at the chance to stay in the game in some capacity.

Simpson was given a cosy club house close to Vicarage Road, a hut full of garden tools, a wage of £6.10.6 per week (only a slight drop from his players salary) and a budget of £50 per year for seed and other essentials, and was more or less left to get on with tending the pitch.

So Gladys' formative years were spent in a football environment. She often accompanied her father as he repaired divots, painted white lines and carried out general maintenance duties, and the bonny child soon became well known to the players and officials of Watford Football Club, even appearing as club mascot in the team photographs for two seasons in the early 1920s.

As Gladys grew up she attended St. Mathilda's Convent, then Watford Girls High School, excelling in English and sport. Her prowess on the football field had been noticed at a very young age, and before her tenth birthday Gladys was drafted into the Hertfordshire Ladies team. Due to injuries and the Great War, Gladys was given her opportunity at right half, and played a major role in the Herts Ladies reaching the semi-finals of the wartime Ladies F.A. Cup. Their Cup-run ended with a 3-1 defeat by Middlesex at Stamford Bridge before an excited crowd of over 75,000. Gladys was the baby of the team, playing against women three and four times her age, but she won respect and praise from all quarters with her deft tackling and intelligent passing. *The Watford Observer* reported that " The Herts Ladies bowed out of the Cup, just one game from the final, but there is plenty to look forward to.Young Simpson played her little heart out - remember the name, she's one for the future".

By the end of the Great War, Gladys was a regular in the Herts Ladies team and her performances had caught the eye of England manager Lady Dorothy Palmer - Gray. In May 1918 Gladys was called up for an end of season get together of the national squad that was held at Crystal Palace. Gladys won the first of her 64 England 'Bonnets', as they were then called, in a friendly against Scotland played at Brentford's ground, Griffin Park, a game that ended in a 2-2 draw. Her mother, Jenny Simpson was obviously delighted with Gladys' progress in football, but was concerned that her daughter's love of the game would hinder her studies. With Alf away fighting for his country, Jenny was worried that perhaps Gladys would neglect her schoolwork through devoting all of her time to the game. But, although Gladys did skip a number of lessons to attend training sessions, she was blessed with a natural common-sense that has served her well right up to the present day. Her grasp of languages, mathematics and science were well above average, and Gladys eventually left school in 1920 with a completed education.

When Alf Simpson returned home from the campaign in Flanders to begin his new career as groundsman, he was amazed to see that his daughter Gladys had blossomed from a small, innocent girl into a wily, gifted wing-half. Alf had been caught in a mustard gas attack while in the trenches, and his health deteriorated rapidly in the post-war years. Eventually it became obvious that many of the physical duties involved with being a groundsman were too much for him to cope with. The answer to the Simpson family problem was simple; with Harold Bell's blessing, Gladys joined her father on the staff at Vicarage Road as Assistant Groundsman. The father and daughter team were featured in the October 1922 edition of the magazine *National Turf & Grass*. The article told of Gladys' enthusiasm, and of how she sometimes joined in training sessions with the professional players. The black and white photograph shows Alf and his daughter sitting together on the club's ride-on lawnmower, the caption reading 'Alf and Gladys Simpson - keeping Vicarage Road in splendid condition'. As the years went by, Alf handed more and more responsibility over to his daughter, and by the late 1920's she was dealing with the complete running of the pitch and ground maintenance as well as captaining Herts Ladies and having won over 25 England Bonnets.

In June 1931 Watford signed a will o' the wisp winger from Charlton Athletic. The player's name was Ernest Protheroe, and his speed and craft at The Valley had earned him the nickname of 'The Whippet'. Protheroe was signed for £500, a tidy amount for Watford in those days, and his arrival at the club caused quite a stir. *The Watford Observer* ran the headline " The Brewers Sign Nippy Protheroe" on the sports page, adding that the new signing had not been able to gain a regular first team place at Charlton, but it was hoped that he would be able to contribute to Watford's future success. During the Summer of 1931 Gladys was involved in the Ladies European Championships in Basle, where she helped England to the Bronze medal. The semi-final was a spiteful, niggly affair against Italy, the holders, and England went down 1-0.

Seven players were booked, including Gladys for kicking the ball away at a free kick, and the popular press dubbed the game The Battle of Basle. The Italians went on to beat Spain 3-1 in the final to retain the trophy. On a personal basis it was a successful tournament for Gladys. She was the only England player named in the Swiss Press 'Team of The Tournament', and there were rumours that FC Bruges were ready to put a bid in for Gladys, making her the first English professional lady player.

On the first day of training for the 1931/32 season Gladys was hard at work re-seeding the Rookery End goalmouth, and when the Watford squad arrived for the team photograph she and her father helped the photographer erect his tripod. The players looked very smart in their crisply starched shirts, their heavily greased hair slicked down onto their heads. As the players jockeyed for position on the wooden benches, Gladys noticed the shy new signing sitting at the end of the front row. As their gaze met, Gladys noticed how very blue Ernest's eyes were, and somewhere deep inside her, she felt her heart skip a beat.

Ernest Protheroe was a great success at Vicarage Road. The crowd took to his surging runs and inch perfect crosses, and by Christmas he had inspired Watford to one of their best starts to a season for many years. Although the skilful winger and the hardworking groundswoman had only exchanged the occasional 'Good day' both sensed a mutual attraction, and at the club's Christmas party Ernest plucked up the courage to ask Gladys to dance. Within moments the two young people were chatting away like old friends. Ernest walked Gladys home, and as he saw her to her gate he asked whether she would like to accompany him on a country walk the following Sunday afternoon. Gladys agreed. Soon they began to step out on a regular basis. Everything seemed to be going splendidly for the young couple. Ernest was the club's leading goalscorer; his two goals against Southend United on New Year's Day had put Watford in touch with the leaders and in with a great chance of promotion to Division Two. Gladys' playing career with Watford Ladies was going equally well. Watford 'Gals' as they were known, had reached the semifinals of the Ladies F.A. Cup, and were tipped by many experts to go all the way.

By now Ernest and Gladys' romance was common knowledge and there were constant references to the 'Sporting couple' in the local press. The two young lovers had talked of their future together, the possibility of becoming engaged, perhaps buying a small house in nearby Croxley Green and maybe even starting a family. But their plans of domestic stability were thrown into confusion when, in April 1932, Italian giants Verona contacted Watford to say they were prepared to pay 28 million Lira (£14,000, then a record transfer fee) for Watford's star winger. Apparently, Protheroe's skill had alerted the Italian scouts, and they had secretly attended the Watford v. Brighton game in which Ernest scored twice and made the other goal as the home side romped to a 3-0 win.

Watford were staggered by the offer. The club had teetered on the brink of bankruptcy for years, but suddenly here was the chance to pay off all their debts and still have a small fortune to invest in new talent.

The Watford board met on 24th April 1932 and unanimously decided to accept Verona's offer. In those days, before freedom of contract, the management and players had little or no influence in such matters, so when Ernest arrived for training the next morning there was a note pinned to his peg instructing him to go directly to the manager's office. Fearing he was in for a dressing down, Ernest tapped nervously on the door before being invited in to the room full of cigar smoking directors drinking large brandy and sodas. The transfer bid was explained to Ernest, and he was introduced to the Verona chairman, Senor Picca, a neatly dressed man in a huge fur coat.

Ernest was offered a signing-on fee of £2,500 and a weekly wage of over £60, nearly five times the amount he was earning at Vicarage Road. Ernest asked for an hour to think over the offer, which Senor Picca reluctantly agreed to.

On leaving the office Ernest ran down to the pitch where Gladys was re-painting the centre circle. He explained the situation to his love, then told her he was confused and worried. If he turned down this opportunity would he ever get such a chance again? Yet, if he accepted - what would become of their relationship? Gladys told him it was a decision that only he could make. Ernest fell silent for a moment, then cleared his throat and dropped down onto one knee. He asked Gladys to be his wife. It did not take Gladys more than a split second to agree to Ernest's proposal. There in the centre-circle they planned their future. Ernest would sign for Verona, fly out to Italy with Senor Picca and find an apartment where the newlyweds could set up home. Then, after Gladys had served her notice at Vicarage Road and attended to all the loose ends, she would fly out to join Ernest. But first, they would be married.

The wedding of Ernest Protheroe and pretty Gladys Simpson was the talk of the football world. Protheroe's massive transfer fee had stunned the Watford supporters, but they realised that a young ambitious sportsman like Ernest had to accept the challenge that awaited him in Italy. Senor Picca was delighted to get his man, and Ernest put pen to paper in front of a host of pressmen from both English and Italian newspapers.

Verona agreed to wait for a fortnight so Ernest and Gladys could be married in Watford, and Ernest's debut was arranged for Verona's last home game of the season against A.C. Milan. On Saturday morning, 16th April 1932, Ernest made Gladys his wife at the cramped church in Croxley Green. The service was attended by the complete Watford squad, as well as their opponents that afternoon, Leyton Orient. The wedding photographs show that Gladys wore a long white silk dress, with a veil covering her pretty face. Embroidered into the veil were the initials 'W.F.C.', while Ernest looked immaculate in a dark suit with a red rose buttonhole.

The Watford Observer carried a special commemorative brochure with their next edition listing all the guests, told of the moving speeches made by Ernest's fellow players and of how proud Gladys' parents were of their beautiful daughter. Before the kick-off of the afternoon's match, Ernest (now of course officially a Verona player, and therefore unable to play for Watford) and his new bride walked around the touchline to thank the supporters for a lovely carriage clock that they had chipped in for. Watford had to win by three clear goals if they were to make it into a promotion spot, but without Protheroe's guile on the wing they were unable to break down the Leyton defence, and the game ended 0-0. The result meant that it would be Fulham who were promoted, and Watford would remain in the Third Division (South) for another year at least. The newlyweds watched the game, then sneaked away just before the final whistle to a secret destination for their wedding night.

As time was so tight, Gladys and Ernest had decided to have a few days in Brighton, then enjoy a proper honeymoon in Italy later in the summer. The four days went by so quickly, and soon it was time for Ernest to fly from Croydon Airport out to his new club. The two young lovers stood and embraced on the tarmac until the captain could wait no longer. Then with tears in his eyes, the skilful little winger walked up the steps to the aeroplane, turned, waved to his wife, and flew out into the unknown. Gladys watched as the plane soared into the spring sky, and dreamed of the day when they would be together again.

Ernest was an instant hit in Verona. The crowd for his debut was over 80,000, and he capped a fine performance by scoring the winner as his new club beat A.C. Milan 2-1. The fanatical Italian press dubbed him 'Il Protho' and Gladys proudly read about his searing pace and the rasping volley that had won him the respect of the knowledgeable fans. Verona had installed a telephone in Ernest's apartment so he could be in constant touch with his new wife, and they would chat for hours every evening, telling each other the events of their day. Gladys was to leave Watford on 5th May, then fly out the next day to join Ernest. She was full of questions: how hot was it? Were the other players friendly? Did Verona play with a flat back four? Was the food tasty? Had he found an apartment for them?

One of Ernest's fears had been that his huge transfer fee may have made some of the other players jealous, but he really needn't have worried. Apart from three lads who were Verona born and bred, Senor Picca had spent a vast fortune, even by Italian standards, to assemble a top quality squad. There was Corti who had cost £65,000 from Roma, Bertolucci a £50,000 signing from Juventus and Rava the pin-up boy of Italian football who had cost a staggering £85,000 from Internazionale.

In fact, Ernest's fee of £14,000 was looked on as a minor transfer, so his ability, so obviously proved on his debut, made him a real bargain.

Verona's final game of the Italian League season was an away fixture at Napoli. Both sides were in mid-table, and had been involved in disappointing campaigns, although Verona were on a run of eight games without defeat, and many pundits were tipping Ernest's new club for success the following season. The match was played in a swirling storm with rain making the game a lottery. The final score was 0-0 with neither team really playing well. As Ernest sat in the dressing room pulling off his saturated kit, Guisseppe Rava asked him in pidgin English whether or not he would like to come to an after match party. Ernest, keen on making new friends, agreed and asked his teammate how they would get there. Rava told him that they would go in his new Alfa Romeo Sports Car. Guisseppe had only just taken delivery of the shiny red machine, and was obviously keen to show the vehicle off to his friends. The team were to stay in Naples overnight then fly back North to Verona the next morning, so the players were given permission to take in the sights and enjoy themselves.

Ernest, dressed in his new club blazer and a pair of pale grey Italian lightweight trousers, looked every inch the successful young Englishman abroad. Rava turned the radio up so the jazz station they had found on the dial filled the car, and the two colleagues set off for the party at breakneck speed.

The soiree was being held at a select restaurant overlooking the Bay of Naples, and was being hosted by Napoli's number one diva, Gina Vito. By ten o'clock Gina had noticed that her friend Guisseppe Rava had still not arrived, but having known the fun loving footballer for many years, she assumed he had stopped off at a nightclub before going on to her party.

But Gina was wrong. At ten o'clock that night Guisseppe Rava was fighting for his life in ward three of Napoli Hospital. The torrential rain had made the roads as slippery as glass, and when Rava attempted to take a hairpin bend at around 80mph he lost control of the Alpha Romeo, and the car and its passengers had plummeted down into a ravine.

The emergency services were called by another motorist who had witnessed the disaster, and the police were on the scene within five minutes. Two medics dragged Rava from the wreckage, immediately recognising him as Verona's star player. A policeman pulled Rava's passenger from the torn metal, and knew instantly that the young man was dead. The policeman was not a football supporter, and therefore not aware of the victim's identity. The ambulance sped to the hospital, weaving through traffic, blaring its horn and flashing its lights. The orderlies were ready to rush Rava to the operating theatre where an emergency operation on his multiple injuries sought to keep him alive. However, it was not to be. The endeavours of the surgeon were in vain, and by midnight two of Verona's young stars were dead.

The Italian media machine quickly picked up the story, and within an hour the tale of the tragedy was broadcast throughout the country.

Meanwhile, back in Watford, Gladys had spent the night packing her suitcases and collecting various bits and pieces that she thought would make their new apartment in Verona feel more like home. She was expecting a telephone call from Ernest as he had promised to let her know the Napoli result, but by ten she had still not heard. Eventually just before one a.m. the 'phone did ring, but the voice at the other end was not Ernest's chirpy chatter, it was the solemn, rich baritone of Senor Picca. Gladys does not remember exactly what the Verona chairman told her. All she remembers is suddenly being cold, icy cold.

Just how Gladys got through those next few days even she doesn't know. In a few seconds a telephone call from a man she had only met twice had turned her world upside down. The Italians, a melodramatic race at the best of times, went overboard about the tragedy. In a matter of days there was talk of an opera being written about the car crash, with the role of Gladys being played, ironically, by Gina Vito. The press had published wedding photographs of the Protheroes with thick black ribbons pinned to them, and an enterprising ice-cream company had introduced 'Il Protho Morto', a strawberry and vanilla concoction with a small broken heart made from chocolate.

Gladys' father made the necessary arrangements for Ernest's body to be flown back to England, and the funeral took place at the very same church where the wedding had been held just three weeks before.

The generosity and kindness of the Verona supporters touched

11

Gladys deeply, and some of the wealthier fans even travelled from Italy to attend the service. Despite having played only twice for his new club there was genuine grief in Verona, where shops closed, the railways stopped and the factories had a minute's silence on the day of Ernest's funeral. Senor Picca told Gladys that she would never have to want for anything. Verona would pay her a substantial widow's pension, and plans for a testimonial game were already in hand. Guiseppe Rava had not been married, and although he had been a hero at the club for a number of seasons, strangely it was the plight of Gladys, the young widow, that touched the hearts of the Italians.

In August 1932 Verona played the Italian national team in the Protheroe/Rava Testimonial game in front of a crowd of nearly 75,000 spectators, and after the 2-2 draw, Gladys unveiled a bust of Ernest that still stands at the gates of Verona's stadium today. Mussolini's Black Shirts did attempt to tear the monument down at the outbreak of the Second World War, but the Verona supporters fought the Fascists off, and the bust has welcomed supporters to the magnificent ground ever since. Whilst in Verona, Gladys was touched by the kindness of the Italian people. She sat alone in Ernest's apartment and tried to imagine his hopes and dreams as she tidied up his personal effects. Then it was time to return to Croxley Green and try to pick up the threads of her life. She embraced Senor Picca at Verona Airport, thanked him for his understanding, and promised to keep in touch. As her plane flew up and away from Italy tears ran down her cheeks as she felt the last link with Ernest finally break.

But before Gladys could get back on the rails, there was one more tragedy. On Christmas Day 1932 her father, Alf, choked on a turkey bone and dropped stone dead on the kitchen floor. There was talk of some kind of curse on the House of Simpson, but this was dismissed by officials at Watford F.C. as utter nonsense.

Another wrench came when Gladys' mother Jenny told her that she had decided to return to her native Burslem to be with her ailing mother, and suddenly Gladys was left a woman alone. With the money from the Verona testimonial game Gladys was able to buy a modest semi-detached house in Croxley Green, where more than sixty years later she still lives. Watford F.C. had stood by Gladys throughout the traumas of the past year, and they told her that she was always welcome to return to Vicarage Road as head groundsman. So, as the clouds of war began to assemble over Europe, Gladys attempted to put her life back together again.

The Vicarage Road playing surface was reputed to be one of the best in the Third Division (South) and Gladys was often complimented on her work. She would spend most of her days tending the pitch, then train with the Watford Ladies in her spare time. She found that when she was alone and unoccupied her mind would drift, her eyes would fill with tears at thoughts of Ernest and then her father. She decided she must keep busy, and threw herself into the one thing that she knew would never leave her, football.

Watford Ladies had established themselves as one of the premier teams in the country. They gained a reputation for attacking, entertaining play, and Gladys was named captain for the 1936/37 season. Her performances won her many admirers, and Gladys became the first and only lady footballer to be included in Players Cigarette Cards when they released their 1938 collection. The picture shows Gladys in her England kit, while the pen-picture on the back of the card reads: Gladys Protheroe, Watford Ladies, Herts Ladies, England International. Intelligent wing-half, strong in the tackle. Despite standing just an inch over 5 ft. exudes authority on the pitch. Widow of Ernest 'The Whippet', Gladys is currently England's finest lady footballer. 42 England Bonnets.

In September 1939 football as we know it came to an abrupt halt as Hitler and his henchmen dragged all of Europe into war. Gladys was unsure in which direction to turn. Many of the Watford players had signed up immediately, while most of the Ladies team became land girls. A telephone call from England Ladies' manager Lady Dorothy Palmer-Gray cured Gladys' indecision. Lady Dot, as she liked to be called, told Gladys that the War Office had decided that to boost morale amongst the troops there should be a Ladies War Time XI to play the other friendly nations. There had been discussions at the highest level to find the woman to lead the team, and the one name that kept cropping up was Protheroe.

The players were to be selected from the top ladies teams in the country, and the first training session was to take place at RAF Nettledon in North Yorkshire - would Gladys take the job?

Gladys was given the title of Chief Coach, responsible for team selection and tactics, while Lady Dot would deal with the official paperwork and fixture arrangements. The ladies were not officially part of the armed forces, but were expected to wear tracksuits at all times, salute senior officers and keep quiet about the proposed games in Europe. Lady Dot had put together a squad of eighteen of the brightest lady footballers in the land. There were the Armitage sisters from Sheffield, Susan and Emily, the agile goalkeeper Betty Jackson from Hull, the prolific goalscorer Mary Kettledon from Blackpool and the notorious Peg 'Break Your Leg' Parker who played her football for Plymouth, and had been sent off eight times in a stormy and sometimes violent career. Gladys spent her time on the training pitch, and she found the girls to be good humoured sensible lasses who loved football and were keen to help the war effort.

Their first game was against the Free French at Highbury. Due to a couple of injuries Gladys played out of position at left back and her team won convincingly 4-1 in front of a crowd of 55,000 servicemen. The newsreels were there to record the game, and after the final whistle Gladys was interviewed by the man from Pathe. The film has been kept, and when seen to-day Gladys seems articulate, witty and in complete control of the situation. She tells the reporter that hopefully her girls will keep the football fans happy with some exciting play, and when asked if she would like to have a crack at a team of Hun women she replied "rather!"

The Allies had arranged for a World Cup of sorts to be held, and England were drawn to play Belgium in neutral Switzerland. Again, the interest from the Forces and the press was incredible. The game was played at the home of FC Basle, where Gladys had taken part in that spiteful game against the Italian women a number of years before. The crowd for the match was estimated to be 40,000 although many experts feel that the real total was well over 60,000. The Belgians played neat, attractive football and stunned Gladys' girls by scoring twice in the opening ten minutes. But slowly, England's strength and tactical awareness shone through and they went on to win 5-3.

There then followed a bitter, niggly game against Scotland in Glasgow which ended goalless, with Peg Parker and the Scots' flame haired winger Mary O'Rourke being sent off for fighting in injury time.

England then crushed the Welsh 8-0 in Swansea with Gladys scoring twice. The War Office were delighted that their footballing ladies had given such a boost to the troops' morale. Each day the Post Office was delivering sacks of mail from the forces in France, North Africa and Malaya all demanding pin-ups of their favourite players and wanting news and results of the latest games.

Scotland had gone down 3-1 to the Dutch in another brutal game in Glasgow, so Gladys prepared her team for the Final against Holland at Highbury. Tickets for the game were like gold-dust, and the gates had to be closed two hours the kick-off. The Dutch had beaten Poland, Northern Ireland and Sweden before disposing of Scotland. Gladys had seen the newsreels of the games and been very impressed. Their outstanding player was their left half and captain Nelly Cruyff, who was perhaps the most talented lady footballer of her generation. Gladys decided that she would mark Nelly herself in the Final, and although Cruyff did manage a goal, Gladys' woman to woman marking job was a major factor in England winning the game 3-1 to lift the trophy. Nelly gave birth to a son who she christened Johann, who of course, went on to become a major star of the 1970s and to manage Barcelona and Ajax. The newsreel of that England victory was shown throughout the World, and many historians believe that battling performance inspired the British troops, and was a major factor in Hitler losing the upper hand in the conflict.

After the success of the Ladies' team, Gladys was contacted by The

War Office and asked to travel to a secret bunker in leafy Buckinghamshire. There she met with Colonel E.J. Marchmont who offered her the chance to manage the men's Combined Services XI. Most of the star names of the 1930s had been called up, and talents such as Raich Carter, Tom Finney, Tommy Lawton and Wilf Mannion were available for the team.

Colonel Marchmont told Gladys that he was more of a rugby man, but he understood the appeal of football to the average Tommy in the trenches. He had been given authority to have any player Gladys wanted to be made available - was she interested? She was a little concerned as to how the players would take to a woman running the show, but apart from a couple of rather narrow-minded players who she immediately dropped from the squad, she found the lads as good as gold.

The players she had available were the cream of the Football League. They were thoroughly professional, polite and perfect gentlemen. Once again the crowds arrived in their thousands to watch Gladys' team play, and for the first time a song that has followed her around the World rang out from the packed terraces. No-one is certain where the song was first sung, or who wrote it, but it first came to the notice of the national press when Gladys' Combined Services Team played Aldershot at Crystal Palace in 1942.

The khaki clad boys behind one of the goals suddenly burst into "We're Gladys' Boys" after Tommy Lawton bulleted a header into the top left hand corner of the net to give Gladys' team another emphatic victory. Within moments the whole crowd had picked up the song, and they carried on until long after the final whistle.

To this day Gladys maintains that her Wartime team was the best that she has been involved with. They were skilful athletes, fair and sporting - playing the game they adored for the sheer love of it. One of the highlights of Gladys' playing career were the six appearances she made for that Combined Services team, including her appearance in the match against the Russians in Kiev in 1944 when she scored in her team's 2-0 win.

When the War eventually ended, Gladys returned to Croxley Green with a trunk full of souvenirs and a head full of memories. The newsreels had catapulted her to stardom, and on her first early morning jog around her village she was amazed at the kind remarks made by passers-by as they thanked her for her efforts during the dark days of War.

One of the first callers to her home on her return was Watford's newly appointed manager Jack Bray. Bray had been given the job at Vicarage Road and was desperately attempting to get a decent standard squad together for the new season, and he asked Gladys if she would consider accepting the post of player/ coach. She was delighted and set about trying to find the players to lift Watford up the League.

Gladys' first training session with the Watford squad was a gentle reintroduction to the rigours of professional football for all concerned. Fortunately, Jack Bray had inherited the nucleus of the pre-War Watford team. Goalkeeper Harry Robinson had been lost in the Japanese prison camps of Malaya while attacking full-back Stanley Gaunt had been shot down while piloting a Spitfire over the Channel. Apart from these two, all of Watford's squad that had been on duty for their last League game against Portsmouth nearly seven years before reported to Vicarage Road that morning. Gladys soon found that even if Hitler hadn't ended the players careers, then Old Father Time had.

The once fleet-footed skilful youngsters of '39 were now mostly war ravaged men in their late '20s and early '30s. Most had taken up smoking during their time in khaki, and the air was full of wheezing lungs as the squad ran a couple of laps of the pitch to limber up. Gladys organised a practice game that had to be abandoned at half time due to fatigue, and it was obvious that apart from perhaps two or three players, Watford would require a completely new squad if they were to hold their own. It was a difficult task for Gladys to pull the older players from the training session and quietly tell them that their professional playing days were over. For the most part, the players of yesteryear took the news well. They were brave, proud men who had served their country well, and had prepared themselves to hear that Hitler had robbed them of their careers.

In a matter of weeks, Jack Bray had been busy on the transfer market and Watford were able to take the field against Brentford with a new team, including, wearing the number three shirt, Gladys Protheroe. Gladys' debut in the Football League made her only the second woman to play at that level (Susan Armitage had already made four appearances for Sheffield United).

It was the beginning of a brief era when women played a part in English men's football. As clubs found it fashionable to sign players from South America in the late 1970s and early 1980s, in the first few years after the War many clubs had women players on their books, although the number who actually made more than a handful of League appearances were very few. Gladys actually went on to appear 28 times for Watford in the Football League, a record for a woman in the English game. Gladys' appearances were all in the Third Division (South), and at present only two ladies have gone on and played First Division football. Nancy Dixon played at right back for Fulham in the 1947/48 season, and Emily Cuthbert made one appearance for Aston Villa in the same campaign, but neither were retained by their respective clubs, and they eventually returned to the Ladies' game.

Whether women in the future will play a part in the Football League is hard to foretell. Perhaps the physical demands of modern day football have made it unlikely, but maybe a real talent will emerge from Ladies football and pure skill will win over strength and brawn - who knows?

Gladys and Jack Bray slowly began to assemble a half decent squad made up of enthusiastic, raw kids and a few hardened professionals Bray had managed to sign on free transfers. Gladys' coaching techniques were years ahead of their time, and in a few seasons Watford had gained a reputation for being one of the most attractive teams in the South of England. Her astute eye for talent had unearthed a number of fine players such as Ken Williams, John Usher and Hubert Surtees among others.

This crop of youngsters became known as "Protheroe's Pride". They were fit, good ball players and loyal to their mentor. At the end of the 1947/48 season, with more and more of her time being taken up with coaching and training the players, Gladys decided it was time to hang up her boots. A crowd of nearly 20,000 packed into Vicarage Road (then a club record) to see the most famous lady player in English football make her final League appearance against Gillingham. Gladys was carried on her team-mates' shoulders after a hard fought 1-1 draw, and the crowd sang "We're Gladys' Boys" to celebrate the end of a record breaking playing career.

When Jack Bray resigned at the end of the season, Gladys was put in charge of pre-season training until the Board appointed the ex-Arsenal and England star Eddie Hapgood as the club's new manager. Hapgood was at first unsure what to make of his lady coach, but was soon impressed by her knowledge of the game both in England and abroad.

CHAPTER TWO " THE CALL FROM LANCASTER GATE".

It was on Hapgood's recommendation that Gladys was secretly summoned to F.A. Headquarters in Lancaster Gate, West London in July 1950. The England team had just returned from Brazil with their tails between their legs after a horrific World Cup. The final straw was a disastrous 1-0 defeat by no-hopers USA in Belo Horizonte. England, the home of World football had now become the laughing stock, and the top brass at the F.A. had decided that a new broom was needed to launch England into a new, exciting era.

The football writers of the day had been calling for a supremo figure to lead English football out of the wilderness for some time, and at last it seemed as if the F.A. were ready to make such an appointment. Various names were mentioned on the back pages. Gladys' ex-colleague from the wartime Combined Services XI, Colonel Marchmont and Arsenal's no-nonsense manager George Allison were both tipped as possible candidates, but more and more often Gladys' name cropped up. On the morning of her meeting at the F.A. the Daily Sketch ran the headline "England Call For Gladys" across their sports page, with an 'exclusive' story telling the readers that it was possible the F.A. were set to shock the football world by appointing Watford's first team coach as England's new manager. That evening, on the steps of the F.A. headquarters Gladys stood in a royal blue tracksuit flanked by two stern officials as the President of the Football Association read the following statement to the assembled pressmen: " The F.A. takes great pleasure in announcing that Gladys Protheroe has hereby been appointed as England Football Manager. Mrs. Protheroe has signed a five year contract and will immediately be responsible for all playing and selection duties. God Save The King".

Watford reluctantly agreed to release Gladys from her contract at Vicarage Road, although the F.A. did have to hand over a cheque for £15,000 as compensation, a fortune by 1950 standards. There were tears in Gladys' eyes as she said an emotional farewell to the players and officials at Vicarage Road. As Gladys stepped into the taxi with her kitbag under her arm a few of the young apprentices burst into a spine-chilling accapella version of "We're Gladys' Boys", a performance that sent shivers down the spine of all who heard it. Gladys turned and waved as the cab set off for Lancaster Gate.

Gladys' first match in charge was to be the clash with Northern Ireland in Belfast. The new England manager made a number of changes from the team that had disappointed the nation in the World Cup in Brazil, and Gladys announced to the press that she was set to bring in more new players during forthcoming matches. The target was the next World Cup in Switzerland in four years time. Gladys' opening game ended in a 4-1 victory. She was pleased with the overall performance, but there was one player who played particularly well, Tottenham's sturdy full-back Alf Ramsey. Ramsey and Gladys seemed to hit it off immediately, and soon the rugged defender became Gladys' ears and eyes in the dressing room.

England's fortunes began to improve, and with Gladys' good relationship with the press, the England team gained a higher profile on the nation's sports pages. Gladys instigated a more open relationship with the media, often being interviewed on the radio and news-reels, this initiative creating more demand for International match tickets.

In the early 1950s by no means all of England's games were played at Wembley. Goodison Park, Villa Park, Maine Road and Roker Park were just some of the alternative venues selected by the F.A. One of Gladys' first moves was to convince the men at Lancaster Gate that Wembley Stadium should be the England team's permanent home.

Gladys became well known on the International circuit, and her tough talking style became much imitated by football managers all over the globe. England went on a run of just one defeat in twenty games, and that was a bitter affair against Uruguay in Montevideo, in which Gladys was spoken to by the Mexican referee after complaining bitterly when flying winger Tom Finney was brutally tackled from behind.

One game Gladys was looking forward to was the meeting with Hungary at Wembley. She flew to Budapest to watch the Magyars defeat Spain 3-0, and had returned highly impressed with the Hungarians free flowing style of play. The stocky forward, Puskas, had looked top class, and she warned the England players to expect a difficult game. On hearing that Gladys had described the Hungarians as 'Possibly the most powerful team in Europe' she was called before an F.A. Committee to explain her statement. The F.A. were not used to other countries being complimented on their styles of play, and she was told in no uncertain terms that as far as they were concerned English football was the best in the world, and a bunch of communists from a backwater like Hungary should not be compared to players from 'The Home of Football'. Gladys was fined £25.

So, on 25th November 1953 England met Hungary at Wembley, and ninety minutes after kicking off Gladys knew that the winds of change were blowing through the world game. Hungary left the famous old Stadium with a 6-3 victory, leaving Gladys' England team licking their wounds after a lesson in attacking football. Gladys had expected some party pieces from Puskas, Huidegute and their team-mates, but she has never seen such a display of total football from any team before or since. For the first time,

England had been defeated on home soil, but not only that, Hungary had clearly shown that the English way was not necessarily the best way.

After the game, long after the England players had left for their hotel and the supporters returned home to their firesides, Gladys walked out alone to the centre-circle and looked up to the dark sky. She stared up at the stars sparkling brightly in the cloudless heavens, and gently called to her Ernest for guidance. The press at the after-match meeting had been merciless in their criticism of England's performance, although Gladys had defended her players saying that they had simply been outclassed by a superb team. It was obvious that the next morning's papers would be reporting England's defeat in graphic detail, some even demanding a change of manager. As she stood alone on the muddied centre-spot, Gladys heard a slight noise behind her. She spun around and there standing with her in the half light was her tormentor, Puskas.

The tubby Hungarian bowed his head and held out his hand to shake Gladys'. Then in broken English he told Gladys how he and all the Hungarian players admired and respected her. He went on to tell her that back home in Budapest all sportsmen recognised 'Proth-Proth', as they called her, as a leading figure in world football. Puskas told her to stick to her guns and to be confident of her God given talent. The England team could be re-built, and she was the woman to do it. With that, he stepped forward, embraced Gladys tightly, kissed her on both cheeks then turned and went back to his team-mates. Left alone once more Gladys looked to the skies again and thanked Ernest for his help. She had found new strength, and she would continue her work.

As Gladys feared, the daily newspapers reported on the defeat in depth. *"Glad's Lads Humbled"* screamed the *Daily Mirror*, *"Puskas Punishes Protheroe"* , read the back page of *The Express*, while *The Telegraph* told its readers that *"England Prove Protheroe Wrong"*. While the majority of the match reports fairly explained that the Magyars were perhaps the best team in the World, and England had met them at their peak, there were a couple of cheap shots at Gladys. *The Daily Sketch* demanded a change of manager, and even printed the address of F.A. Headquarters inviting its readers to write in and call for Gladys to be sacked. Even *Women's Realm* got in on the act, and in their 2nd December 1953 edition, editor Mary Hinton told Gladys to 'get back into the kitchen'. The piece went on to say that the women of England did not want one of their own being involved in such a boorish, rough sport as football. If Gladys really wanted to continue in competitive sport, why on earth didn't she take up knock-out cookery?

Gladys got back to the training ground with her players just as soon as possible. She felt it was vital to get another game under their belts and hopefully erase the memory of such a bitter defeat. England's next game was against Scotland in Glasgow, and the Scots' manager, Jack McPherson had already lit the fuse for the encounter by telling journalists that no team of his would lose to 'A bunch of Sassenach jessies managed by a wee old girlie'. The annual game with Scotland was always a volatile fixture, but the 1953 game had all the hallmarks of a bloodbath.

Gladys had taken her time after the Hungarian game, contemplating the changes in the team she felt must be made. It was a difficult decision, but she did feel it was perhaps time her favourite player, Ramsey was left out. After a rigorous training session Gladys called the full-back to one side, and told him of her decision. Alf was no fool, and was well aware that he had lost a yard or two. Time had caught up with him, wingers were now able to get to the by-line and get that cross in, whereas a season or two earlier he would have put the flyer into the advertising hoardings. Gladys thanked him for his loyal service, and told him that she would always remember his tenacious performances for his country. Alf looked Gladys straight in the eyes, and told her that as far as he was concerned she was the finest manager he had ever played under, and he would never forget her kindness and decency, but before he left the international scene he must warn her of what he had heard. Alf told Gladys to be careful. There were rumours that some powerful men at Lancaster Gate were not happy that a woman should be in charge of the national team. There was talk of a young turk named Walter Winterbottom being groomed as her successor, and that all the mandarins were waiting for was an opportunity to ditch Gladys. All Ramsey added was to beware of a man in a pair of brown brogues.

In fact, Gladys was to stay in charge of the England team for just three more months. Ramsey had been correct, her abrasive style - leading from the front and being her own woman - had ruffled many feathers at the F.A. The faceless men in grey suits who had never liked the idea of a woman running the show had seen the opportunity of ridding themselves of this turbulent woman. Seeds of doubt were being sown after the defeat by Hungary, and a supposedly 'secret' document detailing Gladys' sacking was leaked to *The Times*. The paper revealed the F.A. had already approached Walter Winterbottom, and that it was almost certain the new man would lead England into the Swiss World Cup. The F.A. refused to comment on such speculation.

Amid all this paper talk Gladys led her England team into the lion's den to play Scotland at Hampden Park in front of over 120,000 baying Scotsmen. Gladys had made six changes from the team torn apart by Hungary. Not only was Ramsey missing, Eckersley, Johnston, Mortensen and Sewell were all dropped, never to wear the famous white shirt of England again.

The Scottish press had been full of McPherson's descriptions of how his team were going to score a hatful against the English, and there was a famous photograph of the Scots manager holding up a pair of women's bloomers and laughing. The caption read 'Jack's lads set to beat the pants off the Jessie Sassays'.

The atmosphere inside Hampden was electric, and when Gladys took her players out onto the pitch for a light training session, the terraces - packed with fans despite it being over two hours until the kick-off - erupted into a bitter barrage of hate against the English. Gladys and her squad were pelted with coins and bottles; even some bras filled with turnips were thrown onto the pitch. The Scots made it crystal clear that they felt football was a man's game, and that women should not be involved.

Fortunately, the English players took the barracking well despite goalkeeper Gil Merrick being hit full in the face with a sock full of bottle tops as he attempted to retrieve a ball from a mob behind his goal. Gladys gave one of her liveliest team talks in the dressing room, telling her men not to get rattled by the fans, but to play their own game. She was certain that England possessed technically better players, and if they could survive the first twenty minutes, they would go on and win the game. As Gladys expected, the Scots threw everything at Merrick and his defenders straight from the kick-off. The Hampden roar, supposedly worth a goal start to the Scots, was deafening. Gladys had expected such a din, and managed to acquire a pair of bright yellow ear muffs that enabled her to keep her head clear and concentrate on the game.

In accordance with her plan, the English got more and more into the game, and at half-time were leading one goal to nil through a fine strike by Ronnie Allen. Gladys could hear her opposite number, McPherson, ranting at his players through the dressing-room walls, and she was convinced that if England kept their heads, they would get the right result.

There was an unseemly incident as the two teams took to the pitch for the second half, which resulted in a couple of punches being thrown in the tunnel. McPherson had shouted to Tom Finney that he was a disgrace to menfolk all over the world by playing for a woman, and the normally placid Preston winger reacted. Fortunately, the fighting was over in a few seconds, but England captain Billy Wright had to have treatment to a badly bitten ear which delayed the kick-off for five minutes. The French referee, Monsieur Papon, spoke to both managers and made them promise that no more such behaviour would take place.

England went further ahead through Broadis, then put the game out of Scotland's reach with a bullet header from Mullen. The Scots managed to pull two late goals back, but England immediately scored again through Nicholls to make the game safe. Gladys was delighted with the performance, and she patted all her players as they left the pitch, still having to duck various objects thrown by the furious crowd.

After the match, the Scots manager burst into the press-conference smelling strongly of whisky and informed the press that England had been lucky, and as far as he was concerned, women had no place in football. He went on to call Winston Churchill 'A wee git', Tom Finney and Billy Wright 'A pair of poofdahs' and Gladys Protheroe 'A silly wee lesbo'.

Gladys, slowly sipping a glass of water did not rise to the bait, but simply told the pressmen that the Scots obviously held their drink as well as they played football. This caused immense laughter in the pressroom, and on that she thanked the journalists for their time, and left to join her players. England's next two games were in Belgrade against Yugoslavia, and the return match with Hungary in Budapest. Gladys attempted to have a 'clear the air' meeting with the F.A. to try and have her plans for the World Cup campaign accepted. The press continued to speculate on whether on not Gladys would be in charge for the World Cup, but when F.A. Chairman Harold Hill announced on BBC Radio that Gladys had the full support of the Committee, that seemed to be the end of the talk of Winterbottom taking over.

The game against the Yugoslavs was looked on as a formality, just a glorified training session for the Hungarian game. But it didn't work out that way with England going down 1-0. Suddenly, the game against Hungary took on a vital significance. Before the match in the Nep Stadium, Gladys was summoned to a meeting with F.A. Secretary Alexander Hunter. She was told in no uncertain terms that a repeat of the Wembley debacle would simply not be tolerated. Apparently at a dinner party for the F.A. the previous evening, Harold Hill had been insulted by a drunken Hungarian businessman who had told him that the Magyars would 'kick the English ladies all over the Nep'. Gladys was told that this sort of lampooning must stop, and soon. As she was being given the warning, she noticed that Hunter wore a pair of brown brogues.

If Puskas and his team had been in superb form at Wembley, then that night in Budapest they simply surpassed themselves. England were left chasing shadows as the men in the cherry red shirts ran riot. The final score was Hungary 7, England 1 - but many experts felt that the Hungarians were a trifle unlucky not to make double figures. The infuriating thing for Gladys was that she felt her team had played to their limits.

It was obvious to her that the training manuals had to be torn up, and the whole way English football operated, from the schools right up to the national team, had to be immediately re-assessed. As Gladys sat with her tortured players in the dressing room, she hoped that perhaps the real football experts, both in the media and at the F.A. would appreciate just how talented the Hungarians were, and realise that the English team were in a period of transition. But her hopes were dashed as she heard a scuffle in the corridor, and a drunken English supporter dressed from head to foot in red, white and blue, broke through the security men and shouted 'Protheroe Out' before he was manhandled away by the embarrassed Nep match stewards.

The England party were surrounded by pressmen as they boarded their coach for the airport, many wanting to know if Gladys was ready to resign.

The newspapers really went to town the next morning. *The Daily Sketch* who had been anti-Gladys since Day One had the story of England's rout on the front page. They published a picture of the England manager sitting on the team bench at the Nep Stadium with head in hands. The headline ran " For God's Sake Woman - GO NOW!" The other papers were slightly less hysterical, with The Telegraph and The Times advising the F.A. not to panic, and to allow Gladys to lead England into the World Cup. They printed articles pointing out that despite the defeats in Budapest and Belgrade there was no-one available to take over who had as much experience as Gladys. She was still the best qualified person for the job.

But, the general feeling was that the die had been cast, and Gladys would be relieved of her duties sooner rather than later. One of the bitterest attacks on the England manager was an acidic piece in the News Of The World the following Sunday. The article called Gladys' dress sense dowdy and named her the country's plainest woman. The paper printed the words to a song titled 'Go, Gladys Go' one verse read:

She is nothing but a silly old bat,
Who tried to manage England, well fancy that!
Her stupid ideas are full of rot,
She has made our great country the laughing stock!

Gladys was summoned to a meeting at Lancaster Gate the following Tuesday, and in a meeting that took just eight minutes was removed from her position as England manager. Within the hour Walter Winterbottom was officially appointed as her successor, and Gladys was out of work just three weeks before the World Cup was due to start in Switzerland.

CHAPTER THREE " DARK DAYS".

Gladys was in a state of shock for almost a week. She would walk around her house in a daze, refusing to answer the telephone or read her post. The press had, for the most, been delighted to have played a part in Gladys' downfall. The headlines read *"Glad She's Gone"*, *"Protheroe Sacked"*, and *"Sweet F.A. For Gladys"*. Only The Daily Telegraph, who printed an editorial titled 'Madness At Lancaster Gate' supported her. The F.A. refused to discuss the sacking, only saying that as far as they were concerned the matter was closed. Three days after her final meeting Gladys received her cards, her share of the F.A. Christmas Club and a Golden Handshake in the shape of a cheque for £500. There was also a card with 'All The Best, We'll Miss You' printed on it, although there were only a couple of signatures from the secretaries in the typing pool.

Suddenly being cut off from the day to day business of professional football, Gladys began to find time lying heavy on her hands, and due mainly to boredom she began to drink. At first it was just a couple of vodka and tonics with her lunch, but in a matter of a week or so, she was getting through a bottle of Premium Russian vodka and a gallon of Dutch lager each day. Within a month the £500 from the F.A. had gone on alcohol, and she had become a well known regular at the local pub, The Fox & Hounds. Her once impeccable dress sense went by the wayside, and she started to wear tatty tracksuits for weeks on end. She would forget to apply any make-up, and her once proud, lean face became puffy and lined. She seemed to change from a girlish, sporting lady to a bitter, lonely old woman.

Gladys' day would not start until noon, when she awoke in her by now reeking tracksuit - sometimes on the floor, sometimes in her garage or even on the front step, wherever she had passed out the previous night when the drink had taken its full, vicious effect.

The curtains remained drawn as she opened a new bottle of Smirnoff, then greedily emptied two large tumblers before her hands would stop shaking. Occasionally she was asked to leave the pub as she drunkenly picked fights with the other locals whenever someone passed a comment on the state of her tracksuit. When she did eventually get home, she sat alone in a drunken slumber. Sometimes, she would go to her attic and bring her scrapbooks down. Then with a bottle beside her she flicked through the pages reliving her days at Vicarage Road and her time with the Ladies Wartime XI. She turned to the page that Ernest's strong eyes stared from. It

27

was then she would slam the book closed, unable to let him see her this way.

The weeks turned to months, and even though the widow's pension from Verona was normally more then enough to live on, her drinking meant that all her money was being spent. Gladys was in fact offered £1,000 by *The News Of The World* to put her side of the story, but Gladys wanted nothing to do with a tawdry expose. They had taken her career, her dreams and her ambitions - but they would never take her pride and self-respect.

Amazingly, Gladys, once so vibrant and full of life, spent over two years in an alcoholic stupor. She would drink all day, every day, only leaving her now ramshackle home for visits to the pub or the off-licence.

Then, one night, Gladys touched the depths.

She sat alone in her kitchen, cold and stinking drunk. On the table were a three quarter empty vodka bottle, five empty Heineken bottles, and the remains of a pack of cheap tobacco. She had recently started to roll her own cigarettes, and the floor was littered with matches and dog-ends. Gladys read, for the thousandth time, the England v. Hungary programme from three years before. Three years? It felt like ten times that since that terrible defeat.

She stood up and staggered to the mirror, where she saw the face of a broken woman. There was the face of someone who had simply given in. Tears fell from her bloodshot eyes as she made her way to the medicine cabinet and reached for a bottle of sleeping pills. She was not sure just how many she managed to cram down her throat, but she swallowed them, one after the other, then downed two huge tumblers brimming with ice cold vodka.

Feeling dizzy and tired, she made her way to her favourite armchair under a signed, framed print of the great goalscorer, Dixie Dean. Once in the chair, she closed her eyes and felt the heavy fog of sleep begin to envelop her. Gladys' breathing became heavier, her head felt too big for her shoulders. Her mind filled with the scenes from her life. There were the packed terraces at Vicarage Road, the twin towers of Wembley Stadium and the silent spinning wheels of an upturned sports car in a far off land.

Then came peace and quiet.

The first thing she noticed was the smell. It was the unmistakable smell of a hospital ward. Within moments of Gladys opening her eyes a young smiling nurse was bending over her and taking her temperature. The Doctor, a charming young man named Dr. Feeney told her she had been lucky, very lucky. If it had not been for the swift actions of Gladys' neighbour, Mr. Pollard, then she would surely have not recovered after the lethal cocktail of alcohol and drugs.

Mr. Pollard had lived next door to Gladys for nearly eight years, and although being one to keep himself to himself, he had always taken a close interest in the various happenings in his famous neighbour's life. On the day in question, Mr. Pollard had noticed that Gladys' copy of *Charles Buchan's Football Monthly* had remained in her letterbox until well into the afternoon. Gladys had not cancelled her subscription to the magazine, and would normally read it from cover to cover to try to keep up with the goings-on in world football.

Mr. Pollard left it until 4pm then he knocked on Gladys' door to check that all was well. He had been aware that his neighbour's drinking had been on the increase, but when he spotted three dustbins piled high with empty bottles, he rang the emergency services.

Gladys was whisked to Watford General Hospital, and after having her stomach thoroughly pumped, was placed under observation. The staff at the hospital were soon aware that Gladys was some kind of well-known personality, but not completely certain of just who she was.

However, one person knew immediately. Jimmy Wilson was eighteen years old and an avid football supporter who spent most of his wages on either going to matches or on kit and rosettes. Jimmy was the keenest member of the hospital football team, and although by no means a talented player, Gladys immediately recognised the spark of a fellow spirit in the youngster. He was at Gladys' bedside as often as he could be, and would run errands for her to the news-stand or the hospital shop.

Soon the two new friends spent hours discussing football. Players, managers, teams and tactics were all put under the microscope. Although Jimmy was too young to reallyknow much about Gladys' days as England manager and her time with Watford first hand, he would astonish her by reeling off statistics about her past. The boy's knowledge of dates, places and results was uncanny. Jimmy would list the games Gladys had played for Watford, the team changes she had made for England - then ask why she had made that particular decision, and why she had felt Player X would be a better bet than Player Y.

Occasionally, Jimmy asked Gladys to come along and watch the hospital team play, but she always refused. She told him that football had kicked her out - she was finished with the game.

Perhaps the critics had been right all along. What could a woman know about a mans' game? This terrible crisis had brought her to her senses. It was now 1960, a new decade, an opportunity to wipe the slate clean and change direction.

Eventually, Dr. Feeney told Gladys that she would be able to take some light exercise, although the years of drinking had taken their toll; it would be some months before she would be allowed home.

Each morning before breakfast Gladys went for a short jog around the hospital grounds. She had borrowed an old tracksuit from one of the matrons, and although it was a couple of sizes too big, the thrill of being dressed in sportswear once again boosted her morale.

It was on one of her morning runs that Gladys chanced upon Jimmy and his colleagues involved in a practise match. She stood alone, hidden from the footballers by a row of conifers, and watched as the fourteen players battled their way through a seven a side game. Gladys winced as she saw pass after pass go astray, shots hit wildly over the bar, tackles mistimed and all the players making elementary errors. Gladys could bear it no longer. She strode out from her hiding place and shouted at the players to stop. She called Jimmy over, and told him to get the squad ready for a real training session. Jimmy agreed and ran over to his colleagues to tell them that they had a new trainer. Gladys did not notice the ear to ear smile on the youngster's face as he sprinted across the pitch. For him, his mission was accomplished. He had achieved just what he had set out to do. He had brought Gladys Protheroe back to the game she loved, the game she needed.

Jimmy and the lads explained the position they were in. The hospital team were second from bottom of their league, and with just six matches of the campaign remaining, it looked like relegation for the third season running. The one bright spot was the National Hospital F.A. Challenge Cup. This year the final was to be held at Wembley for the first time. Because of the harsh winter weather, the first round tie against Charing Cross Hospital had been postponed five times, but was at last due to be played in ten days time.

Before that there was a difficult league game away to Championship challenger Ford Motors. They were a factory team based in Dagenham, and were able to select their side from a huge workforce of over 5,000. The Hospital had lost the home game 6-1 earlier in the season, and after watching her new players train for half an hour, Gladys was rather surprised that Ford Motors had only managed half a dozen.

Jimmy and the players worked hard for their new coach. To say they were not the most talented bunch of players she had worked with was rather an understatement. To be honest, some of them were simply not cut out to be footballers, but they were keen, and she found their eagerness and commitment refreshing. They were young, reasonably fit and ready to learn. In just three days of training, Gladys could already notice a difference in the team. They were starting to find each other with their passes, tackle cleanly and crisply. They were beginning to rediscover their pride. The night before the Ford Motors game Gladys found it difficult to sleep. As in the old days, her mind was full of plans and tactics. Would Terry Wilkins be able to control the right-side of midfield? Did young Jimmy have the pace to trouble the Ford full backs? It was dawn before she finally dozed off.

Usually the team would find its way to away games individually, or somehow all cram into three or four cars, but Gladys changed all that. She hired a minibus, paying the fee out of her savings, and then presented each player with a hand knitted woollen tie she had made in the team colours of blue and white. Instead of arriving just a few minutes before the kick-off and hurriedly getting changed, Gladys arranged for the squad to travel to Dagenham in plenty of time, and to take their places in the dressing room an hour before kick-off. Gladys led her squad into the visitors changing room, closed the door and locked it. For the next twenty minutes, with the aid of a blackboard and some coloured chalks Gladys gave the team talk of her life. At the end of it, she knew she could do no more.

The referee came in to pick up the team sheet, and chatted to a few of the Hospital players. Then, out of the corner of his eye he noticed Gladys as she rubbed linament into the thighs of the giant centre-half, Jackie Dawson.

The official immediately recognised the proud profile of one of England's footballing greats and walked over to introduce himself. He told Gladys that he had stood on the Vicarage Road terraces just after the War and been inspired by her great deeds. Gladys felt obliged to explain just how an ex England manager came to be in charge of such a dog-eared bunch of players. She briefly explained her stay in hospital, then pointed to Jimmy Wilson, telling the referee that there stood the lad who brought her back to football. The referee shook Gladys' hand, wished her the very best of luck, then left the dressing room. But instead of going directly onto the pitch with the linesmen he went to a nearby pay-phone. He made a call to an old friend who worked on the sports desk of *The Daily Mirror*. He asked him one question. Do You remember Gladys Protheroe ?

Gladys took her place on the Hospital team bench and sat next to little Lenny Baker, a sixteen year old she had selected as a reserve. At the end of the bench sat old Bernie Crabtree who had carried the bucket and sponge for the team for more years than anyone could remember.

The Ford team were as Gladys had expected, big, strong and fit. They attacked straight from the kick-off, and for the first twenty minutes continually bombarded Phil Murray in the Hospital goal. Murray was perhaps the most able player in the team, and Gladys had her hopes pinned on him keeping the Ford forwards at bay. At half-time thanks mainly to Murray's heroics, the woodwork and poor finishing by the home side, the scoreline remained 0-0.

A vital factor was Gladys' off-side trap that had continually frustrated the Ford forwards. The trap had proved very effective, but had incensed the home side's supporters who slow handclapped and jeered each time the linesman raised his flag. Gladys had worked for hours with the back four perfecting the system she first developed with the England team some eight years before. The trap had worked well with the national team, but that had been with the assistance of four of the most able defenders in the country. Now she had raw boned, rag, tag and bob-tail players at her disposal, and yet for the first forty five minutes they had managed to keep their opponents out as they gelled into an unbeatable unit. Could it possibly last?

The Hospital's dressing room was noisy and full of excited voices as Gladys strode in. She clapped her hands twice and told her team to be silent. She told them that they had achieved nothing yet, the real hard work was about to begin. At all costs they must keep their concentration, and remember what they had been taught over the last few days. If they did that, and with a little luck, then maybe, only maybe, they could gain the result they were looking for.

As the players emptied their tea cups and filed back onto the pitch, Gladys had a quiet word with each member of the team. Encouraging, cajoling, pointing out the pitfalls and dangers they could expect in the second half.

As Gladys returned to the team bench, she noticed a tall man in a tan coloured raincoat holding a pad and pencil. He took up a position just behind the Hospital's goal with some other supporters, and as the game re-started, Gladys forgot all about him.

Once again the Hospital defence was under the cosh, although now and then Jimmy Wilson and Terry Wilkins did link up and cause a few problems amongst the Ford back four. Gladys had instructed her players to play the ball out to the wing, where the Hospital's nippy flankmen were putting pressure on the Ford full-backs. Gladys had noticed that both full-backs were rather overweight, and now and again Wilkins' speed took him past a tackle and into space. Sure enough as the game wore on this plan started to pay dividends.

With just five minutes left Wilkins won possession and centred perfectly for the Hospital inside forward Harry Dzehociuvelz, a Polish kitchen porter, to rifle the ball into the bottom left hand corner of the Ford net. Old Bernie Crabtree leapt off the bench, overturning his bucket, threw his sponge into the air and embraced Gladys. The Hospital players danced a jig of delight all the way back to the centre circle, punching the air as they celebrated Harry's deft strike.

But Gladys wasn't satisfied. She shouted at her team to keep their concentration, there were still three minutes to go, and it only took a second to score a goal. Indeed, straight from the re-start the Ford centre-forward grazed Murray's crossbar with a long range effort. Those last few minutes seemed like an eternity as the home side pushed all their players forward in a desperate search for an equaliser, but finally the referee blew his whistle for the end of the game.

The Ford manager sportingly shook Gladys' hand, and told her that she had out-manoeuvered him. His players had been unable to break down the Hospital defence, and although he did feel his players were technically more proficient, he admitted that Gladys' tactics had won the day.

The dressing room was full of cheery laughter and horseplay as Gladys and Old Bernie marched in. The players fell silent, then Jimmy Wilson raised 'Three cheers for Gladys Protheroe'.

There were tears in their coaches eyes as her new team shouted out their 'Hip, Hips'. Gladys had been congratulated by many football greats in her time, but no moment had meant quite so much to her before. The team of no-hopers and losers had found a sense of purpose. And in that loud, bawdy dressing room, Gladys too felt a tingle of pride - a sense of satisfaction. Perhaps the old game wasn't that bad after all.

After the celebrations which followed the Ford game, Gladys worked her team hard in training, determined to prove that the result was not just a flash in the pan. The next match was the cup tie against Charing Cross. Gladys noticed a definite feeling of confidence amongst the players, and felt that they were perhaps ready to learn a few more tactical moves. She tinkered with the balance of the mid-field, worked on a flat back four, pushed a fifth man running into the hole to link up with a deep playmaker and also told the full-backs to smile more.

The game against Charing Cross was a difficult, edgy match. They had won the competition twice in the previous five years, but their manager had made the classic mistake of letting the team grow old together. The twin strike force which had broken scoring records for the past five seasons were two gynaecologists now well into their mid-thirties, and Gladys banked on them having lost a yard or two.

The Charing Cross team arrived at the Hospital's cramped, shabby ground. Their players arrogantly strutted around the rutted, uneven pitch joking with one another over who would be the first to score a hat-trick. Gladys had seen teams with this attitude many times, and she had always taken great delight in taking them down a peg or two. Gladys told her players that Charing Cross were already preparing for the next round. The visitors were laughing and joking in the next dressing room, and their boorish predictions of a goal feast were overheard by the Hospital players. Gladys told her lads to listen to the bragging. Then she looked her squad in the eyes, and asked them one by one if they were going to stand for such dreadful behaviour. The players, to a man, told her no - they would not.

Within just five minutes of the kick-of, the visitors realised that the Hospital team were no longer a soft touch. The referee had to be on his toes as Gladys' team tackled like demons, leaving Charing Cross players on the floor after bone jarring challenges. At one point it did look as if the game might get out of hand, and Gladys had to shout to her players to keep calm.

Just before half-time a thundering volley from Terry Wilkins flew into the Charing Cross net, and the small knot of home supporters cheered in disbelief as the referee blew for the interval with the Hospital still leading 1-0. As expected, the visitors ran themselves into the ground searching for an equaliser, but as in the previous match Gladys' tactics frustrated the opponents. The Hospital team grew in stature as the minutes went by, and it was no surprise when Lenny Baker was on hand to scramble the ball over the line and put the result beyond doubt.

The Charing Cross team took the defeat badly, and there were a number of unsavoury incidents as the two teams left the pitch. Old Bernie Crabtree's bucket was thrown across the tunnel by the visitors' mascot, a precocious nine year old named Julian, who then caused mayhem by swearing and spitting at the genial old fellow. The infant was left writhing on the floor when an unknown assailant felled him with a sly, swift kidney-punch. The perpetrator was never discovered, although it was noticeable that Gladys spent a few moments dabbing her right fist with an ice pack when she returned to the dressing room.

The Hospital team managed to win two and draw three of their remaining league games to avoid relegation by just one point. It was in fact, the team's longest unbeaten run for over twenty years.

The second round of the Cup gave the Hospital an away tie against Manchester Royal Infirmary, one of the strongest hospital teams in the country. However, they had been shaken by a scandal in which a number of their squad had been accused of putting an athlete's foot preparation into opponents' half-time tea, and were without six first team regulars who had been suspended.

The game was an ill tempered affair in which both teams had three players booked, but the Hospital team eventually made it through to the quarter-finals with a twice taken penalty from Billy Ryan.

In the last eight, Gladys' team were paired with Hammersmith Hospital, a team that boasted an unbeaten home record stretching back three years. The game was to be played on the windy, open spaces of Wormwood Scrubs, and a crowd of over 2,000 were expected. Gladys took the opportunity of watching the Hammersmith team in league action against Harrow Asylum, and was impressed with their ball skills as they walloped the hapless lunatics 8-0.

For the quarter-final Gladys introduced a 'libero' to stifle the rampant Hammersmith attack, and gave a debut to a sixteen year old trainee chiropodist from Jamaica, Henry Powell. Powell was a strapping lad who stood 6'3" in his stocking feet, weighed just over 15 stone and could run the 100 yard dash in under 12 seconds. Technically, the boy had a lot to learn, but Gladys was impressed with his raw athletic ability, and she was certain his pace would trouble any defence. Powell was to play at centre-forward.

As expected the crowd around the pitch was up to ten deep in some places, and Gladys was delighted to hear that a healthy number of locals had made the trip to West London to cheer the Hospital team on. There was even a chorus or two of "We're Gladys' Boys" just before the kick-off. For the first time since Gladys took the helm at the Hospital, she was in doubt whether her players really could win.. Hammersmith played neat one-twos, opening up the Hospital's leaden-footed defence at will, and only a debatable off-side decision that had the home supporters in uproar kept the game goalless.

Hammersmith's wingers were like quicksilver, speeding down the flanks and knocking in inch perfect crosses for their muscular forwards to run onto. Phil Murray was under incredible pressure, shots raining in on him from all angles and distances. Just before half time Hammersmith made the breakthrough they had always threatened, and the home side's burly centre-forward McBride, helped himself to two goals in as many minutes following a couple of dreadful defensive mix-ups. As Gladys had feared, when the chips are down, no amount of coaching can disguise a basic lack of ability.

At half-time Gladys told her players to get their heads up. There was a long way to go yet, if they could manage to score early in the second half then perhaps Hammersmith would wobble under pressure. Gladys talked to young Henry Powell who had hardly kicked a ball in anger throughout the entire first half. She told him to get involved, to put himself about and try to ruffle a few feathers.

Amazingly the Hammersmith team were so confident of winning the game that Gladys noticed a number of their players stubbing out cigarettes and even draining cans of beer as they prepared to take the pitch for the second half. It was with particular interest that Gladys saw Hammersmith's captain and most inventive player Simpson take a huge pull on a reefer as he ran onto the playing area.

The Hammersmith players were giggling and clowning around as they waited for the referee to blow his whistle, and Gladys was astounded to see their full-back, Hill, urinate on the edge of his own penalty box in full sight of the crowd. As the minutes went by, the Hospital team started to get on top, and it dawned on them that as far as Hammersmith were concerned the game was over. First Billy Ryan, then Jimmy Wilson both wasted good chances to get a shot on target, before a massive goal-kick from Phil Murray bounced well inside the Hammersmith half. The home defence stood motionless as Henry Powell controlled the ball, noticed that Randall the home keeper was sipping from a hip flask, and chipped a delightful shot over the drinking custodian into the net.

Too late, the home side realised that Gladys' team had not just come to make up the numbers, but to win. Their minds confused by alcohol and marijuana, the Hammersmith team threw in the towel as Powell twice more and then Terry Wilkins scored to give the Hospital an incredible 4-2 away win. As the final whistle blew, two Hammersmith players were violently sick in the centre-circle while a nasty looking fist fight erupted between goalkeeper Randall and the drunken winger Goring. There were more remarkable scenes as the home supporters poured onto the pitch to swop punches with their own players who attempted to beat a hasty retreat to the dressing rooms. Gladys ordered her players to change as quickly as possible so they could leave the scenes of bedlam immediately. Suddenly, on the journey home, it dawned on Gladys – she was just one game away from Wembley.

Birmingham Royal Free Hospital were to be the opponents for the semi-final. Gladys and Bernie Crabtree drove up to the Midlands to watch the Brummies play Bromsgrove Old Folks Home in a league fixture. The Birmingham team were well disciplined, fit and dangerous from dead ball situations. News of the Hospital's sensational victory over Hammersmith had reached the Midlands, and after the game, a dull 1-1 draw, Gladys met the Birmingham manager, a mortuary attendant named Dave Black. Black told Gladys that he was looking forward to the semi-final, which was to be played at neutral Northampton. He told her that he had not seen the Hammersmith game, but had heard all about the amazing second half.

He also told Gladys that his team were tea-total.

On the journey home Bernie and Gladys discussed how to plan the semi-final. The Birmingham team seemed to lack any real stars, but often teams made up of hardworking players were very difficult to play against. Gladys knew her team must be on their mettle if they were to make it to the twin towers.

One of Gladys' major headaches was keeping her players feet on the ground. Since the win against Hammersmith the team had started to be recognised in the street, and she had noticed that hat-trick hero Henry Powell had gone out and spent a month's wages on a white suit. For so long, they had been the underdogs, now they had become personalities, so Gladys worked them even harder on the training pitch, drumming into them the fact that as yet they had achieved nothing.

For the semi-final The Powers That Be at the Hospital had decided to run a number of coaches up to Northampton. The interest was incredible. Many bed-ridden patients demanded to be allowed to see the game, and a local businessman agreed to pay for the hire of a huge transporter that was transformed into a mobile ward, complete with beds, drips, commodes and iron lungs.

Two days before the big game, the tall man in the tan raincoat who had been at the Ford Motors game all those weeks before arrived at the hospital reception desk and asked if he could speak with Gladys Protheroe. The stranger told the receptionist that his name was Harry O'Neil, that he was a sports reporter on the *Daily Mirror*, and that he was keen to write a story on the Hospital's remarkable football manager.

Gladys agreed to a short interview, stressing to O'Neil that she wanted the piece to be low-key. The reporter talked with her for nearly an hour, then took a few photographs of the manager putting her team through their paces. After O'Neil had completed his work and left for Fleet Street Gladys thought that perhaps the story would merit a paragraph or two in the paper, maybe sandwiched between the small ads and the gardening column. How wrong she was, for on the morning of the semi-final the Mirror ran the story right across their back page. In one inch headlines the page shouted out *"Gladys Is Back!"*

The article told the complete story of how the ex-England manager had fallen on hard times, but was now reviving her career with a fantastic cup run. And there staring out from the newspaper was the proud, lean face of Gladys Protheroe.

O'Neil had certainly been thorough. He had interviewed Bernie Crabtree, opposing managers and the governors of the Hospital. They were, of course, delighted with Gladys. She had single handedly made their hospital the most famous in all of England, and though none of them knew the first thing about football, they were now being congratulated at dinner parties and other social engagements for their sporting acumen.

Gladys had decided to field an unchanged team for the semi-final and as the team mini-bus drove up the newly opened motorway to Northampton, the players were amazed to see car loads of hospital supporters, some flying banners from their vehicles as they sped towards the ground.

The stadium was owned by The Northampton & District Catholic Sisterhood For The Mentally Unstable. Their team had been, not surprisingly, knocked out of the tournament in one of the preliminary rounds, but their stadium was one of the best looked after in hospital football. The Sisters keenly tended the playing surface, and had gone to particular trouble for the semi-final by re-painting all the seats, and arranging for huge flags representing both teams to fly from newly erected flagpoles. Supporters filled the surrounding streets, and Reg the coach driver had difficulty in manoeuvering the mini-bus through the excited crowd to the car-park. Well-wishers shouted out their best wishes as Gladys and Bernie shepherded their team past the waiting nuns who were acting as crowd control stewards, into the dressing-room. There was still over an hour before kick-off, but even in the depth of the dressing room, the travelling supporters could be clearly heard singing and chanting.

Gladys told her lads to take their time, to try to relax and put the game out of their minds for a few minutes. She pulled a large box out of one of the kit bags, and within moments had smoothed out a 'Subbuteo' pitch. She split her squad into four teams of four, and for over half an hour the dressing room was engrossed in a table football competition. Then the buzzer sounded, and the referee strode into the dressing room to introduce himself. He warned the players against any rough stuff and told them to keep the bad language to a minimum as a nun was running one of the lines.

After the official had left, Gladys gave a brief team talk, then out of another kit bag she pulled a large photograph of Wembley Stadium. She looked at her team, then asked them how many of them would be just ninety minutes away from playing at the grand old Stadium ever again ? Here was an opportunity to play under the twin towers, an experience they could tell their grandchildren about. She told them that many, many great players never had the chance to play at Wembley, yet now, here was their chance. They must take it. She knew, they knew they were not great players, but in everyone's life there came, just once – an opportunity to beat the odds. A chance to throw a spanner in the works. This was their chance, their day.

As the players ran out onto the pitch, the supporters from both teams roared their approval. The ground was packed. The more adventurous fans keen to get a better view were perched in trees surrounding the little stadium, the atmosphere was electric.

Gladys had never really believed in fate. She had always been suspicious of Bohemian, Beatnik ideas of Karma and mystical promises, but that day as she walked to the team bench she felt positive. Her team may not play well, they may not do exactly what she told them to do, but she knew one thing – they would win.

It was not a great game. Forgettable was the word used by most fans who were there. But the facts were that Birmingham Royal Free froze on the day. The Hospital forwards seemed to go through the Brummies' defence like a knife through butter. By half-time Henry Powell and defender Frank Derby had scored to give Gladys' team a healthy 2-0 lead, and goalkeeper Phil Murray had not had a shot to save.

At half-time Gladys told her players to shut up shop. When you're two to the good in a semi-final, it's the right time to rest on your laurels. They kept to her word. As early as the 55th minute centre half Graham Browne, a gangly youth who worked in the kitchens managed to waste five precious minutes by ballooning a clearance into a nearby stream.

As the minutes ticked by, Old Bernie became more and more uptight, until he could contain himself no longer. With five minutes left he pulled a half bottle of brandy from his kit bag and took a mighty swig, then he looked over to Gladys and offered her the bottle. Despite seeming cool and calm, she too was on tenterhooks, and accepted Bernie's offer of a quick nip. She then took a deep breath and counted the minutes as her players played their hearts out.

The referee blew his whistle. The game was over. Gladys Protheroe was back at Wembley. Within seconds Bernie and Jimmy Wilson had hoisted their manager onto their shoulders and she was surrounded by ecstatic supporters. The pitch was invaded by the Hospital fans and they tried to raise the roof off the stand with an energetic version of "*We're Gladys' Boys*". The dressing room was full of pressmen and camera crews as the players tried to get changed and prepare for the journey back to the Hospital. Dave Black did manage to push his way through the throng to shake Gladys' hand and wish her all the best for the final.

As the players were interviewed by the men from Fleet Street Gladys stood alone in the corner sipping an orange juice. She stood there and tried to take it all in. Yes, it was true. She was back at Wembley.

The Hospital was gripped by Cup Fever. Most of the patients, even some on the critical list, demanded that the wards were to be decked out in the blue and white favours of their team. The doctors too got in on the act. Many surgeons wore rosettes and scarves and even carried rattles into the operating theatres. BBC Radio sent a reporter down to interview some of the patients, while a young Kenneth Wolstenhome arrived with a film crew to record a piece for television.

Local coach companies were besieged by supporters wanting to hire mini-buses, coaches and cars to make the journey to Wembley. The success of the football team seemed to have an effect on the patients. Elderly folk who had been bed-ridden for months were suddenly spending mornings and afternoons in kick-abouts on the hospital lawn. The once boring life-styles of the patients had been dramatically altered. Now they felt there was a purpose to their lives. They were going to Wembley.

As a goodwill gesture to Gladys and the players, the Board of Governors arranged for the entire squad to be kitted out in new suits for the final. The photograph taken for the match programme shows the team seated in front of the main doors of the hospital, with Gladys sitting in the centre of the front row flanked by Jimmy Wilson and Bernie Crabtree. The players really look the part in light grey suits, white shirts and blue and white silk ties – a far cry from the scruffy bunch of irregulars Gladys had first started work with. Gladys herself wore a light grey two-piece suit with a blue and white cravatte. The match programme, which is now a sought after collector's item, also featured a full page article on the Hospital's manager, headlined "Glad To Be Back".

Newcastle General Hospital were the team to beat at Wembley. They were the most powerful hospital team of the modern era. They had won the Hospital Cup seven times since its inception in 1948, and had been unbeaten in any competition for over two years. And even then, their last defeat had been by the narrowest of margins,when they had gone down 1-0 to The Montevideo Clinic For Disorders Of The Bowel in the unofficial World Hospital Cup.

Newcastle's centre-forward Harry 'Wor' Stokes had broken all scoring records, and had recently been the subject of transfer speculation linking him with Newcastle United, Sunderland and Tottenham.

On the morning of the final, after a light breakfast of scrambled eggs and orange juice, Gladys took her team for a short stroll around the hospital grounds. It was a bright sunny spring morning, and the smell of newly cut grass was in the air. The players looked immaculate in their suits and Gladys joked with them that they looked like film-stars. She asked them to take a long look at themselves. A few months ago they were a scruffy bunch of no-hopers – now they were smart athletes, preparing to play at the most famous stadium in the world.

Gladys told them to enjoy the day, to take in every second, it would go by so fast. Although she didn't mention it to her team, she felt it was highly unlikely any of them would ever again get the opportunity to set foot on the sacred turf.

The transformation in her players had been nothing short of amazing. The once tongue-tied, shy amateur players were now confident young sportsmen. Jimmy Wilson had been approached by one of the major record companies who had been impressed by his boyish good looks, and hoped to mould him into England's answer to Dion, while Phil Murray had been watched by Brentford and full back Frank Derby had been linked with Fulham.

The luxury coach, covered in blue and white ribbons, arrived at the Hospital to pick up the players at noon. The road was lined with supporters and well-wishers, up to ten deep in some places, each one keen to give Gladys and her lads a great send-off.

Gladys walked down the aisle of the coach gently having a few words with each player, calming nerves and cracking jokes. She sat at the front of the vehicle next to Bernie Crabtree, who also looked a million dollars in a brand new royal blue tracksuit.

As the coach pulled off Wembley Park Drive up Empire Way, the famous twin towers came into view. There were tears in Gladys' eyes as the driver slowly crawled up the road that was packed with fans. It was at that moment that Gladys fully realised what she had achieved. She had been written off, thrown on the rubbish heap by the football authorities, and yet here she was – back at the heart of football. As the tears welled up, she felt a light tug on her sleeve. Without a word, and keeping his eyes front, Bernie handed her a handkerchief.

Gladys and the squad strode about the pitch, waving to their supporters standing at the tunnel end. There was still over an hour before the kick-off, and yet over 5,000 Hospital supporters were already in their places, determined to take in every second of a marvellous day out. They sung and shouted to their favourite players as the team waved to their families and friends.

Gladys signalled to her players to return to the dressing room where Bernie had already laid the kit out. The Governors had arranged for a commemorative shirt to be produced for the final, with the inscription "Wembley 1960" embroidered under the hospital's crest. This decision caused some anger among supporters, who had claimed that due to the Hospital's new deal with a kit company, the Governors were in fact attempting to make a quick profit from the loyal fans, who would buy the new shirt for the final, even though they had only recently purchased one. Gladys did have some sympathy for the parents of fashion conscious youngsters.

The team talk lasted less than a minute. Gladys looked at her team, and told them to just go out there and give it their best. Enjoy it. She told them that if you can't play football here, then you can't play.

The Hospital supporters roared their approval as Gladys led her team out onto the pitch. The stadium was about three-quarters full, and a crowd of just over 70,000 including a sizeable Geordie contingent created a great atmosphere.

But, alas, there was to be no dream ending for Gladys and her team. Newcastle General had obviously done their homework. Straight from the kick-off, Billy Ryan was shadowed by Newcastle skipper Mick Lee and Henry Powell was never given an inch of space. The Geordies played a tight, defensive style, always ready to play the ball back to their goalkeeper rather than take a risk.

Gladys shouted and cajoled from the bench, trying to get instructions to her players, but the noise from the crowd meant that most of her calls were lost in the air.

Just as it looked if the scoreline would remain goalless at half-time, a Newcastle free kick hit the Hospital wall, took a wicked deflection off Frank Derby, left Phil Murray helpless, and flew into the corner of the net. At half-time Newcastle General led 1-0.

Gladys told her players to step it up, to get their tackles in and to keep running. Privately, she felt that the Newcastle team were just too fast and skilful for her lads.

Within ten minutes of the restart, Harry Stokes picked up a loose ball, shook off a couple of half-hearted tackles and struck an unstoppable shot past Murray for number two. For the next five minutes or so Gladys feared her team were going to be destroyed. Newcastle hit the bar, had a goal disallowed for off-side, and missed three easy chances.

Newcastle did score a third goal with ten minutes to go, then seemed to settle for a 3-0 scoreline. In the last minute Henry Powell almost managed a consolation goal for the Hospital, but his shot was brilliantly saved by the Newcastle goalkeeper, Ford.

As the Newcastle team went up the 39 steps to receive the trophy and their medals from the young Princess Anne, Gladys walked among her exhausted team ruffling heads and patting bottoms. There were a few tears shed on the famous turf as the Hospital players waited to collect their runners-up medals.

Then it was their turn to walk up the steps. Gladys followed her players up to meet the Princess, and the huge bank of supporters burst into *"We're Gladys' Boys"* as she shook hands and chatted to her. The Hospital players surrounded their manager, lifted her on their shoulders and set off on a lap of honour around the famous old stadium. After the players had showered and changed, Gladys sat with Bernie Crabtree in a corner of the huge dressing room and sipped a glass of orange juice. The supporters had gone home, the terraces were empty. The Hospital team had got over the disappointment of defeat, and were now laughing and joking, determined to make the most of their day. The governors of the hospital had organised a dinner at The Dorchester to commemorate the day, and the players were changing into their rented dinner jackets.

Jimmy Wilson, his hair still wet from the bath, walked over to Gladys and embraced her. He began to tell his manager how grateful he and his team-mates were, how she had made their dreams come true. Gladys stopped him. She told Jimmy that it should be her thanking him. He and his colleagues had brought her back from the brink, back to the game she loved. Gladys then shook him by the hand, and gave him a light kiss on the forehead. Her work with the Hospital team had been completed. Now there was the future, away from the hospital wards, away from the safety of Jimmy and the lads. Now it was time for Gladys to get back to the real world. The team lined up one last time for their manager, some already changed into their suits, others dripping wet with just a towel wrapped around them. Gladys embraced each one, shook their hands and made them all promise to keep training hard, to continue playing to their best abilities – if they did that, then success would come their way. Bernie Crabtree stood at the end of the line and wept like a baby as Gladys hugged him.

Then the farewells were over, and Gladys left the players to prepare for their dinner engagement. She had decided not to join them for their evening, it was time she got back to her little house and started her new life. The sun was beginning to set, and the last few rays of daylight glinted off the twin towers as Gladys walked up Empire Way to her waiting taxi. Gladys looked back from the cab, wiped a tear away, took a deep breath and looked forward.

CHAPTER FOUR "LA SENORA DE LA BERNABEAU".

Gladys arrived home just before nine o'clock, and was pleasantly surprised to see that her neighbours had kept her garden tidy; one thoughtful soul had even creosoted her front fence.

She watched television for short while, delighted to see a brief report on the news of the Hospital Cup Final. There was shot of Gladys and Bernie on the bench, but most of the item centred on the victorious Newcastle General team.

As she drank a mug of ice cold milk and nibbled a digestive, Gladys idly flicked through the morning's post. While she had been in hospital, all her mail had been forwarded to her, but there were a number of telegrams from well-wishers passing on their best for the final that had only arrived that morning.

The last letter was a rather mysterious affair. It was a bulky package, postmarked Madrid. Gladys reached for her paper-knife and slit the envelope. The letter was on crisp notepaper with gold letterheading. The heading read Real Madrid.

The communication was signed by Senor Juan Gomez, a wealthy Spanish businessman who had just taken control of the club. Senor Gomez was the owner of internationally successful companies, and was renowned for always getting what he wanted. He was now chairman of the biggest club side in the world, and he wanted a manager – but more than that, he wanted Gladys. Enclosed was an air ticket from London to Madrid; the flight left at 11.00 am the next morning. Senor Gomez briefly explained the situation he was in. Real had won the European Cup at Hampden Park, Glasgow the previous month, decisively defeating the West German champions Eintracht Frankfurt 7-3. The game had been described as 'The Match of The Century', and the victory had given Real Madrid the trophy for the fifth season running, underlining the fact that they were without doubt the most powerful team in the world. But, behind the scenes, things had not been going well. Boardroom vendettas and petty jealousies had meant that no chairman had ever really been able to run the club. Financial irregularities, accusations of bribery and then finally a transvestite scandal had ousted the previous Chairman, and Senor Gomez had been approached to take the helm. He had agreed, but only on condition that he had the last word on all transfers, and more importantly was given a free hand to appoint the team manager of his choice.

Senor Gomez had long been a follower of the English game, and had been intrigued by Gladys' recent re-appearance in the public eye. He had meticulously gone through her past records, spoken to many football experts in England and on the continent, and was convinced that she had now rid herself of her alcohol dependency. He was certain Gladys Protheroe was the person to take control of Real Madrid.

Gladys was on the morning flight to Madrid. Her holdall was packed with a few necessities, her head full of wild thoughts. She had had trouble sleeping the previous night.

What would Senor Gomez be like? How would the notoriously macho Spanish players react to a lady manager?

As the plane flew over France, Gladys managed to get a couple of hours sleep, eventually being woken by a polite stewardess who informed her that they would be landing in Madrid within twenty minutes. As the plane taxied along the runway, Gladys noticed a number of arc lights and a posse of people gathered around one of the arrival gates. She supposed that a celebrity was about to land on another flight, and thought no more about it. As the plane got nearer and nearer to disembarkation, Gladys realised that the crowd were in fact T.V. and newspaper reporters, and they were obviously waiting for someone on her flight. She looked around the other passengers, attempting to recognise a famous face, perhaps a film star or a television personality, but no-one looked familiar.

The plane came to a standstill. The passengers started to collect their hand-luggage then prepared to descend the steps. Gladys waited patiently for the dozen or so passengers in front of her to leave. Suddenly, as Gladys reached the aircraft door there was an enormous surge from the waiting pressmen, flash bulbs popped, cameras clicked and there was a shout from the crowd, "La Gladys!"

Within seconds of her arrival on Spanish soil there was another push from the reporters as they desperately tried to get a picture of Gladys. Just as it seemed she would be crushed against a barrier, three huge bodyguards appeared and whisked the startled Englishwoman through a side door into a small, private lounge. The room was empty except for a well-stocked bar in one corner, a low table and three comfortable leather arm chairs.

Gladys took the opportunity to rest her legs, and she sat down and helped herself to a glass of fresh orange juice.

Outside in the arrival lounge, she could hear pandemonium as police and airport staff attempted to control the baying mob. Then the door on the other side of the lounge opened, and in stepped a short balding man with a deep Mediterranean tan. He was immaculately dressed in a light blue suit, a white silk shirt and red tie. He wore a heavy gold bracelet on one wrist and a huge, jewelled Rolex on the other.

Gladys rose to meet him. He introduced himself as Juan Gomez, shook Gladys by the hand, then kissed her on both cheeks. Senor Gomez apologised for the scenes in the airport, but he explained that the news of her arrival had been leaked to the press, and the media had picked it up immediately. Senor Gomez explained that there were five daily football papers in Madrid alone, so the opportunity of meeting the new manager of Real off the plane was too big a story to miss.

But, he added, the day there was not such a clamour to meet such a beautiful, intelligent woman was the day he would know the world had gone mad.

Gomez had bright, alert eyes and Gladys was immediately impressed by his business-like manner. He told her that it was up to him to keep Real Madrid at the top of world football, and he would stop at nothing to achieve his aim.

He wanted the best, and he felt the best was in this room now. If she would accept the position, he would see to it that she had the funds available to strengthen the squad, and he would do everything in his power to make sure she felt at home.

Senor Gomez offered Gladys the use of the club's number one luxury penthouse apartment overlooking Madrid city centre, a brand new Mercedes Benz and a salary of £25,000 per year (a phenomenal amount in 1960).

Gladys asked for a little time to think over the offer. Senor Gomez agreed, but told Gladys that he must have an answer in 24 hours. If she declined to take the Real job, he would be forced to go for his second choice, the Brazilian coach Jesus Coches, the boss of South American champions Santos.

Gladys woke early, breakfasted on rich black coffee and croissants, then set off for an early morning jog around the busy streets of Madrid. On her run she met with many Real supporters who shouted out their best wishes, passing taxis and trucks tooted out messages of support, housewives bellowed from their balconies and children on their way to school ran with her for part of the circuit.

Gladys was rather surprised to see photographs of her arrival in Spain splashed over the front pages of not only the sporting papers, but of the Spanish national papers too. She could only just make out what the news-stands had printed on their hoardings, but with her basic knowledge of Spanish, she was able to make out headlines like 'Gladys will be Real No. 1' and 'Gomez Gets His Woman'.

She returned to the hotel, showered, changed into a fresh tracksuit, then telephoned Senor Gomez to tell him of her decision. She thanked him for giving her the time to decide, but decide she had – when could she start work?

Senor Gomez was delighted, he sent a car round to the hotel immediately, and Gladys was driven to the fantastic Bernabeau Stadium – her new place of work.

At the gates, a knot of newsmen and photographers surrounded the car, and demanded news of her intentions. Gladys told them in poor Spanish that at present, any arrangement between herself and Senor Gomez was personal and private – but as soon as anything concrete had been finalised, they would be the first to know.

Senor Gomez led her into the beautifully decorated boardroom, where a huge trophy cabinet stood at one end. The cabinet was packed full of silverware, the walls of the room covered in photographs of Real teams of the past, the European Cup teams, Spanish League and Cup winners. All around them were the ghosts of great players, great teams and larger than life managers.

Senor Gomez reeled off the names of the men who had held the coveted position of manager of Real Madrid. Gastez, who had put together the first really invincible Real team, Conchillacha, the Uruguyan coach who had first introduced the libero to Spanish football, and Villova, who had first coined the phrase "You're shit, aaaahhh."

He then went to a desk, opened a drawer, and handed Gladys her contract. Gladys signed it and handed it back to her new Chairman without even reading it. Senor Gomez was flabbergasted. He told her that for all she knew, he was making her sign a terrible contract with none of the bonuses and perks he had promised her. Gladys smiled, and told him that they both knew he was not that kind of man.

The new manager of Real Madrid and her Chairman then went to meet the gentlemen of the press. The club had arranged a press conference in one of their huge banqueting suites, and as the new colleagues entered the room, they were dazzled by a sudden explosion of flash-bulbs. There was uproar as each reporter attempted to get their question answered. Real security men had to restrain photographers as they clambered over furniture, trying to get the picture for tomorrow's front page. Gladys answered all the journalists' probings with the aid of an interpreter, a friendly fellow named Pepe. All the questions Gladys expected were there. Did she really believe a woman could run the biggest football club in the world? How could someone from England expect to understand the complexities of the Spanish game? Wouldn't the language barrier be a huge problem?

Gladys fended off the reporters as best as she could, but by the end of the press-conference, she had decided on one thing. She would learn the language, and when she knew the Spanish words she would make those reporters eat them.

Gladys had inherited a squad of talented, highly paid professionals. Of Real's first team squad of over thirty players, 24 were internationals. They were held in awe by the supporters, they never had to pay for their clothes in the chic boutiques and restauranteurs were falling over themselves to have a Real player eat in their establishment. They were perhaps some of the finest players of their generation, the problem was, Gladys was later to say, that they knew it.

When the new manager of Real Madrid walked into the dressing room to meet her squad of players, she was met with an immediate air of hostility. None of the team stood up, many of them continued gossiping and joking, some read newspapers, some simply stared into space. A number of the players had not bothered to shave, most wore dirty, creased clothes while a few were even smoking cigarettes.

Gladys realised that this first meeting with her players was vital. It was a test, a clear pointer to the future. If she failed now, her time in Madrid would be short and sour. She took a deep breath, fumbled in her tracksuit pocket for her Acme Thunderer, and gave it a long, loud, shrill blow. The piercing sound bounced off the dressing room walls deafening everyone there, but Gladys kept blowing. When her lungs were finally empty, she slowly took the Thunderer from her mouth and returned it to her pocket.

The room was now silent. She summoned Pepe, the interpreter, and told him she wanted the players in a line, up against the wall in ten seconds flat. Pepe relayed the instruction, but none of the players, having now recovered their sense of hearing, moved. She met every stare, standing hands on hips in the centre of the dressing room, ready for any eventuality. Slowly, and rather mockingly, the players got up and shuffled over to the end of the room and stood facing her.

They were household names all over the football playing world. There was the captain, DiStefano, the wily winger Gento, the tall stopper Santamaria and the agile goalkeeper Araquistain. Standing slightly apart from the other players stood Puskas, the man who Gladys had first seen play some seven years before. A little broader around the waist, his hair a touch thinner.

Puskas seemed embarrassed by the icy welcome Gladys had received. He was now in his mid thirties, and although on his day he could still be counted as one of the greatest players in the World, he was obviously aware that there were many youngsters ready and waiting to take his place in the team.

Gladys walked up and down the line of players like a Head of State inspecting a regiment of troops. She would stop for a few moments in front of each player and ask him his name. The player would be astonished that his new manager did not know who he was, then she would look straight into his eyes, nod a few times, then look the player up and down before telling him that either he needed a shave or that his shoes could do with a polish. When she reached DiStefano and Puskas, she said nothing. She stood between them for a few moments, then smiled. Gladys told Pepe to ask them to join her in the manager's office in ten minutes, then she glided out.

The two wily old pros knocked on Gladys' door and were offered some PG Tips and shortbread that their new manager had had the forethought to bring with her in her holdall. Fortunately, both could speak reasonable English, so Gladys was able to dispense with Pepe's services.

Gladys told them both that as far as she was concerned they were both to be vital members of her Real team. She went on to tell them her plans for the forthcoming season. She wanted to use Puskas and DiStefano's vast experience, perhaps not playing them in every game, but using their knowledge and more importantly their influence over the younger players to help keep the team on an even keel.

As the two players ate their biscuits and drank their tea, Gladys continued to tell them what she had in mind. She was keen to sign some new players, to make Real play her way. She wanted to try out some new tactical formations, and hopefully get Real to play in a more English way. The meeting went well. Gladys was determined to gain the players' respect, and she felt that if she could convince Puskas and DiStefano, the two senior professionals at the club, of her abilities as a manager and coach, then the other players would fall into line.

Player power was common at Spanish clubs. Many managers had been hounded out by players determined to get their own way, and even boards of directors and chairmen were frightened of upsetting the temperamental stars.

Real Madrid were to open the 1960/61 season with a tricky looking away fixture against Valencia. Real had not won the Spanish title for three seasons, and Senor Gomez had made it quite clear that that was the number one priority.

Gladys decided to leave the playing staff as they were, and to give them all an opportunity to show her what they could do. For the Valencia game she picked both Puskas and DiStefano in midfield, and gave a league debut to a young winger named Varez. He was sixteen years old and had only just established himself in the youth team, but there was something about the youngster that persuaded Gladys to throw him in at the deep end. The decision caused some bad feeling in the dressing room, as Varez's inclusion meant there was no place for the popular Gento.

The game ended in a nil-nil draw, and Real could have won in the last minute when Puskas hit the bar with a rasping volley. Gladys was reasonably pleased with the team's performance, and on the long coach journey back to Madrid she dozed off, contented that her plans were beginning to turn from dream to reality.

The new season started reasonably well for Real Madrid. After the draw in Valencia, Las Palmas and Gijon were easily beaten at The Bernabeau. Slowly but surely Gladys felt that both players and supporters were beginning to warm to her style of management. She had introduced a strict form of discipline in the dressing room, and although there was some resistance at first, the players had buckled down.

As holders, Real had been given a bye in the first round of the European Cup, and the city went wild with excitement when the draw for Round Two paired Real with their arch rivals, Spanish champions Barcelona. Gladys had been pleased with the early season form, but was convinced that if the club were to make progress she would have to enter the transfer market. She got the go-ahead from Senor Gomez to spend a few million pesetas, and she stunned Spanish football by going back to Vicarage Road to pay Watford £60,000 for goalkeeper Harold Brair and centre half Bobby Knox.

Brair and Knox had been recommended to Gladys by friends at her old club, and they became the first English players to play in the Spanish league. Her next move was to lure old Bernie Crabtree away from the hospital to be the new Real Madrid physio.

Gladys was annoyed by the number of minor injuries the players claimed they were picking up in games. She was certain they were feigning the knocks to miss out on training, so old Bernie's ice cold sponge down their shorts should work wonders.

Tickets for the Barcelona European Cup tie were like gold dust. The Spanish media had gone into overdrive, and were building the game up as a war. The political situation between the two clubs guaranteed that any game between them was eagerly awaited by the supporters, but the added glamour of the European Cup had given this tie an extra dimension. Barcelona's manager Juan Vasquez added fuel to the fire by telling the newspapers that as far as he was concerned, Gladys was a 'little English housewife' who had no business in the game. Vasquez had derided Real Madrid as being like a sewing circle, and cartoons appeared in the papers of the Real players sitting at Gladys' feet in the dressing room darning socks and embroidering shawls. This more than anything caused terrible pressure at The Bernabeau. The players' macho Latin pride had been severely insulted, and a players delegation told Gladys in no uncertain terms that they would not stand for such talk.

Real were to play the first leg at home, and Gladys decided to leave out both Puskas and DiStefano. Brair and Knox made their debuts, and with

Real leading 2-0 at half time, all seemed to be proceeding to plan. However, the home defence became over confident, and allowed Barcelona to score two late goals to draw the first leg. Vasquez was, of course, delighted. He continued to tell the press and television just how it was impossible for a woman, and an English woman to boot, to outwit a man. He went on to say that his brave Catalans would send the senoras of Madrid out of the European Cup, and how he would personally drive the 'Slutty Protheroe' back to English surburbia, where she belonged.

The second leg at The Campo Nuevo was a violent, bitter affair. Bernie Crabtree spent nearly as much time on the pitch as the players. Varez and Gento the Real wingers were continually scythed down in full flight. The Barcelona defenders kicked, punched and spat their way through the first 45 minutes.The first half ended nil-nil, which meant that Barcelona's two away goals were becoming more and more valuable. As Gladys, Bernie and the Real reserves left their bench for the dressing room at the interval they were met with a torrent of bottles, cans and coins. The Barcelona supporters screamed abuse at them, some threw knitting needles and sewing patterns onto the pitch.

Bernie had to work overtime, bruises had to be treated, cuts and even bites tended. Goalkeeper Brair had stud marks running down his back, Bobby Knox had one of his ears badly chewed. Gladys had experienced many types of games, but this was the first time she had witnessed such cold blooded thuggery.

Puskas walked among the players with Gladys, dabbing at open cuts with a bottle of TCP, while his manager told her players to keep their heads, if they kept calm they could win the tie. As the Real players ran out of the tunnel for the second half, the boos, cat-calls and whistles rang out once more. Four of the Madrid team were limping, another three wore bandages and plasters. The second half was equally spiteful, and after an hours play disaster struck as Barcelona scored. The stadium erupted as fireworks and smoke bombs exploded everywhere in a deafening cacophony. Less than five minutes later, the home side put the result beyond doubt, when after a defensive mix up, the tall Barcelona forward Mirueto gave Brair no chance with a rocket of a shot from just outside the penalty box. This time, Vasquez couldn't control his elation. He ran to the Real bench and gestured to Gladys. Within a few moments she was up off her bench and had the Barcelona manager in a Half-Nelson down by the touchline. There was uproar as first the Barcelona reserves, then stewards and finally the Guardia attempted to break up the melee. Players, officials and supporters were swopping punches and kicks as the referee had no option but to halt the game. Finally order was restored, but not before Vasquez had received a hell of a beating. He was badly throttled, his suit in tatters, both eyes blacked, while Gladys returned to her bench without a hair out of place, still splendid in her white Real Madrid tracksuit.

The game restarted, and although Gento gave Real some hope with a goal in the last minute, Barcelona hung on to win the tie 4-3 on aggregate. Amazingly, the media, instead of celebrating Barcelona's victory and condemning Gladys for Real's defeat, paid more attention to the fact that she had given Vasquez a good old fashioned English hiding. The papers told how La Gladys had restored Real's honour, and how Vasquez could never hold his head up again. He had let the menfolk of Catalonia down with his cowardly behaviour, and Gladys was looked on as a woman of strength and dignity.

The Real supporters were obviously disappointed by the Barcelona defeat, but Gladys stated in her programme notes for the home game against Athletico Bilbao, that she was confident she would be able to present the Real fans with the Spanish Championship trophy at the end of the season.

Real went twelve league games undefeated, including victories over local rivals Athletico Madrid as well as a particularly satisfying 3-1 win against Barcelona. By Christmas time, Real were five points clear at the top of the table, and playing some superb attacking football. Gladys had again been active in the transfer market, signing polish international forward Dzeviziodallizoviz Pob from Gornik Zabrz and Swedish full back Senn Arensen from Gothenburg.

By March, the championship was all but won, Real needed three points from their final four games to make sure of the title and to bring the trophy to The Bernabeau for the first time in three years. An exciting 4-3 win in Seville then a 0-0 draw at Ceuta confirmed the title win, and the final match of the season – a home game against Real Zaragoza turned into a fiesta. A Pob hat-trick gave Real a 3-0 victory, and after the final whistle Gladys was carried around the stadium on her players' shoulders, then the packed Bernabeau crowd launched into a pidgin English version of *"We're Gladys' Boys."*

It had been a long, difficult season for Gladys in which she had only returned to her home in Croxley Green twice, for a couple of days at a time, so it was a weary, but satisfied Gladys who arrived at her home for a well earned summer break in May 1961. Senor Gomez had drawn up a new three year contact for her and promised a large cash injection to boost the playing squad for a fresh assault on the European Cup.

Whilst on holiday Gladys arranged with Watford manager Ron Burgess for her Real Madrid team to play a friendly game at Vicarage Road, then she set about trying to sign two bright young stars. Gladys had been in contact with Jimmy Wilson from the hospital who had informed her of two London based players he was certain would become major stars. One was a blonde defender with West Ham named Bobby Moore, the other a wily goal poacher with Chelsea – Jimmy Greaves.

However, both The Hammers and The Pensioners were aware of the value of their new stars and refused Gladys permission to speak to the players. It was one of Gladys' great regrets that she was unable to coax Greaves and Moore to Madrid. Ironically, less than 12 months later Jimmy Greaves did sign for a foreign club when A.C. Milan paid £75,000 for his signature, though Greaves did not settle in Italy, and returned to London with Tottenham Hotspur after just one season. Gladys was convinced that with an English manager, and old Bernie Crabtree to look after him off the pitch, Greaves would have been a great success in Madrid.

The 1961/62 season was bittersweet for Gladys. On the domestic front she could do no wrong. Real once again won the Spanish championship, and the Spanish Cup for good measure – achieving the double for the first time in Real's history.

Gladys restored both Puskas and DiStefano to the Real midfield, and they repaid her faith with a number of breathtaking performances. The tubby little Hungarian now weighed in at a staggering twenty stone, but was still able to glide over the turf.

In the European Cup, Real began their campaign with a difficult tie against Vasas of Budapest. The first leg ended with Madrid winning 2-0, then two goals by Pob and one by DiStefano gave Gladys' team a 3-1 home win to make it a comfortable 5-1 victory on aggregate.

Odense of Denmark proved to be no danger in the second round, with Real winning 3-0 away, then setting the Bernabeau alight with a scintillating 9-0 thrashing of the Danes in the second leg, to move easily into the quarter-finals. The Italian champions, Juventus laid in wait, and it took three games before Real Madrid won through to the last four and a clash with Standard Liege of Belgium. For the home leg of the tie against the Belgian champions the Real ticket office received an application for a seat from a Mr. Ramsey of Ipswich, England. Gladys' old full-back had gone into management and was well on his way to winning the English first division with his home-spun Ipswich Town team just a year after taking them up out division two. Gladys welcomed Ramsey to The Bernabeau and they enjoyed a delightful old English fry-up in the Real bootroom before the game with Standard Liege.

Ramsey saw Gladys' team win through to their sixth European Cup final. beating the Belgians 4-0. The second leg was a formality. with Real increasing the aggregate with a 2-0 victory. The European Cup final was to be held in Amsterdam where Real's opponents would be Benfica of Portugal. Many Spanish experts decided that the trophy was as good as won and had already acclaimed Gladys as Spain's number one manager.

Bernie Crabtree, Senor Gomez, Gladys and Puskas flew to Lisbon to watch Benfica in action against Sporting Lisbon, and were impressed by what they saw. The star of the Benfica team was undoubtedly the dusky centre-forward from Madagascar, Eusebio. His speed and strength were there for all to see, and Gladys was certain she was watching a great star.

Real were on the verge of a record breaking treble, with the Spanish Cup and league already won. Gladys and her squad flew to Holland a week before the final to acclimatise.

The team stayed at the fabulous Hotel Kad, a luxurious complex five miles from Amsterdam. The hotel boasted three tennis courts, a swimming pool, squash courts and a sauna, and to make the Real players feel at home, the owner had even installed a miniature bullring.

Gladys worked her players hard on the training pitch, drumming into them the need to concentrate and to keep the menace of Eusebio under control. After each training session Gladys was besieged by the massive Spanish press presence who were staying in a nearby hotel. They demanded to know if there were any injury scares or whether Real were to change tactics. They also reminded Gladys that her players were representing Spain – and that anything other than victory would simply not be tolerated.

The 1962 European Cup Final was a lively, end to end game full of free flowing, open football. Unfortunately for Gladys Benfica played a scintillating mixture of one touch football and caught the Real defence cold when they roared into a 2-0 lead in the first ten minutes. The film of the game clearly shows Gladys and Bernie Crabtree up off their feet. berating their team. Puskas volleyed in a spectacular goal just before the interval, but then Gladys' worst fears were confirmed when Eusebio broke through twice to put Benfica 4-1 up. Real weren't finished, and Puskas showed his class by bagging two more goals to register a hat-trick. The final five minutes were pure theatre, as the Spanish champions threw everything at the Benfica defence in an attempt to equalise.

But, as Gladys feared, Benfica broke away, and Coluna scored the Portuguese team's fifth to put the result beyond doubt. At the final whistle the players fell to their knees. Bernie Crabtree burst into tears, and Eusebio ran to the Real bench to embrace Gladys. The photograph of the great Benfica striker, naked from the waist up. arm in arm with the Real Madrid manager was published in newspapers and magazines throughout the world, and represented the great spirit in which the final was played. Gladys and her defeated team returned to Madrid, and she experienced the first backlash from the Spanish press. A report in 'El Goala' told of Real's naïve tactics in the European Cup final, and how a male manager would have come home with the trophy, while 'Sporto Espana' carried a banner headline 'Protheroe Must Go'.

After a couple of days at The Bernabeau sorting out a number of players contracts for the next season. Gladys flew back to England to spend her summer holiday at home in Croxley Green. Despite the splendid work her housekeeper Mrs. Cornes put in at the house, her garden had gone to seed, so most of the summer was spent knee deep in compost and herbaceous plants.

Senor Gomez flew in from Madrid to talk over plans for the forthcoming campaign, and was astonished to find that the manager of Real Madrid lived in a modest semi-detached house in suburbia. Senor Gomez was used to visiting huge, imposing houses and was rather taken aback by the frugal home Gladys kept.

The chairman and manager of the biggest football club in the world discussed the new season over fish and chips which Gladys fetched from her local chippy. Once again Senor Gomez was staggered that such a famous personality was able to walk the streets without being surrounded by well-wishers. Gladys explained that Croxley Green was a sleepy backwater; although most of her neighbours were aware she was employed by a Spanish football club few knew that she was in fact boss of Real Madrid. Those who did respected her privacy, while others just looked on her as 'That woman in the tracksuit'. After the hustle and bustle of Madrid, she told Senor Gomez that she needed the peace of her English home where she was able to recharge her batteries and rest before another taxing season.

Senor Gomez said he understood, but during his three day stay with her he did ask her a number of times if Real were paying her enough. Wouldn't she like a house with a tennis-court and a swimming pool? It could be arranged by just one telephone call.

For the 1962/63 season Gladys signed two more Watford players. She paid £50,000 for centre-forward Cliff Holton and £12,000 for wing-half Tony Gregory. She had found the experiment with Watford players at The Bernabeau to have been a success and had no fears over her two new lads.

Once again Real had a great start to the league season – going a record breaking sixteen matches without defeat, including a 4-0 victory against arch rivals Barcelona. Vasquez had been sacked as The Catalans' manager during the summer, many observers remarking that he had never been the same since Gladys had taken the wind out of his sails on that famous night in The Nou Camp. The club looked set for a good run in the European Cup, but it wasn't to be.

Real had drawn Belgian champions Anderlecht, and after the previous season's comfortable win against Standard Liege the Spanish football writers forecast another emphatic Real victory. But Anderlecht obviously hadn't read the script. The Belgians battled to a 3-3 draw at The Bernabeau, scoring two goals in the last ten minutes – then shocked the football World by beating Real 1-0 on a rainy night in Belgium to eliminate the Spanish aristocrats.

Gladys and Bernie Crabtree kept their players locked in the dressing room for over an hour, giving the Real players the biggest tongue lashing they had ever received. Their manager told the players that they had to earn the right to play. Too many of them had felt all they had to do was to turn up to win the tie, but the Belgians had shown them that hard-work and playing as a team were as important as skill and technique. For the first time in her three years in Madrid. Gladys began to notice some dissent in the dressing room. The European Cup exit also gave the newspapers fuel to continue their anti-Protheroe articles. Gladys had, of course, experienced press criticism before and would ordinarily not have taken too much notice of the jibes, but she felt that perhaps the time was right to go before she was pushed. At a quiet dinner with Senor Gomez, Gladys told him of her doubts. She had realised that only three of the eleven Real managers had had the job for over three years. In Spain managers came and went by the month. Despite being relatively new in the job, Gladys was already the third longest serving manager in the Spanish league.

Senor Gomez told her that as far as he was concerned she was still the best manager in the game. He persuaded Gladys to stick with it, to ignore the criticism and to concentrate on winning the League title in style – then set about the European Cup once again.

CHAPTER FIVE "HOME WITH ALF."

After the dinner with her Chairman, Gladys returned to her apartment and had a cup of coffee before retiring. She drank the rich dark brew while attempting to pick up BBC World Service on her state of the art transistor radio. As she fiddled with the dials there was a knock on the door. She opened it to a young telegram boy who stood on her mat with an urgent wire for Senora Gladys.

After tipping and dismissing the lad Gladys sat down to discover just who was in such a rush to contact her. The telegram was marked 'Suffolk. England' and the sender a Senor Ramsey. The telegram read:

"Been offered England job stop. If we are to win Jules Rimet Trophy – need your help stop. Will be on first flight to Madrid tomorrow a.m. stop. See you for elevenses stop. Ramsey. Message Ends."

At just after a quarter past eleven Alf Ramsey sat in Gladys' Bernabeau office sipping P.G. Tips and nibbling Garibaldi biscuits. Ramsey told Gladys of his plans. He had taken Ipswich Town as far as he could. After the League Championship, Ipswich like Real had been eliminated from the European Cup in the first round – by A.C. Milan. But Ramsey's exploits had been noted by the F.A. and with the tournament to be held in England in three years time the one time full-back had been given the responsibility of winning the World Cup for England.

But Ramsey, although confident of his own abilities, felt he needed someone he could trust and rely on at his right hand. He wanted someone well versed in the rigours and pressures of World football – someone who had been there. The English game was very insular, only a handful of players had ever played abroad – even less made a successful transition to the Continent. There was no-one who had experienced the same week in, week out – seen the ups and downs of European football. No-one who had worked with and against talents such as Puskas, DiStefano, Gento, Eusebio and Riviera. No-one that is apart from Gladys Protheroe.

Ramsey went on to say he was aware of the dreadful way Gladys had been treated by the F.A. during her time as England manager, but that was almost a decade ago. The top brass had been replaced, now everyone at Lancaster Gate was pulling together, working towards one goal – The World Cup.

Gladys was placed in a delicate position. Since the Anderlecht defeat the Madrid newspapers had been filled with glossy speculation that Senor Gomez, frustrated by Real's inability to recapture the European Cup, would sack Gladys at the end of the season. This story had been angrily denied by the Real chairman but at the back of her mind Gladys had always wanted to be able to leave The Bernabeau when she was ready – not when the press decided.

Gladys told Ramsey that she would need 24 hours to think over his offer, and he flew back to England after telling her one more thing. Her country needed her.

Later that day there was a knock on Gladys' office door and Senor Gomez popped his head round the corner to ask his manager if she could spare five minutes for a chat. Gomez sat down, and for a few minutes they chatted about the weather and the form of reserve team goalkeeper Julio Inglesias. Then the chairman came to the point. He asked Gladys how Mr. Ramsey was keeping. She was at first surprised that Gomez knew of her visitor but then quickly realised that nothing went on at The Bernabeau without either his knowledge or consent.

Gladys took a deep breath and told him everything. Gomez sat silently, nodding and listening intently. When she had finished, he sat there for a moment then had his say. He told her that when he announced to the board of directors he was keen to appoint an Englishwoman as manager, many of them had called him mad. Some of the newspapers had christened him 'El Bosso Loco'. But he had been convinced that she was the best, and a club like Real Madrid deserved the very best. When he had made his decision, it was from the heart. Sometimes fate throws up once in a life-time opportunities. If Gladys felt that her country called, he would not stand in her way. He did not want her to go, but if she felt she must, he would accept her decision.

The two, who had started as employer and employee had now become close friends mutually respecting each other's talents. Gladys stepped from behind her desk and embraced Senor Gomez. They were both in tears as she told him that yes, she must return to England to win the World Cup.

That night, Gladys telephoned Ramsey to tell him of her decision to take the position as his assistant. Senor Gomez announced to the Spanish media that the First Lady of The Bernabeau was to leave. Fittingly, Gladys' final game as manager of Real Madrid was a home game with Barcelona. The Bernabeau was filled to capacity. Before the kick-off a small boy dressed in the famous all white of Real Madrid stood alone in the centre circle. All was silent as he sang a spine chilling soprano version of 'We're Gladys' Boys'. You could hear a pin drop in the huge stadium. Many of the players were in tears. Senor Gomez had to be supported by a programme seller as he presented Gladys with a bouquet and then 1,000 white doves were released into the Madrid sky. All 22 players ran to the Real bench and adorned it with red roses. For the first time in recent history both sets of supporters forgot their rivalry and stood together to applaud as Gladys took her place next to Bernie Crabtree. The game was an anti-climax after all the pre-match excitement, and ended in a nil-nil draw. That point meant that Real needed just two more from their final four games to be sure of a third consecutive Spanish championship, which they duly gained.

On her return to Croxley Green, Gladys kitted herself out with a number of new tracksuits from Lillywhites in Piccadilly and began another exciting chapter in her life.

The F.A. held a press conference to announce the management team for the 1966 World Cup campaign at The Green Man public house, just a stones throw from Wembley Stadium. Gladys sat on Ramsey's right hand as the media quizzed the pair on how England were going to fare in the tournament. Although the World Cup was still three years away English expectations were high. The Cup was being held in England for the first time, and after a string of poor performances in the previous finals, many experts felt it was vital English football showed the world that the country where the game was invented could still lead the way.

Ramsey seemed slightly edgy during the questioning, far from home under the bright lights, and he visibly flinched under the barrage. This is where Gladys proved her worth. Slowly, but surely, she won the pressmen over. She had, of course, experienced press conferences such as this on an almost daily basis in Madrid, and had learnt many tricks.

One journalist asked her how England would overcome the Brazilians. The Brazil coach had been quoted as saying that England were no longer a world force in the game. Gladys had the room in laughter when she swiftly retorted 'He would say that, wouldn't he?' A few months later, Mandy Rice-Davies used Gladys' catch-phrase in a courtroom during the Profumo affair, and sent Gladys a huge box of chocolates as a thank you.

Gladys had lost touch with the English game during her stay in Spain. She had regularly received all the English football magazines, and been sent reports on promising young players by scouts, but she had not actually seen an English League game for over six years. Her first priority therefore, was to see as many potential members of the World Cup squad as possible. The 1963/64 season was about to begin, and on the opening day Ramsey and Gladys took in Manchester United v. West Ham at Old Trafford.

She was already aware of the talents of players such as Moore and Charlton, but two new names caught her eye that afternoon. One was a spunky little ball-winner called Nobby Stiles, the other was the West Ham wing half Geoff Hurst. There was something about Hurst that impressed Gladys, but she just couldn't put her finger on it. Indeed. after the game she met the Hammers' manager, Ron Greenwood, and mentioned to him that perhaps Hurst was being played out of position. She suggested to Greenwood that Hurst had the look of a centre-forward about him – perhaps he could be given a run in that role? Greenwood thoughtfully accepted Gladys' advice, promising her that he would think about it.

Both Gladys and Ramsey soon came to the conclusion that many of the existing England squad were either too old to be considered for the '66 team, or simply not good enough. They realised that the international games between 1963 and 1965 would have to be used as a period of transition. The plan was to have a stable, balanced squad ready by the Summer of 1965, 12 months before the World Cup tournament. But it wouldn't be easy. The England supporters, and more importantly the national press, would not put up with poor results, even if it was explained to them that these games were being used to try out as many players as possible. Gladys had not forgotten the terrible mauling she received from the tabloids ten years earlier, and did not underestimate the power they had.

Ramsey made it clear that he looked upon the sports writers with little more than contempt. He saw them as people who had no experience and next to no knowledge of the game at the highest level. That attitude did nothing to improve his image of being an aloof, serious, private man. Gladys, with her experience in Spain behind her, patiently explained to Ramsey the importance of courting the press, but he would not be convinced and gladly gave his new assistant full responsibility for all press conferences and interviews.

It is interesting now to look back on the news clippings and TV and radio recordings made by the England management at that time, and see it was in fact Gladys, not Ramsey, who dealt with the vast majority of press duties. Indeed, it was Gladys, on Ramsey's behalf who made that famous prediction, that yes, England *would* win the World Cup.

The first game for England under the Ramsey/Protheroe regime was a clash with France in Paris. The French ran out 5-2 winners and this was followed by a defeat against Scotland at Wembley and a draw with Brazil, not the auspicious start Gladys had hoped for. But slowly, they began to get the balance right. Bobby Moore had impressed Gladys with his cool defending, and she was convinced he was a natural leader. Bobby Charlton, Ray Wilson and goalkeeper Gordon Banks had done enough to convince Alf and Gladys that their places were assured. These players were to be the nucleus of the 1966 team. Obviously, they had to be aware of injuries or a sudden loss of form, but Gladys was confident that they were beginning to put the jigsaw together. Gladys and Ramsey covered thousands of miles during her first season back in the Enlish game, and soon they became well known faces in the director's box at the big League grounds as they ran the rule over hopeful candidates.

60

Occasionally on Saturday evenings Gladys would join Kenneth Wolstenhome, commenting on the day's results on the BBC's newly launched TV programme '*Match of the Day*'.

During the Summer of 1964 Gladys and Ramsey spent much of their time on the Continent watching World Cup qualifying matches. As hosts, England were automatically guaranteed a place in the finals as were the holders, Brazil. Of the teams they saw, the West Germans with the strike force of Haller and Seeler caught the eye. Gladys was particularly impressed by an elegant young defender named Franz Beckenbauer. She mentioned to the German press that he had the confident stature of a Kaiser, a nickname that stuck.

Portugal with the great goalscorer Eusebio, Italy with Mazzola and Rivera, Spain, Switzerland and Hungary were also on course to qualify.

There had been reports from South America that Brazil had unearthed a new batch of young stars to add to the superb skills of Pele, and Gladys had also been aware that Uruguay and Argentina were emerging as forces to be reckoned with. The England management partnership flew to Montevideo to take in the Uruguay v. Chile game and left shocked after witnessing a game full of cynical fouls and gamesmanship. Gladys realised that if England were to succeed in the World Cup, they must be made aware of such tactics.

Time was beginning to pass quickly, and World Cup fever started to grip the country. In January 1965, Gladys and Ramsey launched the 'World Cup Willie' campaign at a luncheon at The Dorchester, and in March Gladys recorded a pop record, "We Can Do It" which was released on the Pye record label. This record was one of the first ever football releases, and although the disc only managed to reach No. 16 in the Hit Parade, it was a project that was to pay rich dividends in years to come.

The record was the idea of music entrepeneur Dick James. He had persuaded both Gladys and Ramsey that a pop single would capture the imagination of the teenage population. and with the F.A's blessing. Gladys recorded "We Can Do It" c/w "The Twin Towers Theme" in a Tottenham Court Road recording studio. Gladys possessed a bright, bluesy voice not unlike a sober Billie Holliday and she was backed on the session by Dick James' studio band. They were a competent four-piece and Gladys soon struck up a friendship with the bespectacled pianist. He told Gladys that he was a keen football supporter and that his uncle in fact had played professionally for Nottingham Forest, appearing in the 1959 F.A. Cup final. The pianist's name was Reg Dwight, but he confided to Gladys that he was considering changing it.

The England management continued to tinker with the make up of the squad. Gladys was delighted to learn that Ron Greenwood had taken her advice and switched Geoff Hurst to centre-forward. Hurst became a regular scorer in the First Division, and Gladys persuaded Ramsey to give him an opportunity at international level. The West Ham man was a whole hearted player, and Gladys liked the way he was always ready to listen to her advice.

In May 1965, after the Home International Tournament, Gladys and Ramsey attended the draw for the World Cup rounds. England were to open the tournament against Uruguay at Wembley. Mexico and France made up Group One. The main benefit was that England were to play all their group matches at Wembley, and Gladys had worked out that if everything went to plan, it was possible to play both the quarter and semi-final at the grand old stadium. This would mean that while England's rivals travelled to various parts of the country for their games, the English squad could be settled at a Home Counties base just a short coach trip from Wembley.

In the Summer of 1965 Gladys took a well earned holiday, and flew to Madrid to stay as a house guest of Juan Gomez. Unfortunately, Real Madrid had been unable to recapture the form they had shown under Gladys' management, and Gomez had appointed and sacked three coaches in the two years since Gladys left. Many of the players Gladys worked with had moved on, although Bernie Crabtree continued as Real's physio, even taking charge of team affairs on a caretaker basis for a brief spell. Bernie had settled into the Spanish way of life, and to someone not knowing his background seemed to be born and bred in Madrid. Bernie told Gladys he would be returning to England to take in the World Cup, and they arranged to have a good old fashioned knees-up in Croxley Green.

Back in England Gladys and Ramsey met up at the little house in Croxley Green to plan the final twelve months. Friendly matches against Austria, West Germany, Poland and a visit to Madrid to play Spain had been arranged. Together they made a list of fifty players who were in contention for a place in the final twenty-two. They left a couple of spaces blank, open for any players who made a late bid, but in reality, even with a full year to go sixteen or so players had already been pencilled in, leaving only five or six spots to be fought over during the 1965/66 season. Once again Gladys was to be seen at Highbury, Goodison, Old Trafford and the other First Division stadia monitoring the progress and form of the England players. By Christmas Ramsey and Gladys were being offered advice for the squad by the world and his wife. The Sunday papers were filled with writers and players selecting their teams. T.V. and radio pundits spent many hours giving their opinion on who should and who shouldn't be included. Suddenly everyone had become a football expert – even Gladys' postman stopped her on the garden path and told her not to dare leave Jimmy Greaves out of the squad.

England's final games before the World Cup were to take place in Scandinavia and Poland. Ramsey, Gladys and a squad of 30 players left London knowing the next match they took part in on home ground would be the opening match of the 1966 Jules Rimet Tournament against Uruguay.

The results against Finland, Norway, Sweden and the Poles were encouraging. The defence under the guidance of Moore was tight and efficient. Bobby's brother, Jack Charlton of Leeds United had blended in well to the back four adding height and authority. Stiles was a tiger in midfield, while the young flame haired Ball of Blackpool was a little dynamo. The one point of disagreement between Ramsey and Gladys was who should link up with Bobby Charlton and Roger Hunt in the forward line. On the Scandinavian tour, Jimmy Greaves had been at his sharpest, scoring four times in the 6-1 rout of Norway in Oslo. But there was something about the chirpy Londoner that Gladys was not convinced of. She had spotted the Tottenham forward drinking from a small bottle during the half-time interval in the Finland game, and although Greaves had claimed the bottle only contained a cough linctus, Gladys suspected that it was in fact vodka. She didn't say anything to Ramsey about the incident, but decided to keep a close eye on Greaves for the rest of the tour.

On their return to the UK, Ramsey and Gladys went together for a weekend in Devon. Gladys had rented a small fisherman's cottage for a couple of days with the intention of finalising England's 1966 World Cup squad. The sixteen finalists' complete squads of 22 players had to be registered at FIFA headquarters by the following Monday at noon. The two partners drove down to the South West and started work immediately on their arrival. Gladys had brought a large blackboard with her, and with white chalk wrote the numbers 1 to 22 on the left hand side. She made a huge plate of cheese and pickle sandwiches while Ramsey brought a crate of Double Diamond in from the car. They began work at nine that evening, and in less than two hours only four spaces remained blank. Names such as Banks, Cohen, Moore, Ball, the Charltons, Wilson and Hunt were already up there in white chalk – assured of a place in the greatest sporting competition in the World.

Gladys had put forward a case for the young, exciting Chelsea forward Osgood but Ramsey disagreed. Then it was her turn to use the veto when Alf had suggested Stepney of Manchester United for the third goalkeeper's spot. But Gladys told Ramsey she had seen him drop a number of crosses in a league game against Sunderland, so his name was deleted.

They worked on until dawn when only the number 10 shirt was vacant. Gladys remained silent as Ramsey put names like Wignall, Hateley and Bridges forward. Then it was her turn: she told Ramsey there could be only one man for that shirt – it just had to be Geoff Hurst. Alf wasn't convinced. True, Hurst had scored goals at all levels, but his approach work and technique did not impress Ramsey. He felt Hurst lacked pace and was vulnerable in the air. Eventually, just as the clock chimed nine a.m. Ramsey relented. He told her that if Gladys was so certain, then Hurst would be in the squad. She stood up, walked over to the blackboard and wrote 'Hurst, West Ham United' next to the No.10. So it was settled. Ramsey immediately rang the squad through to the F.A., FIFA, then Reuters. By lunch time the England squad would be national, indeed international news, but by then the England management team would be fast asleep in their bunk beds catching up on lost sleep.

Chapter Six "GLORY IN '66".

There was now just a fortnight until the finals, and already some of the competing nations had arrived in England. The stern well-disciplined West Germans flew in first and settled into their training camp in the North East. Next were the mysterious little men from North Korea, then the charismatic Brazilians with Pele at the helm.

Ramsey, Gladys and the squad were now involved in either training sessions or publicity work every day. The England headquarters were at Hendon in North West London, just a few miles from Wembley Stadium. The squad had been kitted out in their World Cup suits (a lightweight grey two-piece for Gladys) and were pictured in the press at The Tower of London, with World Cup Willie outside Buckingham Palace, and various other stunts were dreamt up by the marketing men to keep interest in the tournament at fever pitch. The training sessions went well, there were no injury worries and Ramsey and Gladys had already secretly decided on the team to kick off against Uruguay.

Three days before the opening ceremony, FIFA held an official welcoming cocktail party at the Savoy. Representatives of all sixteen competing nations attended. Gladys and Ramsey were accompanied by captain Bobby Moore. As Gladys stood chatting to the North Korean manager Sim Pan Noo, she caught sight of the Spanish delegation. There in a white suit clutching a glass of white wine stood her old adversary from Barcelona, Vasquez. The Spaniard seemed to be drinking heavily, and was loudly telling the West German captain, Seeler, just how well the Spanish team would do in the tournament.

Gladys continued her conversation with the polite little man from the East, but she couldn't help noticing Vasquez stopping wine waiters every couple of minutes. He downed seven or eight glasses in the ten minutes Gladys was watching him, and his hearty laughter was echoing around the room. He was beginning to slur his words, and he looked a little unsteady on his feet.

About half an hour later Gladys was talking to the Italian inside forward Gianni Rivera and the giant Russian goalkeeper Lev Yashin. The three discussed the forthcoming fortnight, and their mutual respect was apparent. It was then that Vasquez, on his way to the gents, clumsily barged into Rivera, spilling the Italian's orange juice. Vasquez turned drunkenly towards them and suddenly recognised Gladys. He cackled a vulgar, wine soaked laugh, mockingly made a curtseying gesture and in an alcohol stewed voice told Rivera how honoured he must be to speak with the great Senora Protheroe. He plucked a glass of wine from a passing waiter's tray and downed it in one, dropping the empty glass on the carpeted floor. He swayed in front of the three astonished guests, and now in a louder, wilder voice told them it was his Barcelona who had knocked the swines from Madrid out of the European Cup. Heads turned as Vasquez shouted out for more wine. He now had a manic look in his eyes, his tie was undone, his hair ruffled. He spoke, feigning sincerity, telling how marvellous it was to meet Senora Protheroe again. The room was now totally silent but for the drunken rantings of the Spaniard. After another long draw on his wine glass, he shouted out how funny he found it that a woman should be involved with the England team. Were there no English men anymore?

Gladys noticed Bobby Moore pushing through the partygoers to reach her side. She motioned to her captain with her hand that everything was under control. Vasquez then turned his gaze to Moore, looked him up and down and asked him what it was like to take orders from an old woman. He called Moore a blonde pimp and a mother's boy. The Spaniard then insulted the Queen, Harold Wilson and The Beatles. He called Gladys a stupid old bitch whose trouble was that she had never had a Spaniards cock up her. One of the Spanish squad, clearly embarrassed by the scene his countryman was causing attempted to pull Vasquez away, but he shook his arm free and called for yet more wine. Bobby Moore quietly suggested that he had drunk enough, but this advice only further inflamed the Spaniard. Once again he insulted Gladys, but this time his words were met with a vicious uppercut that left him in a crumpled heap on the floor. The Russian Yashin had heard enough, and he could take it no longer. Where he came from, the icy wastes of Siberia, to insult a woman in public was the sign of a coward. He had been biting his lip throughout the Spaniard's dreadful display, but he was unable to control his Soviet temper any longer.

The prone Vasquez was hurriedly carried out of The Savoy by a number of wine waiters, while the Spanish Ambassador and the team manager apologised to Gladys and the other guests before leaving. Yashin was discreetly ushered away by the Soviet delegation, and the party continued.

Fortunately, no journalists had been present, and although a few stories appeared in the press alluding to some kind of incident, the affair was soon glossed over. It was an indication of the kind of pressure the English management and players would be under during the next two weeks, and the following day Ramsey and Gladys used the Vasquez incident to press home to the players the importance of them being on their very best behaviour during the World Cup.

On the 11th July 1966, three years of planning were over. After an hour of speeches, and hundreds of schoolchildren representing the competing nations parading around Wembley Stadium, the opening game of the eighth World Cup kicked off.

Gladys and Ramsey surprised many experts by picking the Manchester United winger Connelly. Uruguay made their intentions clear from the very first minute, when first Ball was scythed down, then the South Americans refused to retreat the full ten yards for the free kick. The English forwards toiled away in the heat, but were unable to break down the Uruguayan defence. Greaves and Charlton were man to man marked, and when an English player was able to find a little space he was stopped by fair means or foul as the visitors battled for a point.

The Uruguay team celebrated as if they had won the trophy itself when the referee blew the final whistle with the scoreline 0-0. There was some booing from the England supporters as Gladys and Ramsey walked down the tunnel to the dressing room. The game proved how difficult it was going to be for England. Every opponent was going to be determined to try and stifle the English forwards; Gladys and Ramsey reminded their players that patience was the one thing everyone needed.

Gladys was aware that the players needed to have their spirits lifted before the next match against Mexico. The newspapers had criticised England's performance against Uruguay, saying that their play had been naïve.

For the Mexico game, Paine of Southampton and Peters of West Ham came in for Ball and Connelly. Once again the England players were frustrated by a packed defence. The Mexicans pulled every player back behind the ball, quite happy to clear the ball anywhere, not even attempting to attack. At one stage, Gladys feared another drab goalless draw until Bobby Charlton picked the ball up just inside the England half. Charlton looked to play the ball out wide, but the Mexican defenders kept retreating. Gladys whispered to Ramsey that she felt Charlton was ready to shoot. The balding centre-forward continued on his run, still no Mexican prepared to tackle him. Then, from about thirty yards out, Charlton unleashed a ferocious shot that flew into the Mexican net. The delight and relief of the England bench was plain for all to see, Gladys jumped up and embraced Peter Bonetti, as England's World Cup challenge moved up a gear at last. A well taken effort by Roger Hunt gave England a comfortable 2-0 win, and barring a freak result against France, had put England into the quarter-finals.

Roger Hunt was the hero against the French when he bagged both goals in another 2-0 victory. The tournament was into the sudden death stages, and England were drawn against Argentina in the quarter-finals. The Argentinians had won through to the last eight with some physical displays.

They had eliminated the Spanish, coming second to West Germany in Group Two, but already had two men sent off and five more booked. Ramsey and Gladys feared that the South Americans would continue where Uruguay, and to a lesser extent Mexico, had left off, attempting to frustrate the English players, push the referee to his limit, then try to score on the break.

Gladys told her players not to get involved in any retaliation, and to simply play their normal game. The one problem for the England management was that Greaves had picked up an ankle injury in the French match, and would have to miss the quarter-final. Ramsey and Gladys spent over an hour discussing who should play in his place. Ramsey was well aware of Gladys' support for Hurst, but he was impressed with the way she discussed the other options. However, Hurst had looked sharp in training and he eventually got the nod to link up with Hunt and Charlton against Argentina.

The game was played in searing heat which suited the South Americans. As expected, the English forwards were subjected to some horrendous tackling as Argentina tried to kick their way into the semi-finals. The Argentine captain Antonio Rattin had a running argument with the referee, and Gladys was concerned that perhaps the tall defender would intimidate the match official into giving the Argentinians some advantage. She shouldn't have worried. Midway through the second half Rattin overstepped the mark, when for the umpteenth time he sent Bobby Charlton tumbling with a wicked tackle from behind, then argued with the referee over where the free-kick should be taken from. The referee's patience had finally been used up, and he sent the Argentina captain off. There was uproar as first Rattin refused to leave the pitch, then he went off and his team followed him.

It took ten minutes for order to be restored. Gladys with her knowledge of Spanish acted as an interpreter on the touchline. Eventually she persuaded Rattin to leave the pitch, but not before a blazing row. There is a famous photograph of the incident which shows Rattin towering menacingly over Gladys as she gives him a severe dressing down for being so stupid. Gladys earned a standing ovation as she ran back to take her place on the England bench, but she was soon back on her feet as she celebrated Geoff Hurst's header that gave England a 1-0 win.

England were through to the last four. West Germany, USSR and Portugal who were to be England's semi-final opponents had also made it through. Both Ramsey and Gladys were quietly pleased with the performances, and obviously delighted that their team had yet to concede a goal in the competition.

Jimmy Greaves was battling to regain his fitness, but although his ankle injury was improving day by day, it was unlikely he would be ready for the Portugal game. But as Gladys said to Alf, how on Earth could they think about leaving Hurst out after his great goal against Argentina?

After being on the receiving end of Eusebio's goalscoring prowess while at Real Madrid, Gladys was determined that he would not be given the opportunity to put one over her again. This would be the first time the England defence had been up against a World class forward who was bang in form. Eusebio was the leading goalscorer in the World Cup after having hit a hat-trick in the quarter-final match against North Korea.

Gladys suggested to Ramsey that Nobby Stiles was the ideal player to tame 'The Panther' as Eusebio had been dubbed by the press. She spent two complete training sessions alone with the tenacious Manchester United man, teaching him the art of man to man marking and passing on some of Eusebios tricks.

The semi-final game was to be played in the evening, which pleased everyone in the England camp. The temperature for the Argentina match had been over 90 degrees and all the players had been dangerously dehydrated by the final whistle.

Another contrast to the quarter-final was the sporting way Portugal played. Instead of stifling, negative tactics, the red shirted Portugese played a swift attacking game. The Wembley crowd were enthralled with one of the most entertaining games of the tournament. Gladys' decision to put Stiles on Eusebio was a success. The two players were inseperable, the short-sighted, toothless Englishman played out of his skin as he snapped at his opponents' heels, and did not give him a yard of space throughout the 90 minutes. However, Eusebio did get on the scoresheet when he blasted a penalty past Gordon Banks - the first time Banks had been beaten in almost five games. Fortunately, England had already made sure of a place in the final through two Bobby Charlton goals. When the referee blew the final whistle the England bench celebrated a great victory. Eusebio made a beeline for Gladys Protheroe, and the two great characters swopped shirts.

In the other semi-final West Germany had beaten the Soviets, so it was to be Seeler, Haller, Beckenbauer and company who stood between Gladys and the World Cup. The Germans were confident about their chances, and for the first time in the tournament the press started to doubt whether England could do it. Some newspapers began to criticise England's 'Wingless Wonders', saying that the Germans were technically superior in every department.

Gladys and Ramsey had nearly a week to work with their players before the final, and after all the excitement of the last few weeks, they decided it would be a good idea to let the squad relax. No training would make them any fitter, it was decided to give them a few days off and hope they would be able to keep their minds off the biggest game any of them would play in their lives.

The one problem for the management team was the fact that Jimmy

Greaves had recovered from his ankle injury. Ramsey was keen to put him back in the team, he felt the Tottenham man's experience would be vital in such an important match, but Gladys disagreed. Once again she had to fight Hurst's corner, and it wasn't until the morning of the final that Ramsey relented.

It was Gladys who broke the news to Greaves that he would not be playing. The player took it badly, and to this day he refuses to speak to her. Indeed, when Gladys was a guest on the ITV quiz show 'Sporting Triangles' in December 1988, some twenty two years after the event, there was an unseemly row between the two in the studio canteen that led to the security men being called. Gladys has been quoted many times saying that she rates Jimmy Greaves as one of the all time greats, but it seems that this particular wound remains as open as it did on that July morning in 1966 – a pity indeed.

The England squad left their Hendon headquarters in the team coach at eleven a.m. on the day of the World Cup Final. The day was overcast, and a light Summer drizzle made the air sweet and fresh. As usual Gladys took her seat just behind Roy the driver, next to Terry Paine. The street were filled with supporters waving and cheering, some holding up banners that read 'Show 'Em Gladys' and 'Alf and Gladys for King & Queen', With still over three hours before the kick-off. Empire Way was packed with fans eager to wish their heroes all the best. Gladys and Alf took the players out onto the pitch to feel the turf which was soft and springy due to the rain.

There was little to tell the players, they knew what was expected of them. The hopes of a nation were on their shoulders. The Germans had already scored one psychological point over England by their choice of kit for the game. As both countries traditionally wore white shirts, obviously one would have to change. The Germans won the toss, which meant England would take the pitch in a new look red shirt. Gladys wasn't pleased, but there was nothing she could do about it.

The 1966 World Cup Final will of course be remembered for Geoff Hurst's marvellous hat-trick, but then there has always been speculation over whether Hurst's second goal did cross the line. One interesting piece of evidence is the BBC film of the game. One of their cameras was directly in front of the England bench, and when one looks back at that film today, one can clearly see Gladys jump off the bench to hug Ron Flowers when Hurst's shot bounces down off the bar. With her undoubted knowledge of the game and her perfect eyesight, even the most cynical of observers are left in no doubt. Yes, it was a goal.

When one remembers that July afternoon there are a number of pictures that spring to mind. One is big Jack Charlton kneeling in the centre-circle sobbing like a child, then there is Nobby Stiles' manic toothless dance around the great old stadium. But for many people, the most potent image is that of Alf Ramsey and Gladys Protheroe totally oblivious to the herd of photographers and supporters around them, holding each other in a tight embrace at the foot of the 39 Wembley steps.

As Bobby Moore received the Jules Rimet trophy from Her Majesty the Queen, the England supporters erupted into an emotional rendition of "We're Gladys' Boys", and once again looking back at the film footage, it is interesting to notice that both the Queen and Prince Phillip join in on the chorus.

After the game the England squad were driven to The Savoy for a celebration dinner, Gladys sat between Alf Ramsey and Bobby Moore at the top table, and the next morning the Sunday papers were full of pictures of the three great friends wearing ear to ear smiles.

After dancing with each one of the 22 England players, and the last waltz with Alf Ramsey, Gladys left early – leaving the younger ones to celebrate well into the small hours. She took a taxi back to Croxley Green. returning home at just before 2 am.

It was a strange feeling as she sat in her kitchen with a glass of milk. After all the years of hard work, she had achieved the greatest feat in football. Gladys pulled her out her small World Cup winners medal and cradled it in her palm. She then looked up to the heavens and asked what Ernest thought about it all. She knew that up there, somewhere, Ernest was looking down on her. She had felt his presence on the bench that afternoon. One day of course, they would be together again. But before that day, there was more work to be done. Where it would take her Gladys didn't yet know. She placed her medal on the mantelpiece, turned out the lights, and went to bed. It had been a busy day – now for tomorrow.

It took a few days for the reality of the situation to sink in. For the next few weeks Gladys and Ramsey appeared on all the major TV chat shows, and interviews with them were syndicated to newspapers and magazines throughout the World. Gladys was seen on Dee Time, Juke Box Jury, and even appeared as herself in a special episode of The Man From U.N.C.L.E.

By the end of the Summer Gladys felt drained. She had been working too hard, and the England team doctor recommended a few months of complete rest.

Bernie Crabtree had left Real Madrid to take over as first team coach with Swiss first division club Young Boys, and he contacted Gladys to offer her the use of a small chalet near his home.

She flew to Zurich, and was met at the airport by Young Boys Chairman Paul Gustz. Gustz was honoured that such a well known character was gracing his club with her presence, and he proudly introduced

Gladys to the Young Boys supporters before their league game with Lausanne.

Gladys took to the clean, fresh Swiss air, and often went on nature rambles in the Alps. She bought a bicycle and took up water colours. She was now almost sixty years old, and although she felt as fit as a flea, had the sense to realise that it was impossible to keep up the kind of workload she had taken on with the England team.

One morning a telegram arrived for her. It was from Alf Ramsey, and told her that her England manager was now Sir Alf. Her captain, Bobby Moore had received the O.B.E. and both friends had been summoned to Buckingham Palace to meet the Queen. In later years Gladys did candidly admit she was slightly disappointed not to have been honoured, but she would laugh it off, only half joking that perhaps the Queen would have been a little intimidated by the first lady of football.

Gladys was to spend just over eighteen months in Switzerland recharging her batteries, and became something of a celebrity. Her chalet was only half an hours drive from Charlie Chaplin's home, and after being introduced at a dinner party, they became very close. Both were Londoners, and found they had a great deal in common. Chaplin had started to write songs, and Gladys would occasionally help out whenever he was unable to find a suitable rhyme or phrase.

Gladys was reading regularly. She had never achieved high academic status, and had always felt she had missed out on a real education due to her football commitments. Soon books by Kafka, Salinger, Sartre, Hemingway and Capote were eagerly devoured. In a matter of months she became something of an authority on 20th Century literature.

English journalists regularly arrived at Gladys' chalet for interviews that appeared in the U.K. press. She would tell them she was contented and happy, resting in such a beautiful country. The one question they all asked was, would she be with the England team in Italy for the European Championships?

Sir Alf Ramsey (as he now was) had been in touch by telephone on a regular basis during Gladys' Swiss soujourn, and had flown to Zurich twice to meet his assistant.

He had managed to get England through the qualifying games alone, but was not confident of success in the European Championships without his right-hand woman. He had begun to question his own ability, and with no Gladys beside him on the bench Sir Alf's decisions and instructions had become confused and muddled. One month before the European Championships were due to begin, Sir Alf arrived at the neat little chalet with a briefcase bulging with files and documents lisiting the players he had available, and their current form.

Sir Alf had a list of nearly forty players, but he had to whittle it down to the squad of 22 – would Gladys help? The two old friends embraced on her front step, then she cooked her visitor a traditional Swiss meal of veal in cheese. They took their coffees and liqueurs overlooking the beautiful countryside surrounding the chalet, and she looked through the list of players, marking the players who impressed her with a red biro.

Since the World Cup England had lost the services of the Fulham full-back George Cohen through injury, Nobby Stiles and Jack Charlton had lost form, and Ramsey had replaced the three of them with Newton of Blackburn, Labone of Everton and Mullery of Tottenham. Although not having watched any League football for some time, Gladys was well aware of the attributes of the new trio. She had also received good reports on a new crop of players including Reaney, Lee, Hughes, Astle, Bell and Summerbee. As far as she could see, Ramsey's list was as complete as it could be, and she told him so.

This news obviously calmed Ramsey, and he was a far more relaxed man for the remainder of his stay. Before he left for London he asked Gladys if she would take her place on the England bench for the European Championships. She took a deep breath and told Sir Alf that no, he must go alone. The World Cup had taken its toll on her mentally and physically and she explained that she would not be able to do the job justice.

A disappointed Ramsey flew home, and a few days later Gladys read that Harold Shepherdson of Middlesborough had been appointed as the new England trainer. The report in the newspaper stressed that Ramsey was keeping the door open for Gladys whenever she was ready to return to the England set-up. Ramsey was quoted as saying that Shepherdson was a fine trainer, but Protheroe was a trainer, diplomat, tactical genius and natural leader all rolled into one – and only one such talent comes along each generation. Gladys was touched, and she still keeps that cutting in her purse, even now.

England were disappointing in the European Championships, losing to West Germany and Yugoslavia before defeating USSR. They were eliminated from the tournament, and although it was never publicly stated, many felt England's poor showing was directly due to Gladys' absence.

Ramsey was criticised in the press, but he remained defiant telling the journalists that the main priority was Mexico 1970, where England would defend their World Championship. Someone at a press conference asked if he was certain Gladys Protheroe would be with him in Mexico – he pretended not to hear the question.

Time began to drag for Gladys in Switzerland. The two years she had spent on vacation had been relaxing, but now she was rested and ready to return to the world of football. During her prolonged holiday she had been linked with a number of managerial vacancies both in England and abroad. One of the more interesting approaches had been from Boca Juniors of Argentina. Ironically, the Boca captain was none other that the World Cup player Rattin, with whom Gladys had the much publicised row at Wembley. It seemed that the Boca board liked what they had seen, and were keen to inject some discipline into their squad of petulant players. However, Gladys wasn't keen to work in South America, so the offer was politely declined.

After thanking Bernie Crabtree and Paul Gustz for their hospitality, she promised to keep in touch with Charlie Chaplin. Unfortunately, Chaplin passed away later that year. After the funeral, Gladys was delighted to receive an old hat-pin from his estate. Gladys wears it to this day as a tribute to the great man of comedy.

On 12th August 1968, Gladys was on a Swissair flight back to Heathrow, fit and ready to carry on her work. The Protheroe home had been kept aired and ready by local char Emily Cornes. The house was as bright as a new pin, and Emily had hoisted a 'Welcome Home Gladys' banner across the drive. Many locals lined the road as the taxi drew up, and as the driver unloaded her luggage from the boot an impromptu version of *We're Gladys' Boys filled* the evening air.

The 1968/69 season was about to kick-off, and Gladys was Guest of Honour at Vicarage Road to watch Watford open their League campaign against Chesterfield. It was the first English league game Gladys had taken in for well over two Years, and despite it being a Third Division fixture, it soon whetted her appetite. Indeed, on a number of occasions in the second half Gladys' voice was quite audible in the Main Stand as she shouted instructions to the Watford team.

For the remaining months of 1968 Gladys kept a reasonably low profile. Apart from appearing on the BBC Television programme *Panorama* to take part in a debate on the student riots in Paris Gladys was busy in her garden, planting a new herbaceous bed.

On 15th January 1969, the day before her 62nd birthday. Gladys was invited by the F.A. to be their guest at Wembley for the friendly international between England and Rumania. It was her first visit since that famous afternoon in July 1966. She received a standing ovation from the crowd, and the supporters launched into a vociferous version of her theme song just before the kick-off, quite overpowering the Rumanian anthem.

Sir Alf had made a number of changes since the European Championships. New names such as Wright of Everton, Hunter of Leeds and the Arsenal pair of McNab and Radford were in the team. Gladys sat just behind the Royal Box, and watched with interest as Ramsey tried to lure his players on to greater things. The game was a slight disappointment, ending 1-1, with Jack Charlton scoring for England.

CHAPTER SEVEN. 'ELTON & BERNIE'

After the game, Gladys attended a small cocktail party in her honour at the nearby Wembley Conservative Club, and spent a happy hour or two chatting to various football personalities. There was a piano player sitting in the corner of the room gently running through a few numbers. He had a pleasant voice, and there was something familiar about him. She walked over to where he played, and for a few minutes stood, enjoying the music. When he had completed his set, Gladys introduced herself. The pianist reminded her that they had in fact met before when he had played piano on Gladys' World Cup disc. He told her that since they last met he had changed his name from Reg Dwight to Elton John. She thought for a moment, and told him that the new name did have a certain ring to it.

Elton told Gladys that he was trying to break into the recording business. Although he was satisfied with the tunes he was coming up with, he felt he needed someone to work with, contributing lyrics. Gladys thought for a moment, then remembered the young lad who sometimes helped her in the garden with the heavy digging. On her return from Switzerland she had placed a postcard in the newsagents window asking for help two mornings a week.

After a few days, a lion-haired youth called offering his services. At eleven o'clock, after the lad had been working for two hours, Gladys usually brewed up a pot of tea and they would spend ten minutes chatting. He had mentioned to Gladys that he was a songwriter, and one morning brought a sheaf of lyrics for Gladys to inspect. Although she felt most of the songs were a little too obscure, she was impressed by one he had written. It was called *Your Song*. The name of that boy was Bernie Taupin.

Gladys mentioned Bernie to Elton, and suggested that perhaps he would like to pop round to her house next morning to meet the lyricist. Elton readily agreed and set about his second set with a new energy.

At around midnight, Gladys thanked the F.A. officials for a splendid night, said goodbye to Elton as he packed his equipment into a battered Ford van then left in a taxi for home. As she was driven home she looked back on a thoroughly enjoyable evening. In future years, millions of pop fans would have cause to thank Gladys for bringing the two most talented songwriters of the 1970s together. For that night signalled the beginning of Captain Fantastic and The Brown Dirt Cowboy.

The next morning Elton arrived in Croxley Green and was formally introduced to Bernie Taupin. The two aspiring songwriters seemed to hit it off immediately, and Gladys left them alone in her front room with her old piano and a pot of good strong tea.

After an hour or so Elton came running into the garden to find Gladys, and asked her to come inside and listen to the fruits of their labour. Elton, like Gladys, had seen potential in Bernie's *Your Song* and had spent the morning putting a tune to the words. Elton sat at the piano and nervously played the first ever John/Taupin composition. When he had finished, the two young musicians eagerly awaited Gladys' opinion. She was silent for a few moments, then walked over to the piano and told them that as far as she was concerned, they had a great future together in showbusiness. Gladys has said in later interviews that she is no pop music expert, but there was something about that song that convinced her Elton and Bernie were on the verge of great success. Of course, she had no idea just how successful the two youngsters would become.

Elton and Bernie told Gladys they would like to dedicate *Your Song* to her, and to the present day Elton always introduces the song at his concerts with the story of how Gladys brought Bernie and him together. On the sleeve of the *Your Song* single, the message 'To Gladys – without you, none of this would have been possible. Love E&B.' runs underneath a photograph of Elton. Some three weeks later, Gladys was woken at four in the morning by a telephone call from Elton who excitedly told her that he and Bernie had just been offered a recording contract. Gladys was delighted, she wished Elton well but warned him to keep his feet on the round, and not to get carried away by the success that was certain to come.

Your Song went on to sell many millions of copies throughout the World, and catapulted Elton John and Bernie Taupin to massive super stardom. But, as successful and wealthy as they now both are, the two great songwriters never have forgotten the role Gladys Protheroe played in their careers. To this day Croxley Green residents often see the two stars arriving at Gladys' home bearing gifts and flowers.

By the Summer of 1969, Sir Alf Ramsey had persuaded Gladys to join him and the England squad in Mexico the next Summer. The players, particularly those who had been involved in 1966 were delighted that the old partnership had been restored.

Gladys and Sir Alf took an England squad to South America in June '69, 12 months before the World Cup was to take place. The trip was arranged so the players and management would be able to experience the climate, altitude and training facilities. Games against Mexico, Uruguay and Brazil had been arranged. England drawing, winning and losing them respectively.

The nucleus of the squad still comprised loyal, dependable players such as Moore, Charlton, Banks and Ball, but time had caught up with a few of the heroes of '66.

Wright, Newton, Lee and Mullery had all settled into the team, and Gladys was pleased with the enthusiasm of the younger players. She confided to Sir Alf, that perhaps this 1970 squad could be even stronger than the one in 1966.

The atmosphere in South America during that 1969 tour seemed to be definitely anti-English. Once again, Gladys' Spanish was a tremendous asset. Whilst Ramsey's taciturn, arrogant attitude aggravated the Latin journalists, Gladys' ability to joke and gossip with the writers in a far more relaxed manner was a vital factor in presenting the England regime in a more accessible light. It was Gladys who took charge of the press conferences as she had done four years earlier.

Gladys advised Ramsey that it was important for England to try and make as many friends as possible on the tour. In twelve months time the relationship with the press, and through them the neutrals, would be vital. Gladys went out of her way to build up a good rapport with the locals, but Ramsey was not convinced of the need for such openness.

Despite all Gladys' efforts, the England squad left South America labelled as secretive, cold and insular. Ramsey and Gladys had learnt the strengths and weaknesses of their major rivals on the pitch, but they had been unable to win over the Mexican supporters. England were to return in a year's time as holders of the Jules Rimet trophy, but few Mexicans expected 'Gladys' Gringos' as the squad had been dubbed, to retain the trophy.

CHAPTER EIGHT: 'THE TROUBLE WITH GEORGE'

When Gladys returned to England in July 1969, she received a letter from Sir Matt Busby, the manager of Manchester United. Busby told her that he was having problems with his Northern Ireland international player, George Best. Best had been missing training sessions, and Busby feared the reason was drink. Would it be at all possible for Gladys to travel up to Manchester to speak to the player?

Busby was convinced that the wayward winger would listen to her. The alcohol problems Gladys had endured during the 1950s had been well documented, and Sir Matt felt that the influence of a fellow football personality who had experienced a similar crisis would help the situation. Gladys agreed, and on 14th September 1969 she caught an express train from Watford Junction to Manchester Piccadilly where she was met by Sir Matt Busby and club captain Bobby Charlton. That evening Gladys had dinner with Busby, Charlton and Denis Law. During the meal Gladys listened as the three men told her their problem. Best was the most talented player in Europe, and second only to the great Pele in the World. But he was insecure and surrounded himself with an entourage of hangers-on and fairweather friends. He had been given bad advice and become involved in a number of financially unsound ventures.

Best had been spotted regularly in Manchester night spots drinking well into the small hours, had stopped shaving and put on over a stone in weight. Initially, Busby had been prepared to turn a blind eye to Best's occasional absence from training, but soon the drinking bouts began to last days instead of hours, and Busby had no option but to discipline the player. The result of a club fine had been that Best had disappeared for three days, and missed a league game against Arsenal at Highbury. He had eventually turned up at half-time wearing odd shoes, no socks and smelling of strong drink.

Sir Matt had no alternative but to suspend the Irishman, and the Board of Directors made an official statement to the press announcing that unless Best mended his ways, he would never play for Manchester United again. The situation between Best and Busby had become intolerable. The player had refused to speak to his manager, and his behaviour had caused discontent amongst the players in the dressing room.

Bobby Charlton, having seen at first hand Gladys' skills of diplomacy and discipline, had recommended her to Busby. Charlton, although disgusted by Best's drinking and bad timekeeping, admired his superb skills,and was determined to do all he could to save his team-mate from more self abuse.

Over coffee and After Eight mints, Gladys agreed to spend a month at Old Trafford in an attempt to get Best back on the rails.

The next morning Gladys reported to United's training round on the outskirts of Manchester at 8 am, and sat with the first team coach Wilf McGuiness. Training officially started at ten, and by nine thirty most of the squad were already out on the training pitch kicking a ball about. McGuinness left Gladys alone in the dressing room as he went off to lead the players through a variety of limbering up exercises. All the first team had arrived apart from Best.

At a quarter past ten there was still no sign of him, and Gladys was about to join the players for training when she heard a car pull up outside. Looking out of a window she saw Best, bearded and dressed in a dinner-jacket thrusting a handful of notes into a taxi driver's hand.

Best's hair was shoulder length, his bow tie undone and his white silk shirt unbuttoned to the waist. Gladys watched him as he carefully crept through the shrubbery so to keep out of sight of the training pitch. She was sitting waiting as he clambered through the toilet window into the dressing room. There was a mixture of embarrassment, surprise and anger on the Irishman's face as he saw Gladys cooly sitting in the corner sipping a cup of tea.

Neither said a word as Best changed into his track suit. Gladys noticed the roll of fat around his waist, and watched carefully as the player, obviously still the worse for drink attempted to tie his boot laces. The once slim, lithe, athlete's body was now heavy and bloated. Best belched loudly as he walked past Gladys and tried to open the dressing room door.

But Gladys had locked it, and she held the key in her hand. The Irishman pushed and shoved the door a dozen or more times before he realised why it would not open. Gladys showed him the key, then quietly but firmly told him to sit down. He obeyed, and she brewed up a fresh pot of tea. She told him that he had the World at his feet. He could be a millionaire if he just agreed to buckle down and work with his manager and coach. He had been born with a God given talent, it was his duty to use it to its potential.

Suddenly, Best turned on her, demanding to know what right she had to keep him a prisoner. He just seemed to snap and went berserk throwing football boots, training tops and bottles of linament against the wall. He screamed how everyone was against him, and how Busby was determined to drive him out of Old Trafford. With his full beard, long flowing hair and wild, glazed, eyes Best looked like the wild man of Borneo. Gladys had to be on her guard as another salvo of studs, jock-straps and shin pads came crashing towards her. Suddenly there was a banging on the locked door. The fracas had disturbed the training session, and the players fearing that Gladys was in danger were trying to break the door down. Brian Kidd ran to get the caretaker who had a masterkey, but by the time he returned, the dressing room was silent and still.

Bobby Charlton was the first player to enter the room. He had never seen such chaos. Everywhere was broken glass, tables were upturned, chairs were smashed to matchwood, players' clothes were scattered over the floor. He was half expecting to see the small frail figure of Gladys Protheroe battered and beaten, but there in the corner she sat with George Best cradled in her arms like a small child. Best was weeping uncontrollably, and Gladys immediately ordered Charlton and the other players from the dressing room.

Slowly, Best calmed down, and after some persuading agreed to travel down to stay with Gladys for a few weeks. Sir Matt Busby arrived at the training round and was staggered to see such destruction. A couple of apprentices had already started clearing up the mess, and a bonfire had been lit to burn the broken furniture.

Gladys, Busby and McGuinness had a brief meeting and all were of the same opinion: that a short time under Gladys' influence could be just what Best needed. Gladys borrowed a club car from goalkeeper Alex Stepney, and within half an hour she and Best were heading South. They had a pleasant drive down, the only disappointment being Stepney's taste in music. He had an eight track stereo in the vehicle, but Gladys and Best could not find a single tape to their taste. The glove compartment was full of Edison Lighthouse, The Archies and Roger Whittaker. Best, now fully recovered from his tantrum, suggested throwing the tapes out of the window, but Gladys wouldn't hear of it. They stopped off at a garage and bought a James Brown tape for the rest of the journey.

George Best stayed with Gladys for nearly three weeks, and during that time did not touch one drop of alcohol. She persuaded him to shave off his beard and they went on early morning runs together. Gladys was in touch with Sir Matt Busby on a daily basis and the Manchester United manager was delighted to hear that progress was being made. United were missing his skills, and without Best the team had dropped out of the early season pacemakers. Gladys told Busby that, all being well, Best should be available for first team selection by mid-November.

Soon the residents of Croxley Green became used to seeing Best on his training jaunts, and the Irishman enjoyed the friendly atmosphere of the relaxed Hertfordshire village. Unfortunately, the Fleet Street newspapers soon found out where Best was staying, and on a number of occasions Gladys crossed swords with prying journalists. One particular reporter from *The Sun* newspaper was an old drinking partner of Best's and Gladys intercepted a message from him asking the player out for a drink at the nearest pub. Gladys was well aware of the danger the reporter posed.

Although Best had been on the wagon for some time, it would take only one drinking session to ruin all the good work.

Photographs of Gladys and Best on their training runs began to appear in the press, and within a few days television crews from all over Europe had camped outside Gladys' door waiting for a glimpse of the infamous player. It became obvious to Gladys that it was impossible for Best to continue staying with her. The press circus outside her front gate was beginning to irritate the neighbours, and the arc lights from the TV cameras had made it impossible for anyone in the road to get a night's sleep. After getting the O.K. from Sir Matt Busby, Gladys decided to enlist the help of Elton John and Bernie Taupin.

Elton was on a club tour of Great Britain, and after a few telephone calls she managed to reach the young singer. He was starting a four night stint at a small club in the North of Scotland and Elton was more than happy to be of help. The plan was that Best would join Elton, Bernie and the band on tour as a roadie, obviously in disguise. The tour ended in Manchester in a fortnight's time, and then the player could be returned to Old Trafford.

At three in the morning, with George Best hiding under a blanket in the boot, Gladys sped through the press cordon in Alex Stepney's car and headed North. A few of the journalists attempted to follow, but some agressive driving from Gladys shook them off by Newport Pagnell services.

Gladys stopped for petrol at Watford Gap and released Best from the confines of the boot. They drank coffee and discussed the next stage of their plan. Best had, much against his will, dressed in a few of Gladys' clothes that she had picked up in Madrid some eight years before. He wore a light blue silk blouse, a pair of tight scarlet red breeches and a pair of Adidas training shoes. His hair was covered in a floral print scarf. He had refused to wear any make-up, and because he had not shaved since the previous morning, the Irishman had started to sport a five o'clock shadow, making the drag outfit look bizarre to say the least.

In fact, in later years, Best would admit that he would have probably created less interest had he marched into the service station dressed in his full Manchester United team kit.

The two new friends drove on through the night, eventually arriving at The Blue Moon Club in Buckie just before noon. Elton and Bernie were there to welcome them, and they told Gladys that the first night at the club had gone reasonably well, and they were certain Best would be able to mingle in with the road crew. The long drive North had tired her out, and Gladys decided to book into a local hotel for a few days before returning South. She was looking forward to seeing Elton in concert, and after making certain that George Best was safely delivered to his room, took a shower and went straight to bed. Elton kitted out Best with a pair of faded blue denim flares, a tie-dyed T shirt and an old leather hat. Gladys also noticed that Bernie had pierced one of the Irishman's ears. Just what Sir Matt Busby would say she couldn't imagine.

The concert went very well, and although the club was far from full, Elton's material impressed Gladys. For the encore Elton Sang 'Your Song' and as he introduced it, he beckoned Gladys up onto the stage. He introduced her to the audience, and she joined him on the chorus, proving once again that she possessed a fine voice.

After the performance, or 'gig' as Elton and Bernie called it. Gladys had a brief talk to the musicians. They promised to keep an eye on Best, to keep him away from drink and women and to deliver him to Old Trafford alcohol free and in prime fitness the week after next. Gladys embraced Best, giving him a peck on the cheek, then set off South.

Gladys' scheme was such a success no journalist ever discovered Best's whereabouts, and with Elton and Bernie's help he arrived back in Manchester in time for a league game against Leeds United, fit, eager and ready to play.

CHAPTER NINE   'DRAMA IN MEXICO'

After the Best affair, all Gladys' thoughts were directed towards Mexico. She met with Sir Alf Ramsey a number of times during the last months of 1969, and they discussed the probable and possible members of the final squad. Terry Cooper of Leeds United and Peter Shilton of Leicester City had caught Gladys' eye, and Ramsey agreed that they could well both be international players of the future.

Once again Gladys had been approached to make a record to promote England's World Cup campaign. This time however, she suggested a song recorded by the complete squad instead of one individual. Gladys met with the songwriting duo Martin and Coulter at The Dorchester on Boxing Day 1969, and over a buffet lunch they composed the song *Back Home*. The idea was for the whole squad including Sir Alf and Gladys to record the song at Martin & Coulter's recording studio in Wardour Street. At first Ramsey was a little reluctant, but eventually he saw the importance of having a hit record.

So in January 1970 *Back Home / Cinnamon Stick* was recorded. The disc went on to become the first (and so far only) football record to reach the number one position in the British charts. The fact that Gladys had made number one, and until the Summer of 1990, Elton John had not, was a constant source of jokes between the two friends. Of course, when Elton did eventually make the top of the charts with *Sacrifice* no-one was more delighted than Gladys.

It is interesting to see Gladys arm in arm with Bobby Moore at the filming of *Top Of The Pops*. Ramsey had refused to appear on the BBC pop show, so it was left to Gladys and Moore to lead the squad through the recording. The players dressed formally in Dinner Jackets and black ties while Gladys was tastefully kitted out in a dark blue silk evening dress with a string of pearls. Most people had never seen her in anything but tracksuits or playing kit, and she caused quite a stir amongst the male members of the viewing public with her sultry performance.

While *Back Home* was at the top of the charts, a group calling themselves The Terrace Boys had a minor hit with a rock version of *We're Gladys' Boys*.

At the end of January Gladys and Sir Alf flew to Mexico City to inspect the hotel facilities and witness the draw for the finals. Rumania, Czechoslovakia and the mighty Brazil came out of the hat in England's group.

England were to play their group matches at Guadalajara in the North of the country. Gladys was impressed by the stadium and the playing surface, but was concerned by the threat posed by the heat and altitude. It was vital England should have time to acclimatise themselves before the tournament began, so while in South America Ramsey arranged friendly games against Colombia and Ecuador.

Once back in England, Gladys set about turning her garage into a special training gym. She had realised the importance of the players being able to play for the full ninety minutes in the Mexican sun. With the use of silver foil, a number of electric blow heaters and a box of black bin liners, she was able to recreate the parched atmosphere of Guadalajara in Croxley Green. Ramsey was delighted by her initiative, and over a period of two months over forty potential members of the England squad were put through their paces in Gladys' garage.

Gladys would bring the players in three by three, dress them in the bin liners, turn the blowers up to their maximum then put them through a tough training session. She realised that to keep the lads in such an environment for longer than twenty minutes would be dangerous, and indeed both David Sadler and Francis Lee had to lie down on Gladys' spare bed to recover after particularly arduous sessions.

A number of club managers did raise objections to Gladys' training methods as a few players returned from the sessions over a stone lighter, but Gladys and Ramsey met with all the First Division managers and put their minds at rest.

Gladys also realised the importance of the players being able to eat the food of their choice while in Mexico. The water situation was also a cause for concern as the Mexican drinking water was infamous for causing stomach upsets.

Gladys approached the owner of a local bistro, a rather eccentric young man named Keith Floyd, and over a good bottle of Chablis Floyd agreed to travel with the England squad as team cook. Gladys and Floyd set about creating a number of tasty meals that would be easy to prepare under the trying conditions they were bound to experience in Mexico, this plan too proved to be a big hit with the players.

Quiches, soups, omelettes and filled jacket potatoes were particularly popular with the team, and Gordon Banks soon became a big fan of her meat and potato pie.

Gladys was being as thorough as she could, trying to foresee any problem that may occur while the players were thousands of miles from home. Most of the squad were married men, and Gladys thought it would be a good idea if the players' wives were allowed to go to Mexico as well. Ramsey was worried that women being so close to the players might distract them from their training but Gladys convinced him that with her supervision, the ladies would actually be an asset.

During the remaining weeks of the 1969/70 season Gladys and Sir Alf watched as many games as possible. Everton were running away with the League title and Chelsea were about to win the F.A. Cup for the first time in their history.

Gladys was delighted to see that George Best had rediscovered his form, and Sir Matt Busby sent a huge bouquet of red and white roses to her when she sat in the Director's Box to take in the Manchester United v Tottenham league game.

The bookmakers had made Brazil favourites to win the World Cup, with England and Argentina just behind. If England were to retain the trophy they would have to become the first European team to win the tournament in South America. Many experts believed that the heat and altitude would put paid to any European challenge.

Both the Italians and the West Germans had been in touch with the F.A. to ask if it was at all possible to observe Gladys' training methods. It had been rumoured on the soccer grapevine that the England players had benefitted from the routines she had devised, and the Germans in particular were keen to try out any new ideas. The F.A. agreed, and in March 1970 a number of West German players arrived in Croxley Green to observe Gladys putting the England players through their paces. Gladys had got to know many of the top European players over the last decade or so, and during the Germans' stay she would often spend the evenings discussing tactics and great games from the past with Haller, Mueller, Beckenbauer, Seeler and the others. On the night before the Germans were to return home, Gladys hired the small room behind the local pub The Fox and Hounds and an unofficial England v West Germany cribbage match took place. Gladys had prepared a sumptuous buffet, and with the help of a couple of barrels of strong Theakstons Ale everyone had a marvellous time. There are a number of photographs of the evening that appear in Uwe Seeler's biography *Uwe, Uwe* (published by Bruchen, 1972).

Whether those few days the Germans spent in Croxley Green made the difference when the two countries met in Leon for the World Cup quarter-final, we will never know. But Franz Beckenbauer is on record as saying that Gladys' methods were ten years ahead of their time, and his one wish was that she had been born German.

Gladys drove the West German minibus to Heathrow the next morning and helped the players through passport control. They all promised to keep in touch and meet up again in Mexico. Gladys was Guest of Honour at both the 1970 F.A. Cup final at Wembley and the replay at Old Trafford. The Chelsea v Leeds games were to be the last she attended before flying to

South America. England were to take a squad of 30 players, then whittle it down to the necessary 22 just before the tournament started.

The first match of the pre World Cup tour was a difficult looking fixture against Colombia in Bogota. The English party arrived a week before the game and after a couple of days rest, they set about getting used to the thin air. One of the first things Gordon Banks noticed was just how quickly the ball moved through the air at altitude. In the first training session Gladys whipped a thirty-five yard drive past the hapless goalkeeper. It is unlikely she would have scored from such a distance at sea level.

The temperature during the sessions was well over 90 degrees, and the use of salt tablets was vital. Many of the players finished a gruelling stint well over half a stone lighter, Gladys herself shed five pounds in weight which worried the team doctor. She weighed in at only seven stone, and had been described as having less meat on her than a butcher's apron. But fortunately, with liquids and a light snack she soon made up the weight loss. The England players soon settled into the new conditions, and Sir Alf realised how important those hours in Gladys' garage had been. The cooking arrangements were also a success. Keith Floyd flew in from England to deal with the kitchen duties, and all seemed ready and prepared for a successful couple of months. Gladys and Sir Alf had done all the homework, leaving nothing to chance. The groundwork behind the scenes had been thorough and complete. No other team would be better prepared; now it was up to the players.

Keith Floyd had brought some good news with him. The World Cup record *Back Home* had reached number one in the U.K. pop charts, and despite the squad being involved in arduous training, Sir Alf and Gladys allowed the players to celebrate with a few cans of cool Colombian beer.

As reigning World Champions, England's presence in Bogota caused immense interest amongst the locals. Apart from the players and officials, there were a few hundred England supporters and a large entourage of British press who followed the squad everywhere eager to find new angles on stories for their editors back in London. Indeed, Gladys likened the whole experience to a travelling circus. The journalists were constantly quizzing Sir Alf and Gladys for any news of team tactics or injuries, and on more than one occasion Gladys had to smoothe things over after Ramsey upset a reporter with a curt, sometimes rude answer to his question.

There was speculation on who the unlucky eight players not to make the final 22 for Mexico would be, but Gladys would not be drawn and remained tight lipped. All she told the press was that the final squad would be announced after the match with Ecuador.

The England management were aware that a number of South American journalists were taking an unnatural interest in the team's general movements. Gladys had heard from an unofficial source that there would be an attempt to discredit the English, and the players were warned to be on their guard at all times. Security was also stepped up when Gladys spotted an unidentified intruder rummaging through the players' personal belongings during a training session. She gave chase, but the dusky youth was a little too nippy for her, disappeared over a wall and was away. Gladys did give the local police a description of the man, but they seemed uninterested and put the incident down to souvenir hunting.

There did seem to be an undercurrent of anti-English feeling in Colombia. Gladys had seen a number of obscene drawings on walls depicting (she supposed) herself and England players engaged in various sexual acts. There had also been a rather heavy-handed press campaign attempting to label the England squad as late night drinkers and gamblers. An outrageously faked photograph of Gladys dancing topless on a table with a crowd of drunken England players clapping and cheering was published on the front page of *Colombia Sporto*, the best selling newspaper in the country. The headline read 'English Slut And Her Pimps Drink Until Dawn'.

The game against Colombia was a satisfying run out for the England management. A comfortable 4-0 victory against a very average team was an acceptable result considering the searing heat. After the game, Gladys took charge of making certain all the team received enough salt tablets and liquids to replenish their parched systems.

That evening at the England hotel Bobby Moore and Bobby Charlton asked Gladys if she would like to join them for a light supper and then a browse around the local shops. She agreed, and after a shower and a change into her England blazer she met the two players in the lobby. They ate at a nearby seafood restaurant, and enjoyed a delicious meal of grilled sole with a huge fresh green salad. The three of them split a bottle of chilled Chablis, and they talked over that afternoon's game and of course the forthcoming few weeks. Gladys had always got on very well with Moore, but had never really got to know Charlton. That night he told her just how grateful everyone at Old Trafford was for the way she had worked with George Best, and by the time the coffee arrived she had both her colleagues creasing up with laughter with her impression of Sir Matt Busby.

During the meal all three were constantly interrupted by autograph hunters. Gladys was impressed with the way the two players, aware of the fact they represented their country, gladly signed menus, serviettes and autograph books. The two Bobbies were polite and diplomatic to all the well-wishers, and when they had finished the meal the three of them posed for a snap-shot with Luis, the headwaiter.

Just beyond the restaurant were a number of interesting looking boutiques, and Gladys suggested buying a few souvenirs. After visiting a leather goods shop in which Moore purchased a beautiful driving licence holder for his wife Tina, the three shoppers entered a chic looking jewellers.

The girl at the counter looked particularly nervous, but Gladys wasn't too surprised. After all it couldn't be every day that three of the most famous names in World football strolled into your shop. Gladys was impressed with the interesting range of Aztec and Inca jewellery and a stunning gold and diamond bracelet caught her eye. She studied the piece through the glass case for a couple of minutes and inquired after the price. The shop assistant replied that the bracelet was 65,000 pesos, which was the equivalent of just under £900 sterling. Bobby Moore noticed Gladys' interest in the bracelet, and asked to inspect it at close quarters. The girl unlocked the case and handed the piece over to Gladys. The three English footballers marvelled at the intricate detail and workmanship, and all agreed that a similar bracelet in London would be at least five times more expensive. Charlton and Moore left Gladys to admire the bracelet alone for a few minutes, then returned to her side and asked her if she would like it as a gift. They explained how the players had already decided they would like to buy her a little something to commemorate the World Cup, and the money they had already collected was enough to pay for the bracelet.

Gladys was touched, and after a few moments of thought told them that she would be delighted and honoured to receive such a gift. They decided to buy it when the team left the hotel the next morning, to save having to leave such an expensive item in the hotel safe overnight.

Gladys thanked the shop-girl for her help, and handed her the bracelet back. Then the three English footballers left the shop and started to make their way back to their hotel. Before they had gone twenty yards a high pitched alarm went off, and the girl came running out of the shop. Within seconds armed police had manhandled Gladys, Moore and Charlton into a nearby doorway. There was a sudden explosion of flashbulbs, and as if from nowhere, a pack of photographers appeared on the scene eagerly recording the incident.

A large black police wagon screeched to a halt, and amid scenes of total confusion, the three shoppers were dragged through a gauntlet of taunting Colombians. They were then bundled into the back of the wagon, the driver immediately roaring off at speed with the English prisoners handcuffed to swarthy Colombian policemen.

The police vehicle sped through the crowded, narrow streets of Bogota with its siren wailing and lights flashing. Pedestrians ran for their lives as it lurched from side to side, mounting the pavement on a number of occasions to dodge oncoming traffic.

Gladys had her arms handcuffed behind her back while Moore and Charlton had been thrown to the floor with four policemen pinning them down. One of the burly officers had his pistol drawn, and Gladys was left in no doubt that the wild-eyed cop was only too keen to start blasting away if given an excuse. In a few minutes they squealed to a halt and the back doors pulled open. Once again there was a barrage of flashbulbs, and this time the blinding arc lights of television cameras lit the scene. There was utter pandemonium in the reception area of Bogota Central Police Station; it seemed like Bedlam as hundreds of voices shouted over the screaming of women and children.

Officials attempted to keep the journalists away from the English prisoners, but microphones were pushed into their faces as they were roughly dragged through the melee into the station. Gladys attempted to make some sense of the situation by asking in Spanish what was going on, but her questions were met by laughing officers who simply ignored her. Gladys noticed that Moore had a cut over one eye, and Charlton's nose was bleeding profusely, his white shirt splattered with blood. Gladys herself had been struck a number of times around the head with a truncheon and savageley kicked in the ribs by a frenzied police cadet.

The three were frogmarched through dark corridors still pursued by the press, then taken into a maximum security area which was surrounded by a 12 foot barbed wire fence and machine gun turrets.

The journalists were refused access to the cells, and Moore, Charlton and Gladys were grabbed by several warders and hurled into a large cage, already home to several winos, thieves and cut-throats. The police started to clear the station of any press, and as the three friends dusted themselves down, Gladys began to realise the predicament they found themselves in. She went over to the two Bobbys and inspected their wounds.

Their cuts were still bleeding, and Moore obviously needed stitches. In the next cell a number of members of a Latin street gang cat-called and screamed insults at the Gringos, whilst the smell of sweat and urine began to make Gladys feel bilious. She shouted out for some medical help for her colleagues, but her call was ignored by the guards and only caused amusement amongst the other prisoners. The police had taken their watches and other personal effects, so Gladys was unable to ascertain just how long they had already been held. She hoped that the news of their arrest had reached Sir Alf Ramsey, and that he was doing all he could to gain their release.

After what seemed an eternity, the cell block door opened, and an official looking Englishman flanked by two sour-faced guards walked up to the cell bars. Looking nervous, the man explained that his name was Bebbins and he was from the British Consulate. He had been informed that Charlton, Moore and Protheroe were being held on theft charges, and would be in court at eleven the next morning. This meant that they would have to spend the night in the cell, and if found guilty would face up to twenty years in prison. On hearing this Charlton burst into tears, but Gladys ordered him to pull himself together.

It seemed to Gladys that Bebbins was going along with the police version of the incident, and he was taking it as read that the three of them were thieves. She looked him straight in the eye, and in a calm, detached manner told him that she wanted to speak to his superior, and she wanted Sir Alf Ramsey and the best lawyer in Bogota in the cell within half an hour, otherwise she would have him sacked. Bebbins was staggered by Gladys' reaction, and dryly told her that he would do all he could. He explained that in South America things took a little longer to organise than they did in the U.K. and mentioned in passing that Britain could do without football hooligans dragging the Queen's name through the gutter.

Gladys asked Bebbins if he would be so kind as to step a little nearer the bars. As he did she shot out a hand and grabbed him by the collar. She told him that he obviously didn't hear her. He was to get Ramsey and a lawyer to the cell *now*. Bebbins went pale with fear as Gladys held him up against the bars for a few seconds longer, all the time staring him directly in the eyes. She asked him whether they understood each other, and the man from the Consulate, spluttered that they did.

As Bebbins turned to leave the cell block, the gang members from the adjoining cage gave a hearty cheer. They liked what they had seen, a Gringo woman with plenty of spirit. Gladys told Moore and Charlton to keep their heads up, it was vital they showed courage in such adversity. After all, they were innocent, and when they were free they would be able to clear their names.

The street gang in the next cell were in custody for petty theft and public disorder and with her fluent Spanish Gladys was soon able to strike up a conversation. There were eight in the gang, and they called themselves "Los Dragonos". Their leader was a tall, thin youth named Joe.

He told Gladys it had been rumoured on the streets for some time that there would be an attempt to discredit the English before the World Cup. Joe had heard the Argentinians, still smarting from their quarter-final defeat in 1966, had instigated a plot for the three most famous English personalities to be shown up as nothing more than common criminals. He went on to say that the Bogota Police Department were well known to be vicious and corrupt, and Gladys and her companions were fortunate to have received only minor injuries. Apparently when Sweden played Colombia in a friendly international some three years earlier, the Swedish centre-forward Tom Olaffson was arrested for a minor parking offence, held for three weeks, then sent back to his club Malmo with three fingers of his left hand missing. Joe told Gladys that if they had not been so famous, they would have all been beaten senseless for sure.

Joe offered Gladys a cigarette, which she gratefully accepted, and he continued his story. He said that "Los Dragonos" were from a shanty town in the South of the capital, and were being constantly harassed by the police. Whenever arrest rates were down, the police would raid the shanty town, pulling in anyone they could find and charging them with whatever crimes were unsolved that month. This meant that the police were seen to be highly efficient, and their clean up rate of 97.8% was the envy of South America. A number of Joe's friends and family had been imprisoned for crimes they had not committed, and he himself had only just been released from a six month sentence for stealing a donkey, a charge that had been completely fabricated. He had his own donkey, he told Gladys. Why would he want to steal another?

"Los Dragonos" were all football supporters, and underneath their rough, macho manner Gladys found them polite and helpful. Slowly, Moore and Charlton were getting over the shock of their arrest and joined in the conversation. Although the players' Spanish was by no means as fluent as Gladys', with the help of mime they managed to communicate with the gang. Their injuries had now stopped bleeding, and instead of the bright red of newly spilt blood, Moore and Charlton were covered in a dark, crusty brown.

Unknown to the prisoners the World's press had been alerted to the goings-on of the last few hours, and the streets surrounding the police station were teeming with journalists and photographers. Sir Alf Ramsey and Keith Floyd had both been on the telephone to London. Ramsey had spoken directly to Prime Minister Edward Heath, and he was told that two of the top men at the Foreign Office were about to catch the first flight to Bogota to get to the bottom of the matter. Heath was worried that the incident could become a diplomatic nightmare, and he urged Ramsey to do all he could to calm the situation.

Britain's Ambassador Sir Basil Phillips had been in conference with the Colombian Minister for Law and Order for over an hour, but did not seem to be making any headway. The Colombian government were well known for their harsh treatment of thieves and trouble makers, and they saw an opportunity to show the World that they would have no truck with criminal activities. Bebbins had been making some enquiries into the alleged theft, and was soon convinced that the three were, as Gladys had insisted, innocent. The shop in question was owned by a shady character who had business links with Buenos Aires, and, what's more, was a season ticket holder at Boca Juniors. Apparently, Antonio Rattin had been spotted at the jewellers only a week earlier.

Sir Alf Ramsey was certain that the Argentinians had stage managed this cruel trap and despite being known as a man who rarely showed his feelings that night in Bogota he openly wept. His assistant and two senior players were rotting in a prison cell and Ramsey was close to breaking point. Keith Floyd wrote in his account of the affair, 'Floyd in South America' (BBC

Books, 1989) that Ramsey told him that he would tear Rattin limb from limb if he ever got his hands on him.

Floyd and Ramsey sat for nearly three hours outside the Colombian Minister's office until Sir Basil finally agreed bail. The bail bond had been set at 6 million pesos, a staggering half a million pounds. It took a further hour and a half to have the money wired from F.A. Headquarters in Lancaster Gate. Eventually the English party took a taxi from the Ministry to the city police station. Ramsey, Floyd and Sir Basil fought their way through the press men and into the reception area. After signing and countersigning dozens of official forms, the burly desk sergeant gave permission for the release of the three prisoners, and they were escorted into the cellblock.

Ramsey had been concerned over Gladys' well being. He knew that Moore and Charlton were strong, professional athletes at the peak of their fitness. A few hours in a prison cell wouldn't have affected them too much. But Gladys, when all was said and done, was a frail woman. She was 63 years of age, thousands of miles from home, an innocent woman amongst a gang of ruthless, vicious criminals. As he walked through the damp, stinking corridors towards the cells, Ramsey was a worried man, wondering in what state he would find his assistant. He had already organised an ambulance to rush Gladys to Bogota General Hospital, and arranged for her to be flown immediately back to London. He imagined the scene in the cell, Gladys cowering in a corner, tears pouring down her face, her terrified whimpering, an old woman shivering with fear – pining for her warm, cosy home.

As the police escort lead the England manager and his colleagues nearer the cells, Ramsey could clearly hear raised voices. He feared some kind of disturbance or perhaps a riot was in progress. Suddenly the thought of his three charges being lynched by a baying mob of murderers and rapists filled him with terror. But as one of the police guards hurriedly began to unlock the huge steel doors, a familiar sound greeted his ears. The noise was not that of a violent struggle, but a rather shaky version of *We're Gladys' Boys*.

Gladys stood on a bunk leading the cell mates through the famous old song. Joe and the rest of "Los Dragonos" were singing at the tops of their voices banging their tin plates and cups against the cell bars while Charlton and Moore stood together conducting the motley choir.

Ramsey tended to his players cuts and bruises while Gladys described the prison food to a disgusted Keith Floyd. Sir Basil informed 'The Bogota Three', as they had become known, of the bail arrangements, and at 4.45 a.m., some ten hours after being arrested Moore, Charlton and Protheroe were officially released from police custody. Before leaving the cellblock, Gladys shook hands with Joe and the others in his gang, and as she turned to leave "Los Dragonos" burst into one last chorus of the great old terrace anthem.

Once again there were chaotic scenes outside the Police Station as TV crews, pressmen and curious locals fought to get a better view of the English. Gladys was offered a blanket to hide under as she was shepherded to the waiting car, but she refused, telling the policeman she was innocent and would hold her head high. The BBC news footage of the release clearly shows Gladys defiantly giving the Churchillian V for victory sign to the waiting crowd before being driven off at speed by Keith Floyd. Sir Basil had suggested that perhaps it would be safer for the 'Bogota Three' to stay at a secret address instead of returning directly to the team's hotel. Ramsey agreed; the other players had already been bothered enough by journalists, and he was worried that this incident might disturb the squad's build up for the World Cup.

The story of the arrest had become World news, and TV reporters from non-footballing nations such as USA, Japan, China, Canada and Australia had arrived in Bogota to swell the already large number of press. Keith Floyd expected a number of journalists to try and follow their car, and he was right. As he looked in his rear view mirror he spotted a convoy of newsmen. But Floyd's experience of running one of the first ever pizza delivery services held him in good stead, and after twenty minutes of breakneck driving he managed to shake them all off .

Sir Basil had arranged for the use of a house in the mountains that had once belonged to a cocaine baron. The drug dealer had been imprisoned in late 1968, and his house had been seized by the Colombian government. The car eventually arrived at the safe house just as the sun was rising. Charlton and Moore had managed to get some sleep during the journey, and Gladys used the time to give Sir Alf and Sir Basil a full account of the arrest. Keith Floyd quickly prepared a hot breakfast for the weary travellers, and after eggs, bacon, mushrooms and fried bread washed down by hot, sweet tea the English players and management caught up on their lost sleep.

England's last game before the World Cup was to be in Quito against Ecuador. The arrests had thrown the travel plans into disarray and it was vital that Sir Alf and Gladys gathered the complete squad together as soon as possible.

Moore and Charlton's head wounds had been tended by Keith Floyd who was fast becoming the most valuable member of the party. He had given the players fresh beefsteak to drape over their faces as they slept, and after six hours rest they seemed to be regaining full fitness. Gladys herself had picked up some swelling around the eyes, and decided to wear sunglasses until it subsided. During the enforced absence of Gladys and Sir Alf, coach Harold Shepherdson had been left in charge of the squad. Sir Alf telephoned him to confirm the travel arrangements, and was told all was well. The players would be on the noon flight from Bogota to Quito, while Floyd would drive the management duo and the two senior players to Ecuador.

After another long drive, the complete England squad was once again together at the Quito Holiday Inn. A mile from the hotel Floyd cleverly swopped their car for a butcher's delivery van, and he managed to avoid the waiting press by a adopting a heavy Spanish accent and driving the van through the tradesman's entrance. There were emotional scenes as Gladys, Moore and Charlton were reunited with their colleagues. Sir Alf allowed the players to have a few beers in the hotel bar, and the evening ended with Gladys leading them through a splendid version of *Back Home* much to the delight of the other guests. Sir Alf had arranged a press-conference for the next morning while Gladys took the players through a training session. The Foreign Office officials had now arrived in Bogota, and they too were convinced that the bracelet incident had been nothing more than a heavy handed set-up. The girl from the jewellers had mysteriously disappeared, and all the police files on the arrest had vanished. Ramsey told the press that the England team would not rest until their names were officially cleared.

Gladys suggested to Sir Alf that it would be in their interests to have someone in Bogota, close to the investigations, who would be able to report back to the team with news. Ramsey agreed and the young goalkeeper Peter Shilton who was not to be in the final squad of 22 was selected to be the man.

Shilton was briefed by Sir Basil Phillips, and told to be discreet. He was given living expenses from the squad's petty cash, and left on the night train to Bogota. The plan was that Shilton would telephone any information to the England hotel in Quito, and Gladys would be ready to join him if necessary.

It was a difficult decision for the England management, but both Ramsey and Gladys felt it was important Moore and Charlton played against Ecuador. The two players could certainly have done with a few more days rest, but Gladys felt that the World should see that the English were ashamed of nothing, and that it was business as usual.

There was a small demonstration in the crowd before the kickoff, and a number of local youths booed Gladys as she took her place on the England bench, but apart from that all went smoothly. Goals from Francis Lee and substitute Brian Kidd gave England a comfortable 2-0 win and both Moore and Charlton had reasonable games.

Afterwards Gladys and Sir Alf had to decide on their final 22 for Mexico. Instead of a remote fisherman's cottage as in 1966, the two colleagues sat in Pedro's Tapas Bar in downtown Quito, and with the help of Pedro's biro and the back of a beermat, they picked the 22 players to defend the Jules Rimet Trophy.

Shilton of course, had already departed, and Gladys gathered the other seven who were to be omitted to give them the news all the players had been dreading. They were given the choice of flying back to London immediately, or staying on with the squad throughout the tournament. As most of the players had young families Gladys totally understood when they all opted to return home. The night before they left for England Gladys and Keith Floyd organised a farewell buffet. Emlyn Hughes, Bob McNab and the others were obviously disappointed, but respected the way Gladys had done her best to make them feel useful members of the World Cup bid.

The England party arrived in Mexico one week before the first game against Rumania was to take place. .Sir Alf and Gladys had decided on a remote ranch style training camp high in the hills above Guadalajara. The camp was called El Panchez, and comprised of two full size pitches, an Olympic size swimming pool, gymnasium, games room, two squash courts, a nine hole golf course, a thirty seat private cinema and top quality sleeping and dining quarters. Despite being in such a remote position, the camp was only a half an hours drive from the stadium where England were to play their group matches.

As soon as they arrived Keith Floyd took over in the kitchen, overseeing the preparation and cooking of the players' and officials' meals. Floyd was well aware of the sensitivity of English stomachs and the danger of 'Montezumas Revenge'. Since the squad had been in South America there had been nothing more serious than an occasional upset stomach that had meant a player missing a training session. But Floyd had been briefed by Gladys about the dangers of unwashed fruit, infected tap water and rancid meats. The players soon settled into the routine of 'El Panchez' and after a few days rest, Gladys and Sir Alf stepped up training to get the squad nicely tuned up for the tournament.

Bobby Moore had not been his usual self since the Bogota incident, and Gladys had a quiet word with him. She told him to try to put the possible prison sentence still hanging over him out of his mind. His main priority in the next few weeks must be the World Cup; nothing should be allowed to divert him. Peter Shilton had telephoned a couple of reports from Bogota regarding the jewellery incident. The girl who had accused Moore, Charlton and Gladys had been interviewed by a U.S. TV network and tearfully admitted that the whole affair had been staged. As the England hierarchy had feared, an unnamed South American country had been reported as being behind the supposed theft. The Colombian government, obviously embarrassed to have been manipulated in such a manoeuvre, issued a statement to the effect that the England players were to be officially cleared of any charges relating to the incident, and as far as they were concerned the case was closed. The England squad were delighted. With the World Cup just a matter of days away, to have a cloud like that lifted from over them was a superb boost to morale. Gladys thanked Shilton for his diligent work, and wished him a safe flight home. So, although the young goalkeeper was not officially a member of the 1970 World Cup squad, Gladys has always recognised the important role he played off the field, and she often refers to him as the 23rd member.

On 2nd June 1970, England started the campaign to defend the World Cup against Rumania. Sir Alf and Gladys knew very little about the Rumanians, in fact it was one of the few European countries she had never visited. The management expected a tough battle with the men from Eastern Europe. In a tournament like the World Cup it was vital not to lose the opening game, and both teams were well aware that with Brazil in their group, it was going to be tough to make it into the top two qualifying positions.

For the Rumania game Sir Alf had picked a workmanlike side. Newton of Blackburn, Cooper of Leeds and Labone of Everton were in to complement the subtle defending style of Bobby Moore, while Alan Mullery had taken the tiger's mantle from Nobby Stiles. The temperature at pitch level was well into the nineties as England kicked off in their unfamiliar light blue shirts. The game was an uninspiring battle with few chances at either end. It did look as if England were to suffer a repeat of 1966, and take part in a goalless opening game, but up popped the hero of four years earlier, and Hurst scored the only goal to give England a winning start.

After the match Gladys took care of the players as they recovered from the incredible temperatures. All of them were immediately weighed, and as she feared the team had lost alarming amounts of weight. Keith Floyd had prepared a huge meat and potato pie with a gigantic bowl of piping hot mashed potato. Even though some of the players were not too keen, they were forced to eat enormous helpings before being allowed to leave the dressing room. The idea worked, and when they were weighed again an hour later, all had returned to their original weights and then some.

This was an idea that all the other Northern European teams unused to the high temperatures took on board. The West Germans all had a plane load of sauerkraut, bratwurst and suet flown in from Hamburg prior to their group game against Bulgaria, and after their 5-2 win regained their body weights with a large filling meal.

Gladys took advantage of the time between the Rumania and Brazil matches to get to know the squad a little better. She knew most of the players from the 1966 campaign, but a number of the team were relatively new to her. Mullery, Wright, Labone, Cooper and Osgood had only just gained international recognition, and although she was aware of them through their exploits in the Football League, she had not really had an opportunity to get to know them on a personal basis.

On the day after the opening match, Gladys hired a car to go sightseeing and invited Francis Lee and Terry Cooper to join her. The three tourists drove out into the Mexican countryside, and were delighted by the friendly reception they received from the locals. Just before they set off on their day out, Bobby Moore walked over to them and warned Lee and Cooper not to spend too much time in jewellery shops – the last time any of the players went out with Gladys they had all ended up in gaol!

After a couple of hours driving, Gladys decided to stop off at Ameca for lunch. Ameca was a small town about 60 miles from Guadalajara, and the three English footballers enjoyed a tasty lunch of tortillas and cooled Mexican beer at Pancho's Bar. After the meal the travellers went for a short stroll around the town and Gladys walked with Francis Lee, the tough little Manchester City forward. Lee was a bright, alert young man and Gladys immediately took a liking to him. As they enjoyed their afternoon walk they chanced upon a busy little factory. It seemed to be a paper manufacturing plant of some kind, and as they had an hour or so to kill, Gladys suggested having a walk around the works. Lee agreed, and having gained permission from the proprietor, a Senor Rizas, they met the workers and inspected the machinery. Lee took a particularly close interest in the factory, and over a cup of coffee after the tour, Gladys asked him what he planned to do when his playing days were over. Most players at Lee's age had no real plans or ideas how to continue earning a living after they hung up their boots, but Gladys was pleased to see that Lee had obviously given it some thought. He told Gladys he was looking for a small business opportunity, probably in the North West. Gladys thought for a moment, and suggested a paper business like Senor Rizas'. She told Lee there was always a call for paper products, especially tissues, and she felt that any little business run by a go-ahead character like Lee would do very well. When they had finished their coffee, Gladys led Lee back into the factory, and they talked with Senor Rizas for over an hour. The Mexican businessman was pleased to be of help and gave Lee advice on which machines to purchase and which paper products were the most popular.

Gladys acted as interpreter, and with her help Francis Lee was able to learn enough about the paper business that afternoon to be able to start his own project on his return to England. Gladys actually helped him with a loan to purchase the lease on a factory unit and a few lorries.

Since those early days, Francis Lee has become perhaps the most successful footballer turned businessman of all time, his paper business has a multi million pound turn over, and he has now moved into the world of horse-racing, owning and training a string of winners.

Even though he is now a millionaire, Lee has never forgotten that afternoon in Ameca that put him on the road to success. Indeed, one only has to look through the names of some of his racehorses to realise just how much store he put in the advice he received that day. 'Ameca Afternoon'

'Glad Lady' and 'The Paper Woman of Mexico' have all been winners for Francis Lee. Gladys always has a little flutter when she sees one of his horses is running, and over the past few years has made a reasonable profit following the Lee stables. As with most of her ex-players, Gladys still keeps in touch with Francis Lee, and is always delighted to receive a jumbo sized pack of extra soft tissues on both her birthday and Christmas.

The England squad had three days to prepare for the clash with Brazil. The football press had built the game up as the unofficial final, England being the holders and Brazil champions in 1962 and the red hot favourites to take the trophy for a record third time. Gladys and Ramsey were well aware of the power and skill of such players as Pele, Jairzinho, Rivelino and Carlos Alberto, they knew that England would have to be at their very best to win the game. Brazil, like England had started with a win, a rather easy victory over Czechoslovakia, and Gladys was certain if England could pick up a point, then both teams would qualify for the quarter-finals.

The night before the game, two busloads of Brazilian supporters drove up to El Panchez and kept the England players awake with their constant drumming and singing. Twice Gladys went out of the main gates of the training camp to try to calm the fans, but she was unable to persuade them to leave. She then supplied all her players with cotton wool ear plugs, and fortunately they were able to sleep soundly.

On the morning of the game Gladys spent some time with goalkeeper Gordon Banks. Banks had confided to her that he was unhappy with his form, and was especially concerned about missing headers that crept just inside the post. She was out on the training pitch with the 'keeper peppering his goal with bullet like headers. Terry Cooper had volunteered to help out, and his crosses were accuracy themselves. Although Gladys stood at just under 5 foot 4 inches tall, she was able to time her headers superbly, and the power she gained surprised Banks. She beat him a number of times with efforts no goalkeeper on Earth could have stopped. By the end of the session Banks had regained some of his old confidence, and as they all walked off the training pitch to shower down, Gladys and Cooper encouraged him with some rousing chants and songs.

For the Brazil game, Ramsey and Gladys decided to keep faith with the eleven who defeated Rumania, once again Tommy Wright playing at right-back. Gladys had warned Brian Labone about Tostao's electrifying pace and the way Jairzinho and Rivelino interchanged passes on the edge of the penalty box. Obviously, all the squad were aware of Pele's fabulous skills and Gladys thought it would be far better not to dwell on the abilities of their opponents, but instead praise the English style. She told her players that they had nothing to fear, after all it was they and not Brazil who were World Champions.

The Guadalajara Stadium was absolutely packed for the game, and the atmosphere was perhaps the most exciting Gladys had come across in all her years in football. Before the kick-off Gladys popped into the Brazilian dressing room and embraced Pele. There is a famous photograph of the two great celebrities shaking hands, and it was used in the opening credits to the BBC's TV coverage of the latter stages of the World Cup.

In the England room, captain Bobby Moore sat quietly in a corner, and Gladys walked over to give him a few last minute instructions. She knew that a player of Moore's ability needed very little motivation for a game of such importance, but he was grateful for her support. She told him that they had been through so much together for their country, now there was one more challenge on the horizon, and she knew he would not let anyone back home down.

The roar that met the teams as they walked out onto the pitch was deafening. Brazil had a huge bank of supporters behind the far goal, and the sight of thousands of bright yellow shirts in the Mexican sun was an image that was to stay with Gladys for ever. Sir Alf, Gladys and the substitutes took their places on the bench, and after the national anthems Gladys walked among the England team collecting their track suit tops and shouting out last words of encouragement.

England's last defeat in a World Cup match had, ironically, been against Brazil in Vina del Mar, Chile some eight years earlier. Gladys and Sir Alf just hoped they had picked the right team for the game, and that England's fine unbeaten record would be intact in ninety minutes time.

The game started at a frantic pace, and it was obvious to everyone watching that it would be impossible for the players to keep up such a tempo in the scorching heat. Gladys noticed that even the Brazilians, who were well used to the South American conditions, were all perspiring heavily, and their players took any opportunity to have a drink of water whenever their trainer came onto the pitch. Gladys worried how the older players such as Bobby Charlton would cope with the extreme temperature. At pitch level, Gladys' pocket thermometer read 99.5 degrees, and she herself was beginning to feel the effects. Gladys was thankful for her cotton underwear, and glad she had decided against her track suit bottoms and had plumped instead for a light tennis skirt.

At half-time the game was goalless, and Sir Alf was pleased with the way the first forty five minutes had gone. Pele and Jairzinho had been well policed by the England defence, while both Geoff Hurst and Francis Lee had come close to scoring. Brazil seemed to raise the tempo of the game in the second half, with Tostao and Gerson gaining the upperhand in midfield. Gladys suggested bringing Colin Bell on in place of the tiring Charlton, the hope being that the younger man's legs could stem the tide, and after an hours play Sir Alf made the switch.

Gladys noticed that Gordon Banks did not seem too happy in goal, so she picked up a spare kit bag, and with Sir Alf's permission she proceeded to crouch behind Banks' goal. From that position she was able to shout encouragement to the England 'keeper. She told him to keep his concentration, to remember their training sessions and to watch out for Rivelino's wicked curling free-kicks. While she was behind the goal, the ball broke to Jairzinho who was able to get away from Cooper and flight a perfect centre into the England penalty box. Pele rose high above the defenders and bulleted a header towards the bottom right hand corner of Banks' goal. The Brazilian supporters were already on their feet in celebration of a Pele goal when Gladys shrieked at Banks to dive. He did, and just managed to turn the ball around the post for a corner. That save, of course, has been described since as the best of all time. It is very interesting to watch the video tape of the incident, Gladys can be seen clearly stooping behind the goal, and as soon as Banks hears her instructions he dives to make the save. After making the stop, Banks is congratulated by his defenders, then he turns and gives the thumbs up sign to Gladys before preparing for the corner.

As the game went on, Brazil began to exert more pressure, and it came as no surprise to Gladys and Sir Alf when Jairzinho found space to burst through the England defence and plant the ball firmly past Banks for the winning goal. Jeff Astle was sent on in place of Lee, and although both Ball and Astle had half-chances in the last few minutes, it wasn't to be England's day.

When the final whistle blew, Pele ran first to Bobby Moore and then to Gladys, and the three of them walked from the pitch arm in arm. England had lost, but the management knew that a victory against Czechoslovakia would still put them into the quarter-finals.

There were four days before the next game, and Gladys was determined to do all she could to raise the squad's morale. With the assistance of Keith Floyd, she laid on a sumptuous meal for the players – Sir Alf giving his agreement to a few cases of Mexican beer to be allowed into El Panchez. Gladys wanted to make it clear to the lads that, despite the Brazil defeat, they still had a great opportunity to retain the trophy.

Gladys had the idea of showing a film of the 1966 World Cup final, so after a meal of traditional roast beef, Yorkshire pudding and all the trimmings, the squad and management settled down with a few glasses of beer to remind themselves of their great feats of four years earlier. The plan did seem to work, and the atmosphere in the room after the film show was confident, proud and ready. The players did seem to have put the Brazil game out of their minds, and Gladys was delighted to hear Martin Peters lead some of the squad through a beery version of *We're Gladys' Boys* as they all retired to bed.

Sir Alf suggested that the time may be right to make a few changes to the team, and Gladys agreed that shuffling the pack could prove beneficial. Full back Wright had a torrid time against the Brazilians, so it was decided to bring back Keith Newton. Likewise, Gladys had been impressed with the way Allan Clarke shaped up in training. Jackie Charlton, Colin Bell and Jeff Astle were also to start a game for the first time in the tournament.

Gladys took charge of the training sessions before the Czech game. The players were all obviously match fit, and it was important they didn't overdo the physical side of things. She dispensed with any rigorous exercises and relied more on ball play. She also introduced some light-hearted variations such as blind-mans five a side and piggy back penalty kicks. The sessions were a huge success, and Sir Alf was pleased to see that the players were in a relaxed, confident mood before the final group game.

In the dressing room before the Czechoslovakia game, Gladys told the team that it was the result that was vital. In this case, the performance was secondary. A win and England would qualify as runners-up to Brazil. The Czechs had lost their first two games, so were only playing for their pride. Gladys was so confident that Brazil would beat Rumania, she felt that a single point may even be enough, although of course she didn't share this thought with the players.

Once again, the soaring temperatures prevented both teams from playing to their strengths. Czechoslovakia were a tough tackling outfit, but never really inventive enough to trouble England. It took a penalty from Allan Clarke to settle matters, England's first World Cup penalty since Ron Flowers scored against Chile some eight years earlier.

As the England squad were on the coach travelling back to El Panchez, they heard on the radio that they had drawn West Germany in the quarter-finals. The game was to be played in Leon, some three hundred miles North-West of Guadalajara. A training camp had been provisionally booked by the F.A. just in case England were to play in Leon, so after thanking the staff at El Panchez for their hospitality and help, the England party set off on a six hour coach journey across country to their new base. The Camp just outside Leon was called La Bubba, and was owned by a former Mexico inside forward called Jose Bubbullez. At the peak of his fame with top Mexican club Monterrey, he was dubbed La Bubba, so when he hung up his boots in 1965, he decided to stay in the game by opening a neat, compact training unit. The England squad arrived just before midnight after a long, hot journey and were all grateful to eat a light supper then fall wearily into bed.

There were just two days before the quarter-final and the West Germans were determined to gain revenge for the World Cup final defeat of four years earlier. The Germans had won through to the last eight by scoring ten goals in their three group games, and Gerd Muller, the stocky little striker from Bayern Munich, had become the tournament's leading scorer. Obviously Muller, nicknamed 'Der Bomber', was the man to watch, and it was decided that Brian Labone should return to the England back four to keep an eye on him, while up front Hurst returned in place of Clarke.

Once again it was decided not to train the players too hard; the last thing anyone in the England camp wanted were pulled muscles. So, Gladys instigated a tennis tournament, some crazy golf and a series of French boules games to keep the squad on their toes. All these sports were a big success, and as well as keeping the players nicely tuned up, they also kept their minds off the importance of the forthcoming game.

Gladys obtained a film of the West Germans' last match against Peru, and after a light supper of egg salad, the squad sat down in La Bubba's leisure room and watched how the Germans had beaten the plucky South Americans 3-1. Muller did look very sharp, and Seeler despite now being well into his thirties showed he had retained all of his excellent control and was still a formidable player. At the back Beckenbauer had matured from being the novice of four years earlier to a cool, accomplished defender very much in the Bobby Moore mould. But Gladys and Sir Alf were pleased to see how the Peruvians scored one goal, and with better finishing could have had a couple more. The Germans seemed a little hesitant at the back, and this gave the England management a boost to their confidence. After the film show, the squad had a brief discussion about their opponents and Gladys chaired a question and answer session. Before bed, Gladys and a number of the squad took a late night stroll around the grounds. She was pleased with the mood of the players, and everyone seemed confident that England would gain a semi-final place, and then perhaps gain their revenge over Brazil in the final.

On the way to her bedroom Gladys passed the kitchen, and saw Gordon Banks talking to one of the cooks. Keith Floyd had the night off, had gone out on a wine tasting trip into Leon, and was not expected back until much, much later.

Banks was feeling peckish, and he was asking whether it was possible for him to have a light snack before retiring. Gladys dismissed the cook and took over. She had got to know Banks well, and had a soft spot for the burly custodian from Leicester City. She set about making him a sandwich, and after looking through the fridge she found a side of ham and a huge bowl of salad. In a few moments she had created a tempting looking snack. Gladys kept Banks company as he ate his meal, and they chatted about the next day's game. After eating his fill, Banks thanked Gladys for her help, and went upstairs to bed. Gladys washed up the cutlery and plates, then after a last check that all the windows and doors were locked, she joined her colleagues in a well deserved sleep.

Gladys was woken at four in the morning by the unmistakable sound of someone vomiting. She immediately pulled on her track suit and went to investigate. She followed the noise, and discovered Gordon Banks crouched over one of the gentlemen's toilet bowls. Banks was as white as a sheet and obviously in some distress. He told Gladys that he had suddenly been roused from his sleep by sharp stomach pains, and had to run the toilet before being violently sick. Gladys was soon joined by Sir Alf Ramsey and the team doctor Dr. Stanley Meakin.

Ramsey was obviously concerned about Banks, and Gladys had to tell him to calm down and not panic. Dr. Meakin told them it was undoubtedly a severe case of food poisoning, and it was highly unlikely the goalkeeper would be fit to play against West Germany in just over twelve hours time. Banks had already lost at least half a stone, and there seemed to be no sign of the illness relenting. As Banks continued to retch and bring up bile and a rather weird emerald green colour water, the three England officials stood around him discussing their options. After another half an hour of blood curdling throws Dr. Meakin pronounced Banks stomach officially empty, and he prescribed a sleeping draft that would enable the goalkeeper to sleep off the effects of the attack. This meant of course it would be impossible for Banks to take his position between the posts for the quarter-final.

Ramsey and Gladys decided not to worry the other players, and so at 6 a.m. the two management figures returned to their rooms and attempted to get a couple of hours sleep before one of the most important matches in their footballing careers. Gladys found it impossible, so after half an hour of tossing and turning, she quickly showered and once again pulled on her England tracksuit. She made her way to the clinic, where she found Dr. Meakin standing over the sleeping Gordon Banks. The doctor told Gladys there was absolutely no possibility of Banks waking for another ten hours, let alone taking part in the quarter-finals of the World Cup. He had quite the worst case of diarrhoea and upset stomach he had ever seen and the doctor feared that there had been some kind of permanent damage done.

Over breakfast, Ramsey and Gladys decided to break the news to the rest of the players. The squad had already noticed Banks' absence from the morning meal, and a few had asked about the retching noises in the night.

Gladys quietly took the Chelsea goalkeeper Peter Bonetti aside, and discreetly told him he was to be in the side for that afternoon's big match. After the cereal plates had been cleared away, Sir Alf clapped his hands and called for complete silence. Some of the more religious players thought they were about to be asked to thank God for their meal, and held their hands together and lowered their heads, but instead Ramsey explained the situation and told them that Bonetti would be in goal that afternoon.

There was a tense atmosphere in the training camp for the rest of the morning. Kick off in Leon was 4 p.m. local time, and Gladys had arranged for the team coach to leave at 1 p.m. She had hoped that the news of Banks' illness could be kept secret until just before kick-off, but somehow it had leaked out and a gaggle of pressmen had already gathered at the gates to La Bubba demanding to know the latest.

There was speculation that Banks had been poisoned by a German cook who had managed to smuggle a rancid portion of bratwurst into the training camp, or once again the Argentinians had thrown a spanner in the works.

Gladys and Ramsey were coaxed into giving an interview to BBC TV's David Coleman, and watching the video tape of the interview, one is aware how anxious and nervous the England management duo seemed to be. On one occasion Gladys snaps at Coleman and gives him a particularly frosty look when he asks how Banks came to be served a poisoned meal.

On the coach journey to the stadium, Gladys sat next to Bonetti and attempted to lift the goalkeeper's spirits by telling him he was behind the best defence in the World, but Bonetti seemed distant and confused, and even though Bobby Moore led a few choruses of *Back Home*. Gladys felt far from confident as the coach pulled into Leon.

As the two teams stood together in the tunnel awaiting the signal from the referee to take the pitch, Gladys shook hands with Haller, Seeler and Beckenbauer and wished them all the best. One of the younger German players shouted out a rude remark about Gladys' cooking, but fortunately the incident was defused as Seeler made the player apologise.

After the anthems Gladys and Sir Alf sat side by side on the England bench to watch an enthralling 45 minutes of football. The England management and substitutes were all on their feet, when just before half-time Alan Mullery fired them into the lead. At the interval, Gladys made sure all the players got plenty of liquids, and she put her arm around Bonetti and told him that he had done superbly well. But when she looked him in the eyes, she saw he seemed to be somehow elsewhere. She would later say of Bonetti, 'The lights were on, but nobody was in'.

As the teams took the pitch for the second half, Gladys did mention to Sir Alf that perhaps they should get the substitute goalkeeper, Alex Stepney warmed up. But Ramsey reasoned that Bonetti had dealt with all he had to confidently, and it would be best to leave things as they were.

Ramsey's words were given more credence when Martin Peters was on hand to force home a Francis Lee corner and put England 2-0 up. The Germans were dead and buried, and with the semi-final only three days away Sir Alf told Gladys that he wanted to make sure Peters and Bobby Charlton were fresh for the next game. The incredible temperatures took so much energy from all the players, but particularly the older ones, and

Ramsey wanted to be certain that two of the heroes of 1966 were fit and ready for the semi-final. Neither Peters nor Charlton were in their first flush of youth, and Ramsey wanted to replace them with Bell and Hunter, but Gladys did not agree. She felt the tie was far from over. Her knowledge of the Germans and her friendship with some of their players made her certain that there was still a lot to play for, she had learnt that you could never write a German off until the final whistle, and she told Ramsey to keep the team as it was. For the first time in their partnership, Ramsey took no notice, and he ordered Gladys to call Peters and Charlton off. Once again the film evidence is enthralling, the heated row on the England bench is quite evident, and while Alan Ball is taking a throw-in just in front of the England bench, one can clearly see Gladys wagging a finger at Sir Alf who sits impassively ignoring Gladys' words of warning.

Within twenty minutes, England were out of the World Cup. Goals from Muller and Seeler meant that the World Champions were booked on the first flight back to London. The substitutions of Charlton and Peters were seen to have been the turning point, not only for England's World Cup hopes but also for the future of Gladys Protheroe.

In the dressing room after the game, the players sat still in their sodden kit with heads in hands. Bobby Charlton was in tears while Peter Bonetti sat whimpering in a corner. Pressmen were banging on the door demanding to know why Peters and Charlton had been taken off at such a vital time. Sir Alf had not spoken a word to Gladys since the substitutions were made, and now in the dressing room he avoided her gaze.

The jubilant West Germans could be clearly heard singing and celebrating in the dressing room across the corridor. On such occasions in the past, the England players would have suggested drowning them out with a raucous version of *We're Gladys' Boys*, but on that day it was not to be.

Gladys felt there was really nothing she could say to the dejected players. Slowly and silently the team showered and changed into their casual clothes for the final trip back to La Bubba. Gladys noticed that Ramsey had gone off to speak to the press on his own which surprised her; normally he was only too keen to let Gladys deal with the journalists, especially after a defeat. Sir Alf spent over forty minutes at the press conference while Gladys and the players waited for him on the coach.

Eventually Ramsey appeared, and without a word to anyone took his seat and signalled the driver to return to the training camp. The staff at La Bubba had prepared a victory meal to celebrate, but this had been hastily cancelled and a spartan spread of bread and cheese had been substituted.

Many of the players, and Gladys, missed supper and went straight to bed. She took her time packing her kit bag that night, realising that it would almost certainly be the last time she was involved with the England team. Gladys slept fitfully, the visions of Muller and Seeler gleefully scoring past the stranded Bonetti continually filling her mind in that dark room.

Gladys woke at 6.30 a.m. and went down to the reception area to confirm the air travel arrangements. No-one apart from the office worker Jose seemed to be around, and he took time off from enjoying a breakfast of tortillas and coffee to tell her that Sir Alf had arranged for the England squad to catch the 11p.m. flight from Mexico City to London, and that a coach would arrive at six that evening to pick them up. Gladys thanked him for his help, and just before setting off on a morning stroll she noticed the front page of Jose's newspaper. In banner headlines were the words ' La Gladys Loco'. She asked Jose if she could borrow his paper, and read that at the press-conference after the game Ramsey had blamed England's defeat solely on Gladys. He had claimed that it was Gladys' decision to pull off Charlton and Peters and he also told' the press that her cooking had poisoned Gordon Banks. Suddenly Gladys realised just why Ramsey had been determined to speak to the press alone and why he had been avoiding her. Without further ado Gladys went to her room, collected her bag and asked Jose to call her a cab. Within half an hour she was on her way to the airport, and with the help of her American Express was booked in a first class seat on the noon flight to Heathrow.

While waiting for her flight Gladys bought all the newspapers and sports journals and read and re-read Ramsey's accusations. He had certainly done a thorough job. Instead of being upset, Gladys had a wry smile on her face as she drank a cool beer and looked forward to going home.

She sat next to a Texan businessman on the flight, and found it refreshing to talk to someone who knew nothing of football and was not at all interested in the World Cup. They spoke of the weather, the price of oil, Ernest Hemingway, the performance of the recently released BMW 3 series and many other topics. Those few hours proved to Gladys that there was indeed life outside football.

Somehow the British press had discovered Gladys was on the flight, and not for the first time in her life she was met at Heathrow by a huge contingent of journalists and photographers. Apparently she had been reported missing by the F.A. and there were initial fears she had been kidnapped by a Marxist Guerilla unit 'The Sons Of Karl'.

Standing next to the reporters were a band of football supporters, waiting patiently for the England squad to return home in some six hours time. As soon as they spotted Gladys in the arrival lounge boos and jeers rang out, and she was fortunate not to have been hit by an empty beer bottle thrown by one of the group that shattered against an advertising board. Gladys was being made the scapegoat for England's defeat and it was going to be almost impossible for Gladys to put her side of the story. She steadfastly refused to give any interviews or make any comment whatsoever regarding England's World Cup exit, and it took five policemen to keep the pressmen away from her as she collected her baggage. She was grateful to Tom, a baggage handler, who went out of his way to hail her a taxi.

The cabbie, a likeable fellow named Norman, was able to shake off the more zealous pressmen by performing a rather dangerous U-turn across the Heathrow entrance, then set off at high speed towards Croxley Green. Norman was able to tell his famous fare how England's defeat had been reported by the newspapers, and he handed Gladys his copies of *The Sun* and *The Daily Mirror*. As she thought, Ramsey had laid England's elimination squarely at Gladys' door and the tabloid papers had gladly gone along with it. Gladys scanned the back pages and read the headlines with disbelief. 'Protheroe The Poisoner Rocks England' screamed *The Sun*. The report read that she had fed Banks with rotten meat and then gone ahead, without Ramsey's agreement, and pulled off Charlton and Peters. 'Mad Glad Helps Jerries' was plastered across the back page of the *Mirror*, and they ran pretty much the same story as their rivals.

Norman dropped Gladys outside her house in the small hours. She had finally arrived home. Mrs Cornes had been in, and had left a fresh bunch of flowers with a Welcome Home card on the kitchen table – a much appreciated little touch. For the first time in many weeks Gladys was able to lay her head on her own pillow. She slept well, putting the events of the last 24 hours behind her.

Early next morning Gladys typed out a short letter of resignation and posted it off to F.A. Headquarters at Lancaster Gate. World Cup Grandstand showed pictures of the England squad arriving at Heathrow, and there were brief interviews with Bobby Moore and Francis Lee. Gladys was only mentioned once during the programme, in a rather derogatory way by presenter Jimmy Hill who remarked to David Coleman that he hoped his wife had not picked up any cooking tips from Mrs Protheroe.

Gladys was determined not to fall into the pit of depression she had experienced when she last left the employ of the F.A. She had nothing to be ashamed of, and despite the constant barrage of articles in the press, Gladys refused to be interviewed to put her side of the story. She kept a dignified silence over the whole matter. A number of Gladys Protheroe jokes began to surface, as often happens in Britain when an incident is taken up by the media.

"Why did the chicken cross the road? – Because he didn't want to be in one of Gladys Protheroe's Pies" was one such gag that did the rounds in the pubs and clubs of England. Two days after the players arrived back home, Bobby Moore telephoned Gladys and asked her out to dinner. She accepted, and spent a delightful evening with Moore and his beautiful wife Tina in a Watford trattoria. Moore told Gladys that the senior England players were fully aware that it had been Ramsey's decision to make the substitutions, and they had been staggered at the way Sir Alf had blamed Gladys for the defeat. Moore went on to say that Francis Lee had already started a petition, demanding Gladys' name be immediately cleared, and it was his intention to present it to the F.A.

Gladys told Moore in no uncertain terms that she did not want the matter to go any further. As far as she was concerned, the case was closed. Perhaps the time was right for her to bow out of international football and let a younger person step in to assist Ramsey. Certainly she had been deeply upset at the way Sir Alf had turned on her after their many years together, but she did understand the constant pressure he was under. When Moore himself became a manager, then he would realise that an international coach was always under the microscope. Ramsey must have known that defeat in Mexico would put his job on the line, so maybe his actions were that of a frightened man. In any case, Gladys could fight her own battles, and the last thing she wanted was the international careers of any of the players ruined because of some silly petition.

Gladys was touched at the loyalty shown by the Mexico squad, but she made Moore promise that they would let the matter drop. They would only cause trouble for themselves, and more importantly the game in general if they continued their rebellious antics.

Moore inquired as to Gladys' immediate plans. He mentioned that Ron Greenwood would only be too pleased if she could spare some time to help sort out the problems at Upton Park. The Hammers had struggled the previous season, and many pundits tipped them for relegation during the next campaign. But Gladys told the blonde defender and his wife that she wanted a few months out of the spotlight to live a normal, peaceful life again. Anyway, the tabloid press were continuing their spiteful attacks on her, holding her totally responsible for England's World Cup exit. The news of her resignation had not yet been released by the F.A. and only that morning *The Sun* had the headline ' For The Sake Of Allah – Go Gladys' dominating their sports pages. She told Moore that there had been an offer of £25,000 from the *News Of The World* to give her account of the Mexico games, but she had refused point blank to be involved in any kind of gutter journalism.

After a delicious meal of veal and pasta, washed down by a most acceptable Soave Gladys thanked the Moores for a wonderful night out, and promised to keep in touch. As they left for their cars, Bobby Moore asked Gladys if she had a message for Ramsey. She thought for a moment and said no, Ramsey knew where she was, it was up to him to get in contact, when he was ready.

CHAPTER 10: 'ROCKING ON THE ROAD'

It was now September 1970, and Gladys spent her time working hard, at last getting round to planting her herb garden. There were a couple of approaches from Continental clubs, but she declined their invitations and decided to stay out of football for a time. The Ramsey affair had certainly left a sour taste, and for the first time in many years she yearned to be involved in a project outside football. She received a kind letter from Juan Gomez at Real Madrid in which he told her that the door would always be open at the Bernabeau; all she had to do was say the word, and her airline tickets would be ready to pick up at Heathrow.

But Gladys was determined to stay at home. She had seen too little of her house and friendly village over the last few years. She was now 63 years of age, and perhaps it was time for her to do the things women of her age did. Gardening had always been a great love of hers. Taking country walks, cooking and song-writing were hobbies that she was keen to try, things she had no time for while involved in the hectic world of professional football. Now she would make the time.

Within a few weeks of returning home from Mexico Gladys had joined the Hertfordshire Ramblers, Croxley Green Allotment Society, Watford Pastry Cooks and the Herts Players (a local amateur dramatic society). She put everything into the societies, and soon her days were full of coffee mornings, committee meetings and rehearsals. Gladys played the part of a woman detective in the Herts Players' production of Agatha Christie's *Ten Little Niggers* and won some good reviews in the local press. For the Christmas pantomine, her Little John in a lively version of *Robin Hood* also gained rave reviews. On New years Eve, Gladys sat with Mrs Cornes and a few of her pastry cook friends and welcomed in 1971. She had made a new life outside of football, and although her sideboard was covered with cards from players and managers from all over the World (Sir Alf Ramsey had not sent a card for the first time in many, many years), she had lost touch with most of her ex colleagues. It seemed to her that the spell in the limelight was over and now it was time for her to put her feet up.

One evening when Gladys returned from a Hertfordshire Ramblers meeting she was rather surprised to find a rather battered blue Transit van parked outside her house. She thought no more of it, and went inside to put the kettle on for a cup of tea. Just as she was buttering some hot toast there was a knock on the door. Standing on the step was Elton John.

Gladys poured Elton a cup of tea and listened intently as he told her of his predicament. He and his band had been booked on a concert tour of England, but at the last moment his tour manager had been taken violently ill, drugs had been suspected, and the poor fellow had been dragged off to the Emily Fish clinic in Aylesbury to dry out. But this left Elton with no-one to organise his tour, and his whole career was in jeopardy. This tour was a vital one for him, his first L.P. had sold reasonably well in the U.K. and his record company were keen for him to build up a bigger following by playing in some more prestigious clubs and theatres. In the up and down world of rock music it was important for a new performer to keep in the public eye, to cancel a tour at such short notice would be a disaster.

Elton went on to say that now she was free of any footballing obligations, he was hoping that she would be able to take the helm. Her organisational abilities and experience of keeping a team of young men in order would be ideally suited to life on the road. Before making any decision, Gladys asked for more information. She was told by the eager pianist that it was a 16 date tour of England and Wales starting in Manchester the day after tomorrow. All transport and accommodation arrangements had been made. The band were ready – was she? Gladys finished her tea, took a bite of buttered toast, looked Elton straight in the eyes, and told him to give her half an hour to pack a holdall.

Within a few minutes the house was full of musicians. Elton's band had been waiting in the van, and on being told he had a new tour manager he ran to pass on the good news. The band were the same musicians that had backed Elton when Gladys last saw him play. Nigel Olsson, Dee Murray and Davey Johnstone. Bernie Taupin had gone on ahead, and they were to meet up with him at The Revolver Club in Manchester. Gladys made more tea and prepared plate after plate of toast for the hungry lads. The musicians were pale and thin from too many late nights and inadequate food. The plan had been to drive through the night and arrive in Manchester in the early morning, but Gladys would hear none of it. No, they would all get a good night's sleep in Croxley Green, go on an early morning jog in the countryside, get a hot breakfast inside them – then Gladys would drive them up the M1. It was her first decision as Elton's tour manager. Before the band retired, she had a chat with her new team. She told them that she was happy to take the job, but as in football, she demanded complete co-operation from them.

She had been in charge of many, many young men in her time, and although her new squad wore cheese-cloth shirts, clogs and Kaftans instead of tracksuits and football kit, she knew that deep down all young men were the same. Gladys went on to say it was her intention to inject some good old fashioned discipline into the band, and if this was the first time any of them had experienced such a regime they would just have to get used to it. If she was to take the job on, it would have to be on her terms. That was the way she had always worked, and she wasn't going to start changing her style now. The band all agreed on the ground-rules, and after cups of warm milk all round, Gladys' new team went to bed.

Gladys rose at 6.30a.m. and slipped on her England track-suit. She rummaged through her kit bags and came up with five more suits and a number of Real Madrid training tops. She laid them all outside her spare bedroom where the musicians slept, packed one set up for Bernie Taupin, then woke the band. Eventually she got them out of their beds, and after a few incredulous remarks from the rhythm section, persuaded them all to have a cold shower. Within half an hour the five of them were off on a three mile run around Croxley Green. Elton was obviously trying his best, but he had put a bit of weight on since Gladys had last seen him, and ended the run way behind the others. Gladys was pleased with the band's attitude. They had all entered into the exercise with the right spirit, and if they kept up their keen, open minded outlook there was no reason why the tour shouldn't be a great success.

After a breakfast of muesli and freshly ground coffee, Gladys went out to take a look at the band's Transit van. She was dismayed by what she found; the vehicle was dirty and smelt strongly of tobacco and reefers, so before setting off on the tour, she armed her lads with soapy water and dusters, and they gave the van a spring clean. They managed to fill five bin liners with fast food boxes, fish and chip wrappers, empty beer cans and cigarette packs. Elton was in fact delighted to find the words to a song he had written a few months earlier. He had feared the song was lost, but Gladys found them scribbled on a kebab wrapper. Eventually Gladys was satisfied with their transport, and they set off on the long trek up the motorway.

Gladys took the wheel and within no time they were heading North West. Elton told Gladys he had played The Revolver club once before and, having gone down very well on that occasion, decided to start the new tour there. He and Bernie had been busy writing new material, the band had been well rehearsed, and now with Gladys in charge – surely nothing could go wrong. Elton was well aware how badly she had been treated in Mexico, and although he didn't want to dwell on what must have been a most upsetting time for her, he did tell her that he and the band were with her all the way. Gladys thanked him for his kind words, and as the van shot past the Watford Gap services, the band burst into a spontaneous version of *We're Gladys' Boys.*

The Revolver Club was a small, cosy rock venue that had, to be honest, seen better days. There were faded posters from concerts past on the walls. Names like The Yardbirds, Vinegar Joe and Humble Pie had

113

apparently all played there, though the names meant nothing to Gladys. She did notice a musty, sweet smell in the club – the unmistakable aroma of cannabis, or 'pot' as the youngsters called it. One would imagine that Gladys would have been fiercely anti-drugs, but surprisingly she saw no real problem with reefers. Like anything, she thought that moderation was the key. Obviously hard drugs were another subject, and she made it clear to Elton and the boys that she would not tolerate anything stronger than the occasional joint. She did understood that occasionally 'creative' types did need the extra boost that alcohol or 'pot' would provide. The Revolver Club, or 'The Revy' as she noticed the band called it, was littered with empty beer bottles and full ash trays, the dance floor was sticky with spilt beer, and Gladys was sorely tempted to give the whole place the once-over with a mop and bucket of Vim.

The manager of the club, a callow long haired youth named Zak introduced himself, and Gladys told him that she was handling all of Elton's arrangements. On the journey North, Elton had told her what the job entailed. Gladys was to be responsible for the band's equipment and was to be the link between Elton and the club managers. Elton's job was to come up with the goods on stage, and he didn't have either the time or the inclination to deal with business matters while on the road. Gladys had a diagram to show where the band's gear was to be placed on the stage, and she instructed Zak to get his roadies to unload Elton's van.

The roadies were a grubby bunch of denim clad youths, but Gladys soon realised not to take too much notice of their unkempt appearance. After introducing herself, she found them to be polite, helpful young men, although she was rather mystified by their rather eccentric names. They were called JJ, Spliff, Speed, Rokko and Acidhead. After a lifetime around young men named Bobby, Billy and Jimmy, the bizarre names did take a little getting used to.

Gladys oversaw the unloading of the equipment, then went in search of the group. She found the dressing room, a rather cramped, poorly-lit room that only just held the band. Elton was giving an interview to a Manchester rock magazine while the rest of the lads sat around drinking beer and reading newspapers. Elton broke off from the interview and introduced Gladys to the journalist. The writer was intrigued to find one of the most famous names in English football working as tour manager to an up and coming rock act, and he asked her if it was 'cool' to mention her in the article. She didn't see why not and agreed.

After the journalist had left, Gladys told the band that all was ready for their soundcheck. She led them to the stage, made sure all the amplifiers were in the correct position and plugged everything in. She then withdrew to the back of the club, and stood with Zak and Acidhead to listen to the band. Elton and the group sounded in excellent form, and Gladys was impressed with the standard of the new material. As Gladys stood sipping a Coca-Cola, tapping her feet to the beat she felt a hand on her shoulder. She turned round and there stood Bernie Taupin. Bernie had grown his hair longer since they had last met, but still had that boyish glint in his eyes. The two friends swopped stories from their adventures. Bernie told Gladys that he didn't want to open any old wounds, but he said that if he could be any help with regard to the Mexico experience, she just had to ask. Gladys wouldn't hear of it, she told Bernie that was all behind her – now her priority was to make certain this tour was a huge success, and the boys sold thousands of records. Bernie said he'd drink to that, and mischievously finished off Gladys' drink.

When the soundcheck had been completed, Gladys and the band left the club for an Indian restaurant where they enjoyed a light meal before the performance. The band were to stay at the Manchester Trust House for the night, just over a mile from the Revolver Club. Gladys had looked at the budget for the tour, and decided that there was no reason that they shouldn't make a healthy profit from the concerts as long as they didn't get involved in any extravagances. They ate a rather tasty vegetable biriani washed down with mineral water and cold lager. Elton told Gladys that the set would last around an hour, the fee for the night was £200 and Gladys was to pick the money up from Zak after the performance. The roadies would be on hand to load the equipment, then Gladys would drive the van the short distance to the hotel.

When the band returned to The Revolver Club Gladys was amazed at the transformation. Instead of a cold, dark, empty room, the club had become into a noisy, vibrant arena. The dance floor was packed with young fans and Gladys had to push her way through the throng to get to the dressing room. Elton and the boys were delighted by the size of the crowd, and they told Gladys they were determined to get the tour off to a real rocking start. Just before they took the stage, Gladys locked the dressing room door and told the band to keep quiet for a moment. Then, with all the experience gathered from the years in football, she told the lads to go out there and give it their very best. She walked among them ruffling their hair and patting their backs making sure they all had their set lists, spare strings and cans of beer to refresh them during the set. Then with a final few words of encouragement she unlocked the door and sent her team out to a rapturous Manchester welcome.

Gladys stood with Bernie at the back of the club and both really got into the music. She told Bernie that the new material he had written with Elton was superb, and the audience obviously agreed. Elton had the crowd in the palm of his hand, and Gladys was most impressed with his stage manner. Soon young girls were sitting on their boyfriends' shoulders, whooping and swaying to the music. Gladys had experienced many different sporting venues, but she had to admit to Bernie that the atmosphere in the packed Revolver Club was on a par with The Bernabeau, Wembley or the nearby Old Trafford.

Suddenly, Gladys recognised a familiar face at the bar downing a large vodka. The young man had a full beard and long black hair. He was dressed from head to foot in faded denim, and from a distance looked like any other young rock fan, but he wasn't just any music follower. No, Gladys knew immediately who he was - it was George Best.

Gladys knew for a fact that Manchester United had an important game against Everton the day after to-morrow, and she was dismayed to see Best drinking so heavily. She made her way over to the bar and confronted the Irishman. Best looked at her through watery, bloodshot eyes and threw his arms around her. She felt him shuddering and weeping in her arms. Gladys told him to pull himself together, and she asked what on Earth he thought he was doing?

Best calmed down and explained that he had seen Elton was playing in Manchester, and couldn't resist seeing him again. He had started the evening drinking Coca-Cola, but had soon met up with some old drinking partners who had bought him a few vodkas. What with the heady atmosphere of the club, and the beat of the music he had soon realised he'd got through over a bottle of Smirnoff. He told Gladys he was sorry, he had actually cut down on alcohol, but once he had one drink he found it almost impossible to stop.

Best had tears in his eyes as he told Gladys his problems. Since their last meeting he had put on a lot of weight, and with his beard he had started to look far older than his 25 years. The boyish looks that had him dubbed 'El Beatle' were long gone. Wilf McGuinness had now taken over the manager's chair at Old Trafford, and he had made it abundantly clear he would not tolerate any of Best's indiscipline. McGuinness had already suspended the Irishman for a late night incident at a London hotel when Manchester United played Chelsea and stated in the press that he was determined to break Best.

Gladys told Best that she had an idea. If it was acceptable to Elton and Manchester United, why didn't he join the tour as he had done previously? The few days Best had spent with Elton and the band a year before had done the player a power of good, and perhaps a fortnight under Gladys' guidance might cure him of his drink problem once and for all. Best was ecstatic. He told Gladys he thought it was a fantastic idea – he could think of nothing more he would rather do. Gladys, Best and Bernie returned to the dance floor to watch the end of the concert, and after Elton had performed three encores they went backstage to congratulate the band on a terrific concert.

Elton agreed immediately to Best joining the tour, and they arranged to pick George up the following day. Gladys left Best with the band and went to see Zak to sort out the business affairs. Zak told her that it had been a record night, and while he counted out the £200 asked Gladys if it would be possible for Elton to play The Revolver club again soon.

Gladys woke next morning at 7.30 and after a brisk jog around the streets of Manchester she returned to the hotel to begin preparations for day two of the Elton John tour. The next date was at The Cha-Cha club in Carlisle. Gladys had reckoned on a two hour drive to Cumberland, so she wanted the band all ready and willing to leave Manchester by noon at the latest. She telephoned Sir Matt Busby to clear the Best situation with him. Busby was now General Manager at Old Trafford, and although Wilf McGuinness was in charge of the day to day team affairs Gladys thought it would be more apt if she spoke directly to Busby.

She told Busby that Best had been drinking again, and if he was to be any good to United or indeed himself again, it was vital he got away from Manchester and tried one last time to rid himself of his alcohol dependency. Busby eventually agreed to the plan, but he warned Gladys that McGuinness would be furious.

After rousing Elton and the boys she managed to grab a quick breakfast of muesli and orange juice, then set about getting the band on board the van. They picked George Best up at the last petrol station before the M6 as arranged. Best had shaved and looked fitter and neater in a black denim suit with a Frank Zappa T-Shirt on under his jacket. As they drove along, Gladys explained to Best that he would be expected to pay his way on the tour by helping with the equipment. Best said that he would be only too pleased to help, and joked that the physical side of the work would be of more benefit to him than the boring training routines that Wilf McGuinness put the United players through.

The van arrived in Carlisle, and after fighting their way through the town's one way system they eventually found the Cha-Cha Club. The venue was of a similar size to The Revolver Club, and once again Gladys managed the setting up of the band's equipment with George Best being a great help. As he was carrying one of Elton's microphone stands into the club a cleaner, who had been busily sweeping the dance floor, walked over to Best and asked him if he knew he was the spitting image of that footballer. Bobby Moore, she thought his name was.

Once again Elton played a splendid set, and Gladys had started to remember the highlights of the performance. She particularly liked *Skyline Pigeon* and *Val Halla*. The concert ended at just after midnight, and Gladys had arranged for the band to stay at a guest house run by the ex-Carlisle player Ken Horrigan. He was pleased to be of service to two of football's great characters, and kept his small, well stocked bar open later than usual for the band's nightcaps. Gladys kept a close eye on Best's drinking, but was pleased to see that apart from a couple of beers at the club and a small brandy before bed, he seemed to be looking after himself.

That night Gladys sat with Elton and went through the remaining dates of the tour. They were to play Preston, Liverpool, Glasgow, Edinburgh, Newcastle and Leeds on the Northern leg then return South to play dates in Birmingham, Wolverhampton, the South Coast, and finally London. In all there were sixteen 'gigs' as Elton called them, and Gladys was amazed at the names of the various clubs.

They were due at such exotic places at 'The Electric Banana', 'Fat Jacks', 'Denim Heaven' and 'The Big Shag Club' – she couldn't wait. Gladys had found her England tracksuit to be warm and comfortable, but it did tend to get grubby, and she felt rather conspicuous amongst so much denim and black leather. So, the next morning with George Best and Dee Murray acting as experts she visited the Happy Frog boutique in downtown Carlisle and purchased a complete wardrobe for her new career. She bought a pair of fluorescent blue clogs, a Kaftan coat, a pair of faded denim dungarees with the biggest flares they had in the shop, a well-worn US police leather motorcycle jacket, a number of tie-dye T-Shirts with such slogans as 'Keep Cool', 'Drop Out' and 'Keep On Trucking' emblazoned on them, and to top the whole lot off, a huge brown leather hat. This spree cost her nearly £40, but George and Dee both agreed that she had got some really great 'gear'.

Gladys soon got into the life of a rock tour manager, getting used to the late nights and the loud music. She picked up the various rock terms such as gaffer tape, ligger and bum note, and after five or six concerts was able to breeze into a club, tell the manager just where the gear was to go, what kind of sound the band wanted, and when she was to have Elton's bread. After a week on the road Gladys had put all the disappointments of the World Cup behind her, and indeed Mexico seemed another world. The only link with football were the kickabouts with George and the band after the soundcheck, before the club opened its doors to the paying fans. Gladys found it difficult to bend a ball around a defensive wall in her clogs, so she would slip on her trusty plimsoles in the event of any direct free-kicks.

There was a real feeling of camaraderie among the members of the tour. George Best seemed to be in his element, and it was obvious to Gladys that Elton and Best were envious of each other's talents. But that was human nature she supposed. Both of them had incredible natural gifts, but they were frustrated at being unable to dribble past a defender or write a hit pop song. She hoped that their friendship would be one of the many positive points to come from the tour. The band's Transit van was surprisingly reliable. Gladys had put drummer Nigel Olsson in charge of vehicle maintenance, and he had not let her down. Each morning the long haired musician checked the van's water, battery and tyre pressures, and he even gave the windscreen a wipe over with a damp rag prior to each journey.

On the trip to Glasgow, Gladys was rather perturbed to hear on the van radio that Manchester United had announced that unless George Best returned to Old Trafford within 48 hours he would have his contract cancelled, and he would be unable to play League football again. When they arrived at The Exploding Wax club in the East of the city, she drew Best aside and told him about the situation in Manchester. George told her that as far as he was concerned, all he wanted to be was a rock roadie just like Spliff and Acidhead. He had had enough of the goldfish bowl existence of professional football. Yes, he knew he was a talented player, but surely there was more to life than kicking a bag of leather around a field. Gladys told him that he was making a big decision; after all the life of a rock roadie was even more unpredictable than that of a footballer. Certainly, here he was with Elton John and his group, but what about the future? Elton would only tour like this for another few years; it was obvious to anyone that he was set to became a huge international star, but would he always have a vacancy for an ex-professional footballer, even one as famous as George Best? And what about injuries? It would only take one extra heavy box of leads, or a badly packed case of cymbals to put a roadie out with a serious back or neck complaint, and then what?

George told Gladys that he had given it a lot of thought. He had some money put away for a rainy day, enough anyway to buy a house. He was 25 years of age, and he wanted to be able to start making his own decisions, to start living his own life. At Old Trafford it was impossible to express himself as an individual. He was looked upon as a player, pure and simple. Nobody seemed at all interested in him as a person. That's what the difference was with Elton's tour. Everyone was treated as equal. Sure, Gladys was in charge, but she treated everybody with respect. Gladys told George that he must be certain before burning his boats. He still had perhaps ten years at the top left in him, was he certain that he wanted to dedicate his life to the crazy hybrid of rock 'n' roll?

They decided to continue the discussion after the concert as time was getting on, and Elton was keen to run through a couple of newly written songs during the soundcheck. George and Acidhead carried the amplifiers from the van while Gladys and Rokko miked up the drums.

The Exploding Wax Club was a long, narrow room with a cramped stage at one end. There was a bar running almost the entire length of one side of the dance floor, and the floor itself was lit by hot wax projectors, giving the place a psychedelic feel. There were a number of life sized posters of naked girls and a gigantic picture of Mick Jagger in the dressing room. Gladys had arranged a light buffet for the band and roadies, and she was pleased to see that the club's manager Jacko had come up with a tasty table full of sandwiches, mineral water and a case of Glasgow 'Heavy'.

There seemed to be an air of expectancy amongst the band, and the atmosphere got through to Gladys, who sensed that the band were ready to really 'cook'. The Glasgow crowd were renowned for their vocal support, whether it be for their football teams or a favourite rock act. If they liked someone, they were not afraid to show it, the other side of the coin of course being that if something displeased them, then they were only too ready to show the violent side of their temperament. Gladys remembered bringing her Real Madrid team to Glasgow to play Celtic some nine years earlier. Real won 2-0 to go through 4-0 on aggregate. The knowledgeable Glasgow crowd had applauded the Spaniards off the pitch, but then had turned on their own players with a spite and venom that Gladys had not seen the like of before or since. She only hoped that Elton came up with the goods that night. Once again, he was to play before a capacity crowd, and it was so packed in the club itself that Gladys and George decided to watch the show from the side of the stage. There they could enjoy the music and also be on hand in case there were any technical difficulties. As usual, Elton started the show with a blistering version of *Take Me To The Pilot*, before belting into an R&B medley that always had the audience jumping around. After twenty minutes of the set, George asked Gladys if she would like a cold beer from the bar. Gladys had worked up quite a sweat jigging and rocking away to Elton and the boys, and readily agreed to a drink. George set off to the bar as the band launched into *Honky Cat*, one of the new numbers Elton and Bernie had just composed. Gladys really looked the part in her dungarees and T Shirt that proclaimed 'Lets Boogie' and she forgot about George as she 'dug' the sound.

After ten minutes, Gladys started to miss her companion, and she wondered what was keeping him. She was getting very thirsty and could have murdered a cold lager. Gladys set about finding the Irishman, thinking that perhaps he had been recognised and was having to sign autographs for some soccer daft Scotsmen. She pushed her way through the dancing throng and made her way to the bar where Acidhead and Spliff stood chatting to two young fans. Gladys ashed them if they happened to have seen George. Spliff told Gladys that he had been at the bar talking to three or four men in red and black tracksuits a few minutes earlier. Immediately Gladys smelled a rat. She knew full well that the only club that wore red and black tracksuits were Manchester United. What on Earth were four United players doing at The Exploding Wax Club in Glasgow on a Friday night? Gladys knew for a fact that United were due to play at Southampton the following day, and the more she thought about it, the more she began to worry.

Suddenly, she heard a fracas in a store room to the side of the bar. Best's unmistakable voice could be plainly heard shouting obscenities and calling for help. All of a sudden the four tracksuited men burst out of the storeroom, and barging their way past the astonished music fans, rushed to the exit carrying Best by his arms and legs. Gladys did attempt to stop them but she was pushed aside by one of the sour faced kidnappers. By the time

Gladys made it outside, she was only in time to see Best being bundled into the back of a dark blue saloon car. Gladys recognised one of the men involved as John Fitzpatrick, the Manchester United midfielder. Gladys shouted out his name, but Fitzpatrick just looked around, laughed and gestured a V sign to Gladys before ordering the driver to step on it.

The last thing Gladys saw was Best's frightened face pushed up against the rear window as the vehicle screeched out of the Exploding Wax car park and headed South. Clearly Wilf McGuinness had learnt of Best's whereabouts and had sent a kidnap squad to retrieve his player. Gladys ran back into the club, pushed her way on stage and grabbed the microphone from an astonished Elton John. She explained the situation to the crowd and they immediately roared their support. In a matter of minutes a cavalcade of vehicles set off in pursuit of the kidnappers. Gladys drove the group's Transit at top speed through the streets of Glasgow with Elton and Bernie by her side. She had a quick glance in the rearview mirror and could make out a number of motorcycles, a jeep and a couple of brightly coloured vans as well as a fleet of cars. Gladys knew that they did not have a car fast enough to keep up with the kidnappers on the motorway, so their one hope was to catch them before they reached the intersection. There was a carnival atmosphere in the Armada of vehicles. Girls were hanging out of windows screaming and shouting, (some, Gladys noticed, were topless), drivers were tooting their horns and flashing their lights, shouting at passers by as they sped through the Glasgow suburbs. Gladys could see the white knuckles on Elton and Bernie's hands as she skidded into tight corners, and on a number of occasions her passengers closed their eyes as she overtook slow lorries and buses on hills or blind corners. Soon the signs for the motorway and the South came into view, and the followers knew their chances of catching their prey were fading with every mile. Then Gladys recognised the blue saloon car ahead of them, and she really put her foot down. Fitzpatrick and his cohorts obviously thought that the job was done as they cruised along at 90 mph. Gladys and her friends could clearly see the distressed face of George Best bound and gagged in the back seat, while a player resembling the Manchester United defender Francis Burns sat at the wheel. Fitzpatrick was in the passenger seat, while two unidentified players sat with Best in the back. Gladys turned the lights out on the van, and drove right up to the rear bumper of the kidnappers' car. She could now see Fitzpatrick drinking beer from a can and laughing, obviously looking forward to the bonus he had been promised by McGuinness for committing such an evil deed. Gladys shouted to Elton and Bernie to prepare for impact, and if possible arm themselves with the base of a microphone stand or anything else that came to hand. Gladys didn't think the Manchester United players would relinquish their prize without one hell of a fight. Then, she turned the van lights onto full power and rammed the back of the blue saloon. They were taken completely by surprise, and Burns was unable to keep control. Gladys hit the rearside of the car twice, then three times, eventually managing to force it off the road. With a final effort she reversed into the front of it smashing the lights and bursting the radiator. She screamed at Elton and Bernie to get stuck in, and there then followed an undignified scuffle on the grass verge. Within seconds the rest of Gladys' posse had arrived and helped out with the rescue. Acidhead had Fitzpatrick in a headlock, Elton and Bernie had Burns pinned down under a tree, and Gladys dived into the car to free Best, who was unharmed but obviously shaken by the experience. Fist fights continued on the verge for a few more moments before the Manchester United players realising they were outnumbered, turned tail and fled. Elton produced a bottle of brandy from the van, and Gladys poured out a healthy tot for each rescuer. Apart from the odd black eye and a few cuts and bruises no one was seriously hurt. Bernie turned the van radio up to full volume, and they held an impromptu celebration party there on the side of the road. Amid the dancing and laughter, George walked over to Gladys and told her that perhaps he had better return to old Trafford under his own steam to face the music. He said that he was concerned that McGuinness would send another kidnap squad for him, and the last thing he wanted was for Elton's tour to be ruined or, worse, for any of his new friends to get hurt. Gladys agreed that perhaps it was in everyone's best interests for Best and McGuinness to sort the problem out face to face. She offered to accompany Best to Old Trafford, but he declined, so they arranged for George to travel back down South on the back of one of Spliff's Hells Angel friends' motorcycle the next morning. They cleared up the debris on the roadside, then all returned to their hotel for a nightcap and some supper. Gladys thanked all the Glaswegian rock fans who had helped them with their rescue, and promised that Elton would play a special concert for them on the next tour. Elton did, and he is always guaranteed a warm welcome whenever he treads the boards in that fine old city.

There were emotional scenes the next morning as George Best was whisked away by Nuthead on his huge Harley-Davidson 'hog'. Gladys lent George her motorcycle jacket and he wrapped himself up in a Partick Thistle scarf that had been donated by a music fan the previous night. Elton, Bernie, the band, all the roadies, and then of course Gladys embraced the Irishman before watching him roar off back to Old Trafford.

However, despite Best and McGuinness patching up their differences and the kidnapping episode being swept under the carpet by the club, the peace wasn't to last. Best did regain his place in the Manchester United team, but a few short months later Best went missing and was discovered with Miss World, Marjorie Wallace, in a London love nest. Gladys has often thought that if Best had been allowed to stay on that Elton John tour under her guidance, then perhaps she could have helped him really fulfill his potential. Unfortunately, it wasn't to be. One of Gladys' ambitions was to have managed a team with George Best in it. If she had done, many experts still feel that Best would have continued playing at the very highest level right into the mid 1980s.

Elton's tour continued with growing success. Gladys managed to arrange interviews for him on local radio stations in Edinburgh and Newcastle, and he and Bernie were featured in the *Melody Maker* magazine. The writer described them as 'The freshest talents on the British music scene' and a large photograph of Elton appeared on the cover. Gladys could sense that she was witnessing the birth of a superstar. There were now long queues of fans waiting patiently for the band at all the clubs they played, and every date was a sell-out.

The final night of the tour was at the Marquee Club in the heart of London's West End. Elton had built up a large following in the capital, and there were crowds of well-wishers surrounding the stage door as early as noon when Gladys and Acidhead helped unload Elton's trusty keyboard. There was a BBC film unit from the rock programme *The Old Grey Whistle Test* and a number of journalists from the national music press. One of Gladys' duties was to arrange interview times for Elton, after which she went with Dee Murray and Bernie to buy some guitar strings for that evening's performance. Dee told Gladys that the guys in the band wanted to finish the tour on a high note and asked if she would agree to play percussion at that night's gig. Bernie pointed out that she was familiar enough with the material, having attended every date of the tour. They had a tambourine, maracas, bongos and conga drums as well as a number of African instruments. Gladys had natural rhythm and a performers temperament – she would be a sensation.

After giving it some thought Gladys agreed, and she made her debut with Elton John's band at The Marquee Club on Friday 22nd, January 1972. *The Old Grey Whistle Test* filmed the entire performance, and it was transmitted three weeks later on BBC2. Gladys wore a bright yellow cat suit with 'The Allman brothers' written in red on the back and a pair of purple tinted sunglasses that Elton had kindly lent her. In fact her percussion playing and backing vocals are impressive, particularly on a rocking version of *Honky Cat.* The story goes that Elton's record company boss Dick James was so impressed that he offered her a three album recording deal after the show, but Gladys declined. At the post gig party there was a strangely subdued atmosphere. The band and roadcrew had been together night and day for nearly five weeks, and had grown together like a family. Elton and Bernie made short speeches thanking everyone for their hard work and support, adding that they hoped to keep the same team for the forthcoming U.S. tour. Just before Gladys left the party Elton asked her to continue as tour manager for the U.S. trip. She told him that she had only taken the job to help him out, and she didn't really feel that she would fit in with all the long haired young men, but, as the tour had gone on, she had got more and more into it. The answer was yes, if Elton wanted her to continue, she would. A few of the neighbours wondered just who it was alighting from a taxi in the early hours and going into Mrs Protheroe's house. Instead of a track suited figure wearing running shoes and a towel around her neck, it was a strange person wearing a battered Kaftan coat and brightly coloured clogs who trotted up the garden path. The stranger had a set of congas under one arm and and a huge poster of Janis Joplin under the other – was that *really* Gladys Protheroe?

CHAPTER ELEVEN: 'ROCKIN' IN THE U.S.A.'

It was a strange feeling for Gladys to wake up the next morning in her own bed, away from the heady existence of the Rock'n'Roll circuit. For a few days she was unable to get to sleep before 4 a.m., her body clock still working at the pace it had done on the road – a form of jet lag. She had neglected her garden over the previous few months, so decided to dedicate some time to returning it to its former glory. She found the heavy digging and lifting a little difficult at first, after all she no longer had Bernie Taupin to help her, but after a hot bath in herbal salts each evening, she soon got used to the physical exertion. She started using muscles she had forgotten she owned. Gladys got to know the young man at the local plant nursery well, and he would advise her which the best plants were to restock her garden.

Gladys became a well known sight in her garden decked out in garish T-shirts and a pair of track suit bottoms. Soon the garden started to look the part, and passers-by would regularly stop to chat with Gladys and compliment her on her endeavours. By the end of May she half completed her work, and entered the Watford and District Best Garden of 1972 Competition. The judges were impressed with her contribution and she was awarded First Prize in the New Garden section, and won third prize overall. Gladys posed for a photograph for the local newspaper with Watford's mayor and Watford FC manager George Kirby, the headline read 'Ex Lady Soccer Star Still On Top Form'.

Elton and Bernie kept in touch with the preparations for the American tour, and Gladys was pleased to read all the positive reviews Elton was receiving not only in the music papers – but in the daily press too. Gladys had splashed out on a new stereo hi-fi, which cost nearly £100, and she was delighted to receive a huge bundle of LPs from Acidhead. She was not too sure about some of the groups, but after a few plays got into Frank Zappa, The Eagles, Roxy Music and Rod Stewart and The Faces.

In June 1972 Gladys received a letter from Elton John telling her that he had been asked if he would be interested in playing a benefit concert for Watford Football Club. The club were in dire financial straits and desperate for funds. As Elton and Gladys were both local celebrities, Watford had hoped they would be of help. Gladys thought it was a splendid idea and immediately offered her assistance. So later that Summer, Elton John, Rod Stewart, Nazareth and a number of other groups took the stage in front of The Shrodells stand at Vicarage Road and played a superb pop concert in front of over 10,000 ecstatic music fans. Gladys soon got into the feel of the afternoon, and one of the highlights of the concert was a soulful duet between Gladys and Elton, a marvellous version of *I Got you Babe* and the applause nearly brought the house down.

After the concert Gladys attended a cocktail party in the Director's Suite, and a number of photographs of her with Rod Stewart, Elton John, Marc Bolan and Gary Glitter appeared in the press the following day.

Later that week Elton and Bernie arrived at Gladys' home, and the three old friends planned the dates of Elton's US tour. Elton and the boys were to spend a few weeks rehearsing new material in London before leaving for San Francisco where the tour was to begin. Gladys had never visited the U.S.A. before, so she went to Croxley Green library to take out a number of books on America. With the help of a small notebook and a few weather charts Gladys was able to forecast the conditions the group could expect to meet, and she packed her luggage accordingly. When she met Elton the day before departure she had photocopied the various charts which she handed out to the band and roadcrew.

Elton had decided to keep the nucleus of the band from the successful UK tour, but had added percussionist Ray Cooper to augment the sound on stage. Once again Gladys was to be in charge of the roadcrew, and the team of Acidhead, Spliff, Rokko, Speed, JJ and Nuthead were all excited about the trip. This tour was to be far bigger that the UK outing. For a start, Elton had sold five times the amount of records in the USA that he had done at home, and instead of playing small clubs like The Revolver or Exploding Wax Elton was booked into huge ice hockey and football stadiums that could hold up to 75,000 fans. Gladys realised that all her powers of management she had learned during her time in football would be needed if she was to be a success in America. The band and roadcrew were booked on a Pan-Am flight from Heathrow to San Francisco, where Elton and his colleagues would have two days to acclimatise before opening at 'The Talk Of The West Coast', a huge arena that was situated in a natural bowl. 'The Talk', as it was known in rock circles, was a highly prestigious venue, a sign that Elton had arrived on the international scene. As usual for the long haul flight, Gladys had chosen a comfortable England tracksuit and a pair of Adidas training shoes to wear.

There were a large number of Elton's fans waiting at San Francisco International Airport, and after her highly publicised arrivals at Madrid and London, Gladys was intrigued to see just how efficient the U.S. security men were as they coped with the sudden surge of fans and shepherded Elton and his team into the VIP lounge. After a police escort through San Francisco, Gladys was pleased to be able to rest at the band's hotel. Although she was in peak physical fitness, she did feel at 64 years of age that her powers of recovery were not as they were.

After a good night's sleep, Gladys donned her Watford away kit, and went for an early morning run around the San Francisco. She chanced upon Haight-Ashbury, the Bohemian area of the city and as she jogged through the busy streets she was amazed to hear the mix of music booming out of the garishly painted houses and apartments. On every corner there were groups of long haired, wild eyed youths wearing brightly coloured loon pants and tie dyed T-shirts. Some of the kids would follow her as she ran, whooping, shouting and singing.

After running for half an hour, Gladys stopped for a cool milk drink at The Freaky Paisley Bar, a shabby establishment that was decorated by what looked like two huge eyes painted across the windows. The bar was empty but for a few denim clad youths sitting around a juke box listening to a Jimi Hendrix record. Gladys ordered a raspberry milk shake and took a seat close to the window to watch the world go by as she rested. The outrageous fashions the locals wore astonished Gladys; the youngsters wore all the colours of the rainbow, and it was difficult to tell if the passersby were boys or girls. Their hair ran down to their waists, and everyone seemed to have beads, feathers, earrings and all manner of junk jewellery cascading from every conceiveable place. As Gladys sat sipping her milk shake she was aware of a pale youth in jeans and a T-Shirt staring at her. She took no notice and continued to tap her foot to the beat of *White Rabbit* by Jefferson Airplane. After a few minutes the youth plucked up enough courage to come over to Gladys' table. He asked her if he could sit down, and then offered to buy her a fresh shake. Gladys readily accepted. The young man told her that he recognised her face from the Elton John tour posters that had been plastered all over the city. The poster pictured Elton and the band with Gladys on stage at The Marquee on the last date of the UK tour. The young stranger apologised for his manners, and introduced himself. His name was Bruce, Bruce Springsteen. He told her that he too was a musician, and was in San Francisco to try and hawk his demo tapes around the West Coast record companies. He was originally from New Jersey, and had formed a group called 'The E Street Band' but they were having difficulty making any progress in the music business, so he had taken a Greyhound bus across the country hoping to make some connections in San Francisco.

He wondered whether Gladys would be kind enough to pass on a tape to Elton John, in the hope that he would be able to get his career moving. Gladys told Bruce that she was about to return to the hotel, and if he wasn't doing anything he could accompany her. If Elton wasn't too busy then perhaps he would be able to play a few numbers for them all, and Elton would be able to give him the benefit of his experience. Bruce was delighted. He downed his milk in one gulp and returned the back of the bar to pick up his battered guitar case. On their way to the hotel, the two new friends chatted away, Gladys telling Bruce exactly how a limey woman in her mid

127

60s had become tour manager to one of the hottest properties in rock music. Bruce wasn't aware of Gladys' football background, so her stories of the glory days at Wembley and the Bernabeau didn't mean too much to him, but he did tell her that 'Glory Days' seemed a good title for a song, and perhaps one day he would get around to writing it. Fortunately for Bruce, Elton and the band were sitting around the hotel bar having a couple of beers, so after Gladys had made the initial introductions, she asked the bar manager if it would be possible to run through a few numbers on the small bar stage. Each evening a duo called 'Frank & Barbara' entertained the early evening drinkers with middle of the road songs, and they had left their equipment set up ready for that night's show. The manager obligingly agreed, and Gladys helped the nervous Bruce tune up his guitar. Gladys used her expertise to help Bruce get the right sound, and then manned the mixing desk.

Elton, Bernie, Dee, Nigel, Davey and Ray sat down at the back of the bar, unsure what to expect. Certainly they respected Gladys' opinion and musical taste, but they suspected they were going to have to sit through a lacklustre set from some no-hoper. Then Bruce suddenly burst into the opening bars of a song he had just written called *Born To Run* and by the end of the rendition it was obvious to everyone in the bar that Gladys had unearthed a real talent.

Gladys joined Bruce on percussion for the next few songs, rattling the maracas and pounding the conga drums to the heady beat. By the time Bruce and Gladys reached the fifth number, Elton and the rest of the boys had plugged in and were rocking along too. This sudden burst of music had filled the bar with interested spectators, and the manager had to call in extra barmen to satisfy the unexpected morning crowd. Eventually the band were worn out, and despite calls from the fans to continue Gladys announced that the performance was at an end and asked everyone in the house to show their appreciation for a new music star, Bruce Springsteen.

After leaving the bar the band went up to Elton's suite for a bite to eat. Bruce nervously asked Gladys if she thought the audition had gone well. She replied that if he ever did a better one - she wanted to know.

Elton invited Bruce to open the shows on the US tour. Bruce said he would love to, but as his band were on the other side of the country, would it be possible for Gladys to back him with her percussion playing?

Thus the next night Bruce and Gladys stepped out onto the stage of 'The Talk Of The West Coast', and had the San Francisco rock fans dancing in the aisles with their uncompromising rock 'n' roll. The review of the concert in the next morning's *San Francisco Herald* ran under the headline 'Elton Wows U.S.'. It was written by respected rock writer Chet Lewis, and he stated that "Elton John is perhaps the first superstar of the '70s. The concert was a huge success for the English piano player; he is a magnificent talent and is bound to become a household name". But the review also mentioned that the opening act of Gladys Protheroe and Bernie Springman were one to watch. "Protheroe's fantastic rhythms filled the night, her non stop boogie took the crowd to Paradise and back. This foxy rock chick blew this reviewer away - she was awesome" wrote Lewis. Gladys was able to delegate most of her roadcrew duties to Acidhead as her performances with Bruce took up all of her time. Each night, Bruce and Gladys won more and more adulation with their wild rock show. Usually they would join Elton and the band on stage at the end of their set for a blistering encore of *I Saw Her Standing There*.

The tour continued to Seattle, Chicago, Denver, St. Louis, Boston, Philadelphia, Atlanta, New Orleans, Houston and Detroit before ending up in New York where Elton was booked to play three nights at Madison Square Garden.

The media attention that had been building up throughout the tour reached its peak when the tour bus arrived in The Big Apple. Elton had been featured on the cover of both *Rolling Stone* and *Time* while Gladys herself had made the cover of *US Lady*. Tickets were changing hands for over two hundred dollars each and fans packed the lobby of the band's hotel. Gladys had never experienced such pressure and excitement as during those days in New York. In the morning of the first show Elton, Bruce and Gladys appeared on the Breakfast TV Show *Good Morning America*. Gladys wore a Watford first team shirt, and the interviewer was Kelly Jackson, a former Miss Universe. Kelly was interested to learn that Gladys had once been involved in professional sport, and a great deal of the interview was given over to Gladys' stories of her days with the England team. After the interview Elton mimed through *Honky Cat* while Bruce and Gladys were introduced to fellow guests Warren Beatty, Steve McQueen and Ringo Starr. All three were keen to get tickets for Elton's shows, and Gladys told them she would do all she could to help. Later that day, Gladys was interviewed on OKNY75, a rock'n'roll FM radio station, then enjoyed a photo session at the Statue of Liberty with Bruce and Elton.

Bruce was a little edgy before that evening's performance, mainly because for him it was a 'home town gig'. He had many friends and relatives in the audience, and was determined to put on a great show. He needn't have worried, because once again he and Gladys won the crowd over with their set. They had put together a well paced collection of songs, and by their second number the crowd were up off their seats clapping and whooping along.

Elton and the band then tore through their set leaving the audience screaming for more. Gladys and Bruce ran on for an encore, and were joined by John Lennon and David Bowie. The hastily formed supergroup rocked their way through a version of *Blue Suede Shoes* before walking off to tumultuous applause.

The apres-gig party was a glittering affair, attended by film stars, politicians and rock singers. Gladys spent a long while chatting to Ringo and George Harrison, and enjoyed a pleasant half hour explaining the rules of Association Football to Jack Nicholson. Just after 3 a.m. she bade farewell to the guests, and left Elton's suite to retire to bed. The party was obviously set to go on for a considerable time yet, but Gladys wanted to feel fresh for the last two dates of the tour, and she left the younger ones to enjoy themselves.

While in New York, Gladys managed to attend two N.A.S.L. games and had a pleasant supper with Pele and Franz Beckenbauer who were both playing for New York Cosmos at the time.

The final nights of Elton's tour were played in an almost carnival atmosphere. Bruce and Gladys had gained enough notoriety to have built up their own small legion of fans who noisily cheered and stamped their approval after each song. A street wise New York entrepeneur had realised that Bruce and Gladys were fast becoming cult figures and had hastily printed up T-Shirts that read 'Gladys & Bruce - Boogie USA 1972' - they sold like hotcakes. Bruce himself had been inundated by offers from record companies anxious to sign him up, but he confided to Gladys that he wasn't certain he could be a success without her by his side. She told him to pull himself together; he had God given talent; it would be a sin if he did not share his songs with the world.

Madison Square Gardens were charged with emotion on Thursday 17th July 1972 when Gladys Protheroe took to the stage for the very last time. She had confided to both Bruce and Elton that this was to be her farewell. The music press got hold of the story, and as Gladys walked out to her percussion table, the whole audience stood as one and lit their cigarette lighters to create a spine-chilling scene. Bruce stepped out to the microphone, and instead of bursting straight into *Soul Man* he told the fans that if it wasn't for Gladys Protheroe he wouldn't be there on stage in front of such a great crowd. The spotlight picked out Gladys who was wearing a baggy cheese-cloth shirt and a pair of violet dungarees. She waved to the crowd and launched into an energetic solo on her congas. The set was perhaps the best Bruce and Gladys had played. Security men attempted to keep the fans in their seats, but after three songs it was obvious that the crowd were in party mood, and nothing was going to stop them sending Gladys back to England on a New York high.

A couple of fans actually made it onto the stage, and they had to be dragged away from Gladys, but she was still able to keep the pumping beat going, driving the crowd into frenzy. Off stage Gladys could see Elton and the band dancing in the wings. Jack Nicholson, Paul Simon, Muhammad Ali, Margaret Trudeau, Paul Newman, Diana Ross and other showbusiness luminaries were there too shouting and whooping between each song.

As a special surprise Bruce, Elton and the band had secretly rehearsed a rocking version of *We're Gladys' Boys*, and after the final encore Elton and the band tore through the old football anthem, giving it a new depth. Later Gladys was presented with a huge bouquet of red roses by Ed Koch, New York's mayor, and was carried from the stage shoulder high by Elton, Bruce and Bernie.

Gladys was physically and emotionally drained by the performance. She sat with Bernie in the dressing room as Elton played his set to the excited New Yorkers. She told Bernie that she didn't think she was up to joining Elton for his encore; perhaps she would take a quick shower and return to the hotel. There was then a knock on the door, and in stepped John Lennon and his wife Yoko Ono. The Lennons said they were planning to perform *Power To The People* with Elton as an encore, and wanted to know if they could stand next to Gladys?

Gladys did eventually feel strong enough for one last song and agreed. At the end of Elton's performance he asked the crowd for silence, then gave his emotional tribute to 'The Little Lady from Croxley Green'. Once again the auditorium was filled by cigarette lighters, and the audience erupted as Gladys and the Lennons strode out on stage and ripped into *Power To The People*. Gladys found a new strength and leapt onto Elton's piano to perform an impromptu Flamenco dance she had learned during her time with Real Madrid.

Backstage after the concert Gladys was photographed with many of the New York 'Beautiful People'. She hugged Bruce and told him to look after himself. He was set to sign for CBS Records, and after Gladys had read through the contract she told him that the deal looked good to her.

Springsteen is now of course a worldwide recording star, but like Elton John he has not forgotten the part Gladys played in the launch of his career. He recorded *That Little Woman* which was included on the 1979 album *Darkness At The Edge Of Town* which tells the story of Gladys Protheroe. The song includes the line 'She was a soccer woman, a real deep woman, who opened the door and showed me the World'. Gladys and Springsteen still keep in touch, and on the 1987 video for *Tunnel Of Love* Gladys did appear in a cameo role.

Bootleg recordings of that 1972 tour that have become prized possessions of all Springsteen fans and there were rumours that Gladys and Springsteen were set to play together again for Live Aid, but like the much talked about Beatles reunion, it wasn't to be. The morning after the final concert Gladys left the hotel alone and flew back to London. She had enjoyed her time in the rock world, but she felt perhaps it was time for her to return to her first love – football.

CHAPTER ELEVEN: 'GLAD & SHANKS'

As usual, Mrs Cornes had kept her house in pristine condition, and Gladys was pleased to find a small posy of wild flowers on the dining table. There was a mountain of post, so after unpacking and freshening up, Gladys made a pot of good strong tea, and set about catching up with her paperwork.

One of the letters stood out for some reason, it was postmarked Liverpool.

The letter was from Bill Shankly. He told her in no uncertain terms that he had been reading of her 'wasting her time with druggy long hairs'; it was time she got back to the real world and 'got her hands dirty again on the training ground'. Shankly had built not only a great team on Merseyside, but a great club. When he arrived at Anfield in the early 1960s the Reds were an average Second Division club living in the shadows of their more illustrious neighbours, Everton. In five years Shankly had taken Liverpool to promotion, an FA Cup victory and onto European glory. He had formed a superb squad with thrifty signings and a shrewd insight into the game. Players like Hunt, St. John, Yeats, Thompson and Callaghan had gelled to become one of the most potent teams in the country and Shankly had the knack of gently and carefully changing the players in the team over a long period, so giving Liverpool a stable base on which to build for the future.

Gladys had only met Shankly briefly at various footballing functions over the years, and never really had the opportunity to get to know the man at all. She was somewhat surprised to receive such a letter from a manager who she had always regarded as being intent on doing the job 'his way'.

But Gladys was intrigued to find out more about the vacancy at Anfield, and after a brief jog around Croxley Green she telephoned the number given on the letter, and immediately recognised the gruff Scots voice on the other end of the line. Shankly told Gladys that he didn't want to discuss the matter over the telephone, and that he would be at Lime Street Station at noon the next day to meet her, then he hung up. Gladys smiled to herself, and prepared for the train journey North.

Gladys expected Shankly to send one of the reserve players to meet her from the train, but he was there on the platform himself wearing a tan raincoat and holding a bunch of red roses. Gladys was half expecting him to be brusque, even a little rude, but Shankly was every bit the gentleman. He carried Gladys' Watford FC holdall to the waiting taxi, and joked that he hoped nobody saw him with such a dreadful piece of luggage.

The taxi took them to a small restaurant, and over a lunch of steak and salad Shankly explained his reasons for asking her to Merseyside. Liverpool had finished the previous season in third position, just a point behind Leeds United and the eventual Champions Derby County, but it had been eight years since the Championship had last come to Anfield. Shankly was aware that he had a fine team, and with all due modesty, he told Gladys that he believed he was the man to be at the helm. But what he felt Anfield lacked was a different view of things. The famous bootroom was staffed by men who were Liverpool through and through, people like Joe Fagan, Bob Paisley and Roy Evans. Between them they had served the club for well over 100 years, they all lived and breathed the club. But Gladys had seen life on the other side of the fence. She had managed a top club in Spain, experienced different ways of doing things, and Shankly was certain that she would inject a new and fresh impetus into the Anfield set up.

Gladys listened intently to the Liverpool manager as she ate her rare fillet steak and sipped mineral water. Shankly went on to say he felt the club were at the beginning of a fantastic new era. They had experienced professionals on their books like Hughes, Clemence, Lindsay and Heighway as well as exciting youngsters such as Phil Thompson, Phil Boersma and, of course, Kevin Keegan. As the waiter cleared away the dining things, Shankly took Gladys' small strong hand in his, looked into her eyes and asked her to join the management team at Anfield. She emptied her coffee cup, and told him she was ready for the challenge.

Gladys returned to Croxley Green that evening with a two year contract as assistant manager to Liverpool F.C. in her holdall. Shankly had told her that training for the new season was to start in ten days time, so it gave her plenty of time to put all her private and business affairs in order before moving up to Merseyside. Mrs Cornes wasn't in the least bit surprised to hear of her employer's latest career move. Mrs. C. had seen Gladys hit the high points and the low in the ten years she had charred for her, and had grown to care for the tough little sportswoman. Despite working in such diverse places as Madrid and Mexico and having toured the USA with Elton John, Gladys had never been tempted to sell her neat little home, always feeling it was vital to have a stable, safe place she could come back to, somewhere where she could find peace and tranquility, and Mrs. Cornes was a vital factor in keeping the house spick and span. So, no matter when Gladys might return home unannounced, she would always find an aired bed, clean newly ironed underwear in the cupboard and all her houseplants watered and flourishing.

The national press soon got hold of the news of Gladys' appointment, and *The Sun* ran the headline 'Shanks Makes Glad A Scouser' with a picture of Gladys and Shankly standing together on The Kop. Gladys found a small flat to rent near Anfield, and with the help of defender Larry

Lloyd, moved a few personal effects into the apartment.

Gladys jogged to Liverpool's training ground, Melwood, for her first day as a Reds' employee. Bill Shankly and Ronnie Moran were already putting a few of the players through their paces, so she went into the dressing room alone to change. Already stripping down into their training kits were a couple of reserve players and first teamers Alec Lindsay and hardman Tommy Smith. Gladys bade everyone a good morning, introduced herself and set about getting changed into her kit. A number of pegs on the far side of the dressing room were empty of any clothes, so Gladys walked over to one and hung up her kit bag. As she stripped down to bra and pants, Smith walked over, picked up Gladys' kit back and threw it into the middle of the room. There was a hushed silence as a Gladys cooly walked over to the bag and once again hung it up on the peg. This time Smith picked the bag up, turned it upside down and let the contents clatter onto the tiled floor. He then shouted to Lindsay and the younger players that it was a pity the dressing room was getting so untidy, but at least they now had a char woman to clean it all up. Smith snarled at Gladys, then, laughing, started to walk back to the equally amused Lindsay. Before he had got five paces Gladys had him in a half Nelson and pinned him to the floor. She flipped him over, then as he was still stunned by surprise hit him twice in the solar plexus then planted a lighting left hook to his right eye. Within seconds Gladys was on her feet and getting changed while Smith was left in a ball moaning and groaning. Alec Lindsay rushed to help, but Smith swore at him, telling his friend to leave him alone. There was blood dripping from a nasty gash over Smith's eye and his cheek was swollen and bruised. Gingerly, Smith got to his feet, seemed to think about mounting an attack on the now fully kitted out woman, but thought better of it and returned to his corner of the room.

Just then Ronnie Moran entered and demanded to know why everyone wasn't changed and ready to train. He seemed to sense an undercurrent of violence and started to quiz Smith on how he had come by his injuries. Smith and Lindsay launched into a cock and bull story of how he had accidentally walked into the dressing room door, and the two younger players, obviously fearful of any reprisal from the older men, went along with the tale. Moran was clearly unconvinced, but just shook his head, told the players to hurry up then returned to the training session.

Gladys realised that the situation with Smith could cause problems for her at Anfield. She knew all about his reputation as a 'win at all costs' player who didn't take kindly to discipline. Not only had she given the hardman of Anfield a good old fashioned hiding, she had done it in front of an audience. Obviously Smith would be waiting for an opportunity to gain his revenge. Gladys did find the Liverpool players a little suspicious of her during the first few training sessions. Various rumours circulated on how

Tommy Smith had gained his black eye, and there was even been a report in *The Liverpool Echo* that Gladys had given Smith a 'Kirby Kiss'. This story was swiftly denied by Liverpool F.C. but many supporters felt there was no smoke without fire.

Bill Shankly had arranged for a short pre-season tour of Spain before returning to Merseyside to mount a serious challenge for the League title. The matches were to be against Athletico Bilbao, Real Zaragossa and finally at The Bernabeau against Real Madrid. Shankly told Gladys that her experience of the Spanish scene would be invaluable. Liverpool were going through a transitional period. Experienced players like Lawrence, Lawler and Hall were beginning to show their age, while the youngsters such as Cormack, Lloyd and Keegan hadn't really played to their full potential. Shankly told Gladys that one of her tasks on the tour was to get the players to play as a team, to drill them and make them a force to be reckoned with. Shankly badly wanted the League title in the forthcoming season, and this tour of Spain would be a good litmus test to show whether or not he would have to go into the transfer market to improve his squad before the big kick-off.

On the plane journey from Speke Airport to Bilbao Gladys sat next to Kevin Keegan. She had heard a lot about Keegan, who had been bought by Shankly from unfashionable Scunthorpe United, and quickly became a favourite on The Kop. Keegan's partnership with the Welshman John Toshack had been one of the major reasons for Liverpool's success in the last couple of seasons. Gladys exchanged small talk with the curly haired striker for the first half hour of the journey, then casually mentioned that she was a very good friend of Elton John. Keegan's eyes lit up, and he confided to Gladys that he had always harboured hopes of becoming a recording star. He had written a number of songs, but felt that perhaps they needed some expert polishing. Gladys was interested in the little player's aspirations, and agreed to listen to his demo tape and give him all the advice she could.

In fact, none of the songs on that early tape were suitable for release, but during the big freeze of 1974 when Liverpool had four consecutive League matches postponed, Gladys and Keegan went into a recording studio with Elton John's band and recorded *Head Over Heels*. The song was released as a single in 1977, and became a Top Ten hit.

There was a large press presence at Bilbao Airport for the arrival of Liverpool, and once again Gladys had to get used to the popping of flash bulbs. She gave a few brief interviews, and her knowledge of Spanish and the fact that she knew many of the Spanish journalists on a personal basis impressed Shankly and the Liverpool squad. In fact, a number of reporters aware of her past position at Real Madrid thought that she was now the manager of Liverpool, a situation that caused some embarassment to

Gladys, especially when one reporter told the Liverpool chairman that it was about time the Anfield club had got rid of that miserable man Shankly and had the foresight to replace him with someone with as much talent, intelligence and vision as Gladys Protheroe.

Liverpool's first game against the Basque side Athletico Bilbao was a rather tepid affair. It was both clubs' first competitive game for over two months, and with neither able to put together any real attacking moves the game ended goalless.

On the coach journey to Zaragossa Gladys told Shankly that she felt the midfield needed same more imaginative players to provide the passes for Keegan and Toshack up front. She felt that the use of Tommy Smith in the middle of the field didn't seen to work, and she suggested perhaps playing either Boersma or Hall in that role.

Shankly liked good idea. After all, that is what these games were for - to try out different permutations and tactical schemes before the season started for real and there were points at stake. After a brief training session on the morning of the game, Shankly announced the team for that evening. He told Smith that he was to be one of the substitutes. It was the first time he had been left out of any Liverpool team without being either injured or suspended. Smith went totally silent, then in a whisper asked Shankly the reason for his being dropped. Shankly told him Gladys felt the midfield needed a change and had suggested the switch. Smith went completely white and a facial tic of some sort seemed to affect him. The players near him noticed the veins on the side of his forehead stand up, and he started to moan in a low, beastlike way, but after a few seconds he went silent again, then seemed to calm down and accept the situation.

Gladys took her place on the substitutes bench next to Ronnie Moran as the two teams lined up before the kick off. The stadium was nearly half full with a crowd of over 20,000. Eventually the referee blew his whistle to signal to the two captains that he was ready to toss the coin for choice of ends and the substitutes left the pitch. Smith was glowering with rage as he took his place on the bench just two spaces from Gladys. Peter Cormack and Tommy Lawrence sat between them. As the game kicked off Gladys was aware of Smith staring at her, and she overheard him tell Cormack in an evil stage whisper that he was well aware who dropped him from the team, and he would get even with them if it was the last thing he did. Throughout the first half Smith would sarcastically agree with Gladys shouts from the bench, and then cruelly cackle at her tactical calls to various Liverpool players. The other substitutes and the Anfield backroom staff were all aware of what was going on, but with Shankly sitting in the Directors Box, nobody felt man enough to diffuse the situation. They had all seen a vicious, wild Tommy Smith before, and the last thing they wanted was to get involved in a scene with the hardman.

Shankly did have a telephone link-up with the bench, but he wanted to see how Gladys would handle the first half without any help from him. In fact, the tactical changes she had suggested paid off almost immediately. After only eight minutes Boersma crossed perfectly for Toshack to head Liverpool in front. Keegan scored a superb solo goal after half an hour, and just before the interval Toshack scored again to put Liverpool comfortably ahead, 3-0 up at half time.

The Liverpool players were all pleased with their first half performance, and as Bill Shankly walked amongst them expressing his approval Gladys was busy strapping goalkeeper Ray Clemence's right thigh. He had twisted it while saving from a rare Zaragossa attack, but Gladys was able to bring the swelling down with a swift spray of painkiller. Then she tightly bandaged the area to help him keep the mobility in his leg for the second half. During the interval Tommy Smith sat in a corner of the dressing room with an orange juice and muttering to himself.

Shankly decided to keep the team as it was for the second half and Liverpool continued to dominate. The Spaniards had made a number of substitutions but only seemed interested in keeping the score down. One of their subs was a wily old campaigner called Gamacho, who had played against Liverpool two seasons before when he was with Barcelona. During that game he had been involved in a fracas with Tommy Smith, and had obviously not forgotten the incident. Gamacho seemed disappointed that Smith was not involved in the game so they could continue their dispute. With twenty minutes left however, Shankly gave Smith the signal to start warming up as he wanted to give all his players a run out, and told Gladys to call Boersma off.

Within seconds of Smith stepping onto the pitch, Gamacho floored him with a vicious late tackle. The Liverpool player was obviously shaken, but got to his feet immediately. The game continued with the visitors seemingly content to hold onto their three goal lead. With still fifteen minutes left Larry Lloyd fell to the ground holding his knee. There had been no Spanish player near him, he had simply turned badly on the lush turf. It took Gladys and Ronnie Moran only a few moments to realise that Lloyd had torn ligaments, and he was quickly carried from the pitch on a stretcher. There was no defender on the bench, so Shankly decided to play out the rest of the game with ten men.

Suddenly Zaragossa, roared on by the home fans, scored twice in three minutes to cut Liverpool's lead to just one goal. Although the game was only a friendly, Bill Shankly was desperate to win, and he could see that something had to be done. Tommy Smith was losing out in his battle with Gamacho. Since the first tackle, the Spaniard had managed to leave Smith nursing a swollen eye after an elbow in the face, and then scythed him down with another late lunge. Suddenly, Gladys had a brainwave. She stripped off her tracksuit top to reveal the all red of Liverpool with the bright Number 18 on her back. Shankly saw her warming up, and knowing what was going on in her mind gave her the nod. The Spanish crowd realising that Liverpool were about to be boosted by a substitution began a loud, vociferous chant to urge their team on. Ronnie Moran signalled to the referee, and with less than ten minutes of the game remaining, Gladys Protheroe, at the age of 65, made her one and only appearance for Liverpool. The Zaragossa players knew all about Gladys, and as soon as she received her first pass from Steve Heighway she was upended by a late tackle from Gamacho. As Gladys got up, the Spaniard gestured to let her know there was plenty more where that came from.

The game became more of a battle-ground than a football match. Liverpool were keen to keep their discipline and shape and not become involved in any of those off the ball antics that the Spanish were proven masters of. Shankly and Moran were aware of the risk they were taking by throwing a frail old woman into such a white hot situation. Zaragossa had their tails up, and Clemence was called upon three times in as many minutes to save what looked like certain goals.

The simmering feud between Smith and Gamacho continued into the last few minutes of the game. The Spaniard had now taken to spitting at and pinching Smith who was feeling the effects of the battle and was limping from one of many nasty tackles. However, Smith did break free from his opponents attentions, and managed to dribble the ball deep into the home side's half before crossing for Keegan to fire home Liverpool's fourth goal and put the result beyond doubt. Smith was congratulated by his team-mates, including Gladys for his part in the goal, but as he trotted back to the half way line for the kick off, Gamacho ran up on the referee's blind side and floored Smith with a vicious, cowardly punch to the side of the head. The Zaragossa player then quickly ran back into his own half, and innocently bent down to tie his bootlaces up. Most of the Liverpool players had clearly seen the incident, and they surrounded the Portugese referee demanding tough action as Smith lay writhing with agony in the centre-circle. But Senor Hizageux of Lisbon did not want to get involved in any controversies. He had accepted the appointment as official for this prestigious friendly game as it fitted in with his three week holiday in Spain, and the expenses had paid for his accommodation and his flight to and from Portugal. The last thing he wanted was to have to submit an official match report to U.E.F.A. and have his holiday ruined by an official hearing.

So he waved the Liverpool players away and claimed he had not seen the incident. He told the English team that if Smith was not fit to continue the game he should be removed from the playing area. Smith, groggy but recovering, got to his feet and staggered back to take his position in Liverpool's midfield. Gamacho stood grinning, hands on hips, but his smile disappeared when he saw Gladys staring icily at him as Zaragossa kicked off. Within seconds Gladys was at Gamacho's side marking him at a throw in. He didn't seem to be interested in receiving the ball, but Filloz, the Zaragossa full back flicked a pass onto him. At that moment years of experience in the game paid off as Gladys cleverly let Gamacho trap the ball on his chest and shepherded him towards the touchline. Gamacho seemed to think he had proved his point, and prepared to lay the ball off to a teammate, but then Gladys executed a tactic that she had been taught by Puskas some ten years before. She side stepped and hit Gamacho with a thunderous tackle that put the swarthy hatchet man into Row D of the Main Stand. Zaragossa supporters still talk of that tackle today. Gamacho actually left the turf, cleared a line of advertising boards, a ball boy and two Guardia Civil before landing in the lap of a plump lady season ticket holder.

The stadium fell silent; the referee, too dumbstruck to blow his whistle simply stood staring at the scene of the incident. Gladys, with the ball at her feet sprinted off towards the Zaragossa goal, beat two defenders, drew the goalkeeper then centred to the unmarked Tommy Smith who had the simple task of side footing the ball into the empty net.

Smith was jubilant. In over ten years at the club, it was only his second goal for the first team. He was mobbed by his team mates as the referee then blew his whistle for the end of the game. Liverpool had won 5-2, a useful result against such a physical side. As the players left the pitch Tommy Smith approached Gladys. The other Liverpool players noticed and a couple of them hurried over ready to pull him away in case he should be ready to continue his feud there and then. But instead of throwing a punch, Smith held out his hand for Gladys to shake. She didn't just shake his hand, she embraced the man. The two tough old pros buried the hatchet, and as they walked back to the players tunnel they compared bumps and bruises.

That night Shankly agreed to relax his strict curfew laws, and the players and backroom staff went out for a traditional Spanish paella with plenty of rough local red wine. After a few glasses Tommy Smith became a little sentimental. He came over and sat at Gladys' table to explain that he never had meant her any harm. He told her that it was just his way and asked her to forgive him. Gladys told him that as far as she was concerned the matter was closed, and suggested he pass the bottle and tell her once again about how he scored his goal.

The final game of the tour was against Real Madrid, and the Spanish press, having learned of Gladys' appearance against Zaragossa, was full of speculation that she may play for Liverpool against her old club. Shankly did in fact ask Gladys if she wanted ten minutes at The Bernabeau, but she declined. No, her time at Real Madrid was gone, now it was important the Liverpool players of today experienced the thrill of playing at one of the world's great stadiums. Even so, it was an emotional moment for La Senora de La Bernabeau as she once again walked out into the centre circle to wave to the loyal Real supporters.

Gladys received a huge bouquet of white carnations from the Real captain Pirri, and the crowd of over 60,000 stood and applauded as she made her way to the Liverpool bench. A number of supporters did call out, encouraging her to don her playing kit just one more tine, but she declined.

Liverpool maintained their unbeaten record for the tour with a 1-1 draw, Peter Cormack scoring for the visitors.

At the after match banquet Gladys made a short speech thanking the Spanish F.A. and of course all at The Bernabeau for making Liverpool and herself so welcome during their ten days on tour. Liverpool arrived back on Merseyside just one week before the start of the 1972/73 season, and both Shankly and Gladys were aware there was still some fine tuning to do with the squad before their opening match against Manchester City at Maine Road.

Throughout that week Gladys kept the players out on the training ground from dawn till dusk, running various free kick routines and defensive formations into their heads. By the Thursday evening she sat in the Anfield bootroom with Shankly, Joe Fagan, Bob Paisley and Ronnie Moran and told them she could do no more. As far as she was concerned, the lads were ready. She had taught them all she knew and now it was up to Shankly and the players themselves. Liverpool started the season in fine style with a confident 2-0 win over Manchester City, then Gladys was given a rousing welcome by the Kop the following Wednesday evening when Newcastle United were the visitors to Anfield.

The supporters on The Kop were the most quick witted and knowledgeable in the game, and it took them only a few minutes to think up a suitable chant for Gladys. There had been a few verses of *We're Gladys' Boys* prior to the kick off, but some wag launched into *Gladys, Gladys We're All Crazy Now* which was based on the chart topping record by the group Slade. In what seemed like just a few seconds, thousands of Merseyside voices boomed out the new song as Liverpool laid siege to the Newcastle goal.

The Liverpool supporters took Gladys to their hearts, and as The Reds cruised to a 4-1 victory, there was more than one call for her to put on a red shirt and join the fray. By Christmas time Liverpool were three points clear of their nearest challengers, Arsenal, and they knew that a win at Elland Road against their old rivals Leeds United would put them in a great position to go on and clinch the title. Leeds themselves were in third place, five points behind Liverpool, and the Yorkshiremen viewed the match as a great opportunity to keep in touch with the leaders.

The press built the game up as some kind of grudge match. In *The Sun* and *The Daily Mirror* ghosted columns attributed to Don Revie and Billy Bremner warned Liverpool not to expect an easy game, and both papers printed insulting remarks by the Leeds men aimed at Gladys.

Revie allegedly asked 'What kind of club has an old widow woman running team affairs?', while Bremner told his readers that the Leeds players would not take any notice of an old woman who knew nothing about modern day football.

There were allusions to Gladys' past with Elton John and Bruce Springsteen, inferring that she was nothing but a burned out old rocker. *The Sun* also printed a savage cartoon by 'Jak' that portrayed the Liverpool players in petticoats and Gladys as their nanny.

This was just the kind of situation that Gladys had always dreaded. She was thick skinned enough to let press attacks like these wash over her, after all she had been through them many times before. What worried her was the way the players, directors, management and supporters of a great, proud football club like Liverpool would react to being publicly insulted.

In fact the Liverpool board did meet to discuss the paper talk, and asked Shankly to explain the situation. He stood by Gladys, telling them that she was his appointment, and although she had only been at the club for a short time, he was certain she had won the respect of the players and supporters. Surely, he asked, they weren't going to let a particularly sly piece of cowardly journalism rock the boat at a club like Liverpool. That would be just what Don Revie and his cronies wanted.

The Anfield board were aware of the damage this kind of publicity could do to their club, but told Shankly they were prepared to back their management and retain a dignified silence. Indeed a number of directors had raised their eyebrows when Shankly came to them in the summer with the plan of bringing Gladys to Anfield. Liverpool Football Club had always been a bastion of male chauvinism, and the very thought of a woman in charge of training and tactics was an affront to the more conservative members. Even though by now she had proved herself to most people on Merseyside, two of the more prominent directors, Messrs. Wilson and Barrett, had continued to speak out against her appointment. Both were wealthy businessmen who inherited shares in the club from their fathers. They saw the press attacks on Gladys as ammunition to put extra pressure on their new assistant manager.

To the public, it looked as if all at Anfield was calm and settled, but in reality there was the beginning of a boardroom split over Gladys Protheroe. The silent men of football almost always succeed when they want their way, and this case was no different. It took them some time, but eventually they were to force Gladys from Anfield.

Tickets for the Boxing Day clash at Elland Road were like gold dust. The Leeds officials were expecting a record crowd, and the Liverpool team coach travelled across the Pennines followed by a flotilla of Merseysiders, their cars decorated with bright red and white banners and scarves trailing from their windows.

On the coach Gladys tried to take the pressure off the players by organising a card school, then as they drew nearer to Leeds she orchestrated a game of charades. Gladys, decked out in her red Liverpool tracksuit, stood in the aisle miming the titles of books, songs and well known films. Her efforts at gaining the players concentration worked so well that Larry Lloyd and Ian Callaghan had to be separated by their teammates before an unsightly fight broke out. The two players had been voted captains of their respective charade teams, and as the coach pulled into the Elland Road car park, the match was finely balanced at nine points each with Alec Lindsay miming *The Great Gatsby* to the opposition. Gladys held the stop-watch, and she alone decided when the mimer had overrun his one minute. Just as Gladys shouted time on Lindsay's attempt, Lloyd shouted out the title of the film. Within seconds, four or five players were on their feet pushing and shoving each other.

The supporters waiting to ask for the players' autographs were stunned by the sight of the Liverpool squad arriving in such a state of turmoil. Fortunately, Bill Shankly was able to quell the incident, and after a few moments the players were back to their well-disciplined selves. Shankly stood in the aisle and told his team to keep all their aggression and anger for the pitch.

There was a small crowd of fans at the players entrance, mostly good humoured and only wanting an autograph or a quick word with their favourites. But there was also a gaggle of National Front supporters who screamed abuse at the Liverpool squad and Gladys in particular as she alighted from the coach. Leeds was unfortunately known as a hotbed of racist and nationalist politics and the football club had a large hooligan following. Gladys was told to "Get back home and do the washing, like a proper woman" by the thugs in their Doctor Marten boots. But Gladys had experienced the heat of the Bernabeu, and she knew full well that the wild Latin supporters of Real Madrid would have eaten these fresh faced Yorkshire lads for breakfast.

She just smiled, and even had the courage to blow a few of the young men a kiss – this of course generated even more abuse and anger. The police intervened and escorted the Liverpool squad into their dressing room as a hail of beer cans, bottles and half bricks rained down on them. The aggression of the crowd had shaken a few of the younger players, but Gladys clapped her hands a few times, and asked her team to think what the reception for them would be like after they had gone out there and won both points.

Shankly asked Gladys to have a few quiet words with the strike force of Toshack and Keegan. The duo had scored thirty League goals between them so far, but none in the last three games. Shankly was keen to see them among the goals against Leeds, and was banking on his assistant's powers of man-management to shake the players up.

Gladys sat with the two strikers for a few minutes before the team ran out onto the pitch. They both knew the importance of the game, and in reality she had very little work to do. Keegan and Toshack were professionals and well aware of their responsibilities. All she said to them was that the whole of Merseyside was looking for them to do their business. The men who would be marking them were Gladys' old England colleagues, Jack Charlton and Norman Hunter – two of the hardest men in the game. But neither defenders were in their first flush of youth. Charlton was set to retire and Hunter had lost a yard or two over the last season. The game was there for the winning. Gladys ruffled their hair, patted their bottoms and wished them all the best.

The referee, Mr Craigie of Derby, came into the Liverpool dressing room and told the players that he was understood of the importance of the game to both sets of players, but it was vital that everyone kept their heads. He told them that he would not stand for any foul play or dissent. Mr. Craigie kept an eye fixed on Tommy Smith as he warned that any late tackling would immediately earn a booking.

There was a huge roar as the teams ran out onto the pitch. The Elland Road supporters were among the most vocal in the League, and they left Gladys and Shankly in no doubt how they felt about them. As the two managers took their places on the bench a chant of "Shankly Sleeps With Gladys" rang out, closely followed by "Protheroe's A Dirty Slut". But both were experienced football professionals who had heard such abuse from crowds all over the World and Gladys noticed a wry smile on Shankly's face as they prepared for the kickoff.

Within twenty seconds of the referee's whistle, Keegan was left in a heap by a thunderous tackle from Paul Madeley. Ronnie Moran was on the pitch tending injuries a dozen times in the first twenty minutes as Leeds made their intentions crystal clear.

Mr. Craigie took the names of Leeds' Reaney, Charlton and Giles – all for fouls, and Liverpool's Cormack for retaliation. The game had all the makings of a blood bath. There were off the ball incidents going on throughout the first half, and five Liverpool players needed treatment at half time for bruises, cuts and bites.

As for the game itself, there was precious little flowing football played during the first 45 minutes. Apart from a header by Toshack, and a volley from Giles at the other end, neither goalkeeper had been called into any real action.

Gladys walked among the wounded players dabbing cuts with TCP and rubbing linament into bruised thighs and shins. She spent a few minutes quietly talking to Tommy Smith, and reminded him to keep his cool and not be intimidated or forced into any rash retaliation. Smith had been a target for the Leeds players during the first half, but he was too wily by half, and had not risen to the bait set by Bremner and Clarke. Allan Clarke in particular had gone out of his way to fall down heavily as soon as Smith got within five yards of him, then claim to the referee that he had been kicked.

Shankly gathered his men around him as the buzzer sounded to call them out for the second period. He told his players to keep to their plan, play hard, but play fair. If they stuck to that, they would get a point at least because it was clear to him that all Leeds wanted was a bar-room brawl. They couldn't beat Liverpool by fair means, so they were trying to do it by foul – they weren't going to get away with it.

Again the Liverpool players were met by cat-calls, coins, beer cans and apple cores, and just as Gladys took her seat a pair of old carpet slippers hit her on the shoulder. Don Revie had stoked his players up during the interval, and once again tackles were flying in from all angles. At one stage there were three Liverpool players prostrate and needing treatment, so Gladys had to enter the fray, and with the use of a spare bucket and sponge she set about treating Tommy Smith for a badly gashed ankle wound. As she dabbed the open cut, Smith whispered to her that Bremner had *his* coming soon. Gladys warned him to be discreet, and gave him a conspiratorial wink before leaving the playing area.

On the hour, Leeds came the closest so far to a goal. Their nippy winger Gray beat Lindsay for pace and crossed for Jones to rifle a volley onto the Liverpool crossbar with Clemence well beaten. Fortunately for the visitors, Larry Lloyd was on hand to hoof the ball into the crowd. As the players congregated in the penalty area for the corner, Gladys happened to notice Tommy Smith creeping up behind Billy Bremner. She watched in amazement as Smith, with the referee busy seeing the corner kick was taken correctly, grabbed the Leeds captain's groin and squeezed hard before galloping off in the opposite direction. It seemed that no-one else had seen the incident that left Bremner squealing with pain on the ground. The Leeds players rushed to the referee to show him their captain had been felled, and he immediately signalled for Les Cocker, the Leeds trainer to come on. Mr. Craigie stood over Bremner attempting to hear his side of the story, but all the little flame-haired Scotsman could do was point weakly at Smith before passing out.

Bremner was carried from the pitch on a stretcher and replaced by substitute Mick Bates. The referee was in something of a quandary – he was certain that Bremner had been the victim of a violent assault, but he had no proof of who was to blame. Smith, the player Bremner had appeared to blame for the incident, was yards away. Mr Craigie simply shook his head, and ordered play to continue. When Gladys tells the story of Smith's brutal assault on Bremner, she never ceases to be amazed at how many men cross their legs as the tale unfolds.

Leeds without Bremner lost their direction, and as the minutes passed so Liverpool came more and more into the game. Both Cormack and Keegan had goal bound efforts well saved by Sprake, the home keeper. With six minutes remaining, Smith won the ball from Giles then sent Heighway off on a mazy run down the wing. The Irishman centred, Charlton only half cleared, and there was Emlyn Hughes to rattle a twenty yard thunderbolt into the top left hand corner for the matchwinner. Gladys and Shankly leapt off the bench and embraced, as Hughes ran like a wild stallion to the Liverpool fans and celebrated his goal. The Yorkshiremen threw everything at The Reds in those final minutes, desperately battling for the equaliser. But Liverpool kept their heads, and managed to hold out for the final whistle. As Mr Craigie blew his whistle for the last time, tempers did boil over for a few moments. Leeds' frustrations were there for all to see as Giles threw a punch at Heighway, and Gladys had to rush onto the pitch to push Charlton and Jones away from Tommy Smith. The visiting players were booed off the pitch, and Gladys and Shankly had to once again walk the gauntlet of jeers and insults as they made their way back up the tunnel. As the Liverpool players began to pull off their muddy kit and kick off their boots, Gladys told them all to be silent for a moment. You could hear a pin drop in the dressing room; the only noise was the Elland Road crowd baying for blood. Gladys told them that was the greatest noise in the game – they had done a fine professional job against a spiteful, aggressive team – they should be proud of themselves. She then told them to hurry up and get changed because she had laid on a special Christmas treat.

Gladys instructed the coach driver to take a detour and guided him to the Dog & Trumpet at Rastrick, where she had booked the back room for the Liverpool squad. As the game had been played on Boxing Day the players had to leave their families on Christmas Day morning and forego the usual festivities. So, unbeknown to Bill Shankly, Gladys had secretly contacted all the players wives and girlfriends, and they were all there waiting with the Dom Perignon on ice.

Shankly and the players were delighted, and they all ate, drank and danced the night away. Obviously Gladys had been confident of a Liverpool victory as the function had been arranged a fortnight before. Nobody dared mention what would have happened if Liverpool had lost! One of the highlights of the evening was a rendition of *Underneath The Arches* by Gladys and Tommy Smith. The two had became firm friends after their initial disagreements, and Gladys whispered to the player that she wondered what *did* happen to Billy Bremner? Smith took a long sip on his lager and gave Gladys a cheeky wink. The party went on until 3 a.m. when the coach arrived to whisk the weary players and their spouses home to a well earned rest. Gladys stayed on for a few moments to help the staff tidy up and settle the bill, which she paid out of her own pocket.

The tabloid papers were full of Liverpool's win the next morning, and *The Sun* published a photograph of Shankly and Gladys arm in arm after Hughes' goal, the headline reading 'Shanks Is Glad!'

The result at Elland Road had put The Reds seven points clear of Leeds and five above Derby. Everyone in the Anfield bootroom was quietly confident that if Liverpool could keep their heads then the title would be theirs. Gladys was applauded as she entered the Bootroom a couple of days after the Leeds game. All the backroom staff had thoroughly enjoyed the party at the Dog & Trumpet although Bob Paisley and Ronnie Moran told her they still hadn't shaken off their hangovers. As the staff sat in the cosy room drinking hot, strong tea and sharing Joe Fagan's Rich Tea biscuits there was a loud knock. Bob Paisley opened the door, and was met by the stern face of Mr Barrett. Paisley asked him if he would like to join them in a cup of something, but he informed them that as far as he was concerned, Christmas was well and truly over, and - unlike others – he had work to do.

There was complete silence as Barrett told them he had heard that the players and management had been involved in a drunken orgy in Rastrick after the Leeds game, and he wanted an immediate explanation. He continued that the good name of Liverpool F.C. had been dragged into the gutter by an evil influence that had infiltrated the club. He didn't want to name names, but she knew who she was. The drunken binge would be discussed at that afternoon's board meeting, and he and his colleague Mr Wilson would be calling for the strongest possible action. He then haughtily turned on his heels and strode off. There was a stunned silence in the bootroom as the back room staff tried to take it all in. Yes, they had all had a drink, but no-one at the party had acted out of turn. It was Christmas time and they had just won a match that had probably set them on their way to the League Championship – weren't they allowed to let their hair down now and then?

Gladys sat in the corner sipping her tea, while Shankly, Paisley, Moran, Fagan and Evans told each other just how disgusting the whole affair was. Shankly was ready to go up to the Chairman's office there and then, and demand to know what was going on, but thankfully Joe Fagan talked him out of it.

Gladys quietly stood up, finished her tea and told her colleagues she would see them later. As she walked along the Anfield Road towards her small flat, she stopped at the newsagents and bought the latest evening edition of *The Liverpool Echo*. There on the front page was a blurred photograph of Tommy Smith and Gladys, arm in arm performing *Underneath The Arches* at the Dog & Trumpet. The headline read 'Reds Stars in Night Club Booze Up'. The story claimed that Gladys, Smith, Emlyn Hughes and Ray Clemence had been out on the town until 5 a.m. on Christmas night, before the Leeds game. There were also thinly disguised claims that Bill Shankly and Gladys were lovers. She went home to the flat and turned on the television. Granada Sport also carried the story, telling the viewers that the Liverpool board were, as they spoke, meeting to discuss the 'crisis'.

It seemed to Gladys that she had already been pronounced guilty by the media. It was obvious to her that the directors Barrett and Wilson had been responsible for the vendetta, and although it would be reasonably simple to prove that the photograph had been taken after the Leeds game, there was still the old proverb 'There's no smoke without fire' to contend with.

A few minutes after she arrived home the telephone rang. It was Bill Shankly. He asked her if she had seen *The Echo*, and then told her to sit tight, he was coming right over. Fifteen minutes later, carrying a huge bunch of red roses and a chilled bottle of Chablis, he strode into her flat and told her his plan. Apparently the board meeting was still going on, but fortunately Shankly was very friendly with Mrs. Bride the Anfield tea lady who was on duty that afternoon. He had managed to have a quick word with her half an hour ago, and she had passed on the fact that, as Gladys had suspected, Barrett and Wilson were behind the accusations and were now pressing for Gladys to be sacked. The other members of the board had wanted to know if the press reports were true, and Wilson had told them they were. Mrs. Bride had tried to eavesdrop on more of the meeting, but unfortunately her urn ran dry.

Shankly told Gladys that the whole affair stank to high heaven; the bootroom and the players were ready to rebel as soon as they were asked to. Shankly's Glaswegian socialist roots really came to the surface as he stood in Gladys' flat and stridently told her what he and his lads were going to do. Indeed, at one stage with the veins standing up on his temples, he reminded Gladys of Lenin addressing the masses at The Finland Station. During this rallying speech she sat quietly in her armchair, touched by the loyalty and sincerity on display. At one stage he told her that if the Board demanded she should leave Anfield, then Shankly and the entire Bootroom would follow.

After they had polished off the Chablis and Gladys had placed the roses in fresh water, Shankly gave her a quick peck on the cheek, told her to keep her chin up and left.

Alone once again, Gladys turned on the television to learn that the Liverpool board were beginning an in depth investigation into the happenings at the Dog & Trumpet. The Liverpool chairman was interviewed by a reporter, and he told the viewers that Liverpool F.C. would leave no stone unturned until they found out the truth. The TV journalist then asked the Chairman to comment on the rumour of a 'love affair' between his manager and assistant. He refuse to comment and glared at the reporter before storming off. Later, on the eleven o'clock news, the reporter stated that there was a revolt brewing at Anfield. The hot headed Shankly had told the press that if Gladys was hounded out of the club by this witch-hunt, then he would have no option but to resign – and he was confident all the coaching staff and the entire first team would follow him. As Gladys watched the screen a tear fell from her eye.

Twelve hours later Gladys sat in the Croxley Green Café sampling one of their special breakfasts with a pint of sweet hot tea. Within half an hour of that news bulletin on Granada TV she had packed, rung for a taxi to take her to Lime Street Station and caught the night train to Euston.

She sent a letter of resignation to the Liverpool chairman and a more personal note to Shankly. Gladys was many things, but she was not a fool. She could feel the undercurrent of tension at the club, and was acutely aware that a number of directors wanted her out of Anfield. They were obviously determined to get their way regardless of what damage they inflicted on Liverpool Football Club, and despite having only been involved at Anfield for six months she had felt the importance of the club in the community.

Gladys would not stand by and watch loyal, honest men like those in the bootroom throw their careers away just because two arrogant, bigoted directors wanted their way. Gladys had always relished a fight, but experience had also taught her that there were times and places for fights, and she was certain this was the time for a tactical withdrawal.

As she finished off her splendid breakfast Gladys heard on the cafe radio that Liverpool F.C. had accepted the resignation of assistant manager Gladys Protheroe. The press of course had a field day. *The Sun* ran the story on the front page, three inch type screaming 'KOP K.O. BOOZER GLAD' while *The Daily Mirror* printed 'ANFIELD BUST UP OVER BEVVY UP'. Only the *Daily Telegraph* attempted to get under the skin of the story. An American investigative journalist, Rachel Simon, wrote an in depth piece on how Gladys had been set-up on Merseyside. The article had an interview with the landlord of the Dog & Trumpet and a number of witnesses who clearly stated that the Liverpool party had been after the Leeds game, and not as the Anfield directors claimed, the night before. A few days later the TV programme *World In Action* took up the story, and again proved that Gladys had been the victim of a well-planned 'frame up'.

As usual in these circumstances, Gladys kept a dignified silence. As had happened many times before, her small house was surrounded by press men all wanting to know her side of the story. Mrs Cornes kept them at bay and even supplied a tasty buffet and plenty of tea and coffee before reading out an official statement. Mrs Cornes stood on an upturned wheelbarrow in Gladys' front garden, and addressed the gentlemen of the press with: "Gladys Protheroe hereby announces that her contract with Liverpool F.C. has been terminated. She would like to take this opportunity to thank Mr Shankly, his colleagues and all the players for their support, and also thank the fans and supporters of the club for the part they played in making her stay on Merseyside a happy one."

There was no reference to the Board of Directors, or to the cheap way she had been treated. As far as Gladys was concerned life was too short to carry grudges.

Liverpool did go on to win the Championship that season, but the players did not forget the woman who played a decisive role in bringing the trophy to Anfield. When Emlyn Hughes receive the Championship trophy after the final game of the season against W.B.A. he told the packed stadium that they should not forget Gladys Protheroe who had contributed so much to their season. The Kop erupted into a few verses of *We're Gladys' Boys* and then threw in a chorus or two of *Gladys, Gladys We're All Crazy Now* for good measure.

In the dressing room after the game, Hughes was censured by the board for bringing Gladys' name up, and was in fact fined a week's wages for his outburst, but he and the other players thought it was worth it. Although Shankly and the bootroom made no public comment on Gladys' departure, the fact that it was they who paid Hughes' fine does give one an indication of their feelings for her.

Gladys did keep in touch with many of the Liverpool staff, and she was a guest on *A Question Of Sport* Christmas Special in December 1988 when she was on Emlyn Hughes' team. The friendship between the two was obvious, and many TV critics commented that Hughes seemed to spend more time with his arms around his lady guest than he did answering questions.

But perhaps the moment when Gladys showed her greatest respect for Liverpool was at Bill Shankly's funeral in 1982. Gladys wore a Black Chanel suit with a veil and stood between Phil Thompson and Ray Clemence during the service. Her wreath was a simple affair; the card read 'To Shanks, Thanks. Love Gladys'.

For the rest of 1973 Gladys took a long holiday on the South Coast, staying at a small boarding house owned by Bobby Moore's uncle. As usual she received her gratis ticket for the FA Cup final, but instead of travelling to Wembley for the game, she sat with other ordinary fans watching the game on television in a small bar in Brighton.

CHAPTER THIRTEEN: 'BACK TO VICARAGE ROAD'

On her return to Croxley Green, Gladys and Mrs Cornes would take long country walks and picnic in the fields when the weather was clement. She bought a pair of overalls and repainted the outside of her house. As Gladys was preparing the wood for the final coat a number of neighbours stopped to ask her what colour she had chosen?

The red of Liverpool, white for Real Madrid and England?

It was an indication of what was to happen in the future when Gladys bought three large cans of bright yellow gloss.

One thing that did rather depress her during this time was England's inability to qualify for the 1974 World Cup in West Germany. Gladys watched in horror as Bobby Moore's uncharacteristic slip and Alan Ball's sending off led to England being beaten by Poland in Katowice. Then she, like millions of others, was on the edge of her seat as the Poles hung on at Wembley to eliminate the boys in white. That night Gladys sat alone in her kitchen and although she was no longer involved in the international scene, there were tears in her eyes. She had her ups and downs with Ramsey, but she knew England's failure meant the proud manager did not have long left. Of course, she was right.

Gladys had anticipated spending the Summer of 1974 at home, but at the last moment she accepted an invitation from Spanish Television to travel to West Germany for the World Cup. She was on a panel of experts along with old colleagues from her days at The Bernabeau, Puskas and Di Stefano, as well as Jose Labbinez, the manager of Athletico Madrid, an extrovert character who was well known for making outrageously mischevous remarks.

The Spanish, like England, had failed to qualify, but their football crazy population were intent on watching as many games as possible on TV. Gladys appeared twice daily reviewing the previous night's action and previewing the forthcoming games. Because of her link with the U.K. she was also responsible for covering Scotland's progress in the competition. The Scots had been drawn in Group 2 along with Yugoslavia, rank outsiders Zaire and favourites Brazil. The one problem Gladys foresaw was the large contingent of Leeds players in the Scots squad. She mentioned to Gus, the TV producer in charge of all the broadcasts that there may be some bad feeling between a few of the Scots and his new reporter, but he just shrugged his shoulders and told her he would sort it out manana.

As it happened, Gladys and her former adversaries got on like a house on fire. The Leeds players were totally professional and Harvey, Jordan, Bremner and Lorimer behaved like perfect gentlemen throughout the tournament.

Gladys watched the Scots defeat the plucky Zaire team 2-0 in the opening game, then hold World Champions Brazil to a goalless draw. Everything hung on the final group game against Yugoslavia. If Scotland won or even if they managed a score draw, they would be through to the second phase of the competition. It wasn't to be. The Scots forward line were unable to break down the uncompromising Yugoslav defence, and so they were eliminated.

Gladys reported that Scotland had been unlucky – a little more flair up front and she was certain they could have gone on to the semi-finals, then... who knows?

The night after Scotland's match against Yugoslavia Gladys was invited to their farewell dinner. The meal had been arranged by fanatical Scotland supporter Rod Stewart, and he had certainly spared no expense on a fabulous night's entertainment.

Gladys was one of only a handful of Sassenachs invited, and she felt proud to be part of such an enjoyable occasion. Stewart had laid on cases of 'Scottish Wine' and the meal itself was traditional haggis and neeps. A piper led the Scots squad into the dining room of the Hessicher Hoff Hotel, after which Stewart, decked from head to foot in a garish Tartan suit, made a short speech welcoming the guests. He congratulated the team for giving 100% during the tournament. Scotland had become the first team to be eliminated from a World Cup without actually losing a game. The sense of occasion did seem to become too much for the singer, and after a healthy draw on a huge glass of Bells, he spontaneously launched into a boozy, sentimental version of *If You Take The High Road* before being helped to his seat by a waiter.

Gladys sat next to the Celtic midfielder David Hay and the most experienced player in the squad, Denis Law. Gladys had, of course, met Law a few years earlier while she was involved with George Best, and Law spent some time filling Gladys in with the latest developments in the sorry Best saga. The Irishman had continued to miss training, and had been involved in a sordid affair with Miss World, Marjorie Wallace, eventually being accused of stealing a fur coat from her London flat. Law shook his head and told Gladys it was a tragedy that such a great talent should fritter his time away in such a pitiful manner. The initial disappointment of the evening began to disappear as the drink flowed and a number of the squad stood up to take turns leading the diners in raucous sing-songs. By the time the first course arrived, the post-mortems over the Yugoslavia game were over and everyone seemed determined to enjoy themselves.

During the evening, Gladys was asked a number of times about her future. She replied that she had no concrete plans, but she would like to stay in the game in some capacity. Her stint with Spanish Television had not gone unnoticed by the British companies, and back in London Gladys' name had been mentioned at boardroom level as a possible host for a weekly sports show.

While she was finishing off her portion of Black Forest gateau, a rather well refreshed Rod Stewart stumbled over to her, and inquired as to whether Gladys had heard anything from their mutual friend Elton John recently. Gladys replied that she had had no contact with the bespectacled pop star for some time, though she was well aware of his continuing success throughout the World. Stewart, who was by now bleary eyed and slurring his speech, confided to Gladys that Elton had mentioned to him that he was interesting in buying a football club, and had asked whether Stewart himself would be keen on putting some money into the scheme. Just as the conversation was getting to the vital part, Stewart passed out.

The singer had personally accounted for five bottles of Dom Perignon and a decanter of Bells whisky. Gladys called for some assistance, and with the help of the Scotland manager Willie Ormond and burly centre-half Jim Holton she flagged down a taxi, and saw him safely delivered to his hotel. Gladys was intrigued to find out what Stewart was getting around to asking her, but she soon put the incident to the back of her mind and continued to merry-make with the Scots players.

Gladys returned to Croxley Green in July 1974, and spent a number of days in discussion with Thames Television. The TV company had devised a new show to be called *Soccer Science* and after watching the tapes of Gladys' reports from Germany for the Spanish network, had approached her as a possible host. The show was to be a weekly thirty minute programme reporting football news from both Britain and the World. The pilot show was filmed at Highbury, where Gladys chatted with ex Arsenal manager Bertie Mee, Fulham boss Alec Stock and West Ham's new first team coach, John Lyall. The four talked frankly and at length about the problems with the current England set-up, and tried to answer the question why England had failed to qualify for the 1974 World Cup. Watching the video tape of the show now, one cannot help but see that Gladys was in total control. She seems a TV natural. While Stock, Mee and Lyall all seemed to be lost for words, Gladys confidently carried the show along with incisive comments.

However, for some reason, Thames decided against taking the project any further, and the idea was dropped. The Saturday lunchtime show *On The Ball* with Brian Moore as the host continued, although many TV critics felt that Gladys' more direct style would have been a breath of fresh air.

As the 1974/75 season commenced, Gladys began to take more interest in her local club, Watford. Unfortunately, the Hornets, as they were now known, were languishing in the Third Division. Attendances the previous season had dipped to an alarming level, and Gladys always felt a tinge of sadness when she cycled by the ground and noticed how neglected the old stadium looked.

Gladys was in fact in a unique position. On the World football stage, she was bracketed with some of the all time greats. Her name was spoken in revered terms at The Bernabeau, The Maracana and the other great stadiums of the World. Yet on her own doorstep, she was almost unknown. Certainly, most of the locals knew that she had been involved in football to some degree, but her rather Spartan lifestyle and dislike of publicity meant that the great majority thought of her as nothing more than a slightly dotty old woman.

Her connections with Watford FC were almost non existent. Only a couple of elderly programme sellers who remembered her days in the team were still employed by the club, and the present Board of Directors seemed almost embarrassed by the fact that a woman had once represented the club at League level.

Watford continued their decline throughout the season, and by Christmas time as the team battled against relegation to Division Four, there were rumours in the local press that a new regime was preparing to buy the ailing club. There were occasional articles in the newspapers suggesting that a well-known local person was set to be invited onto the board, then ultimately take over as chairman. Gladys was as mystified as everyone else until one night in January 1975.

As she was settling down for a night in with a few mugs of tea and her Rothmans Yearbooks she heard a car pull up outside and what sounded like high heeled shoes clip clopping up the drive. The door bell rang, not in the normal manner, but in a rhythmic, pulsating way. Gladys got up out of her armchair and went to the door. Through the frosted glass she could see the silhouette of what looked like a tall man in a floppy cap. From where she stood in her hallway, her visitor seemed to be well over six and a half feet tall. Who this could this tall stranger be?

The man standing in Gladys' porch wore a yellow and purple cap with bright red feathers jutting out from the peak, a flourescent pink sequinned jacket over a black and white striped T-Shirt and a pair of lime green flared trousers as he teetered on a pair of yellow and blue platform boots with heels that must have been at least eight inches high.

Gladys invited Elton John in and poured him a cup of tea.

After the two old friends had filled each other in with their various exploits since their last meeting, Elton asked her if she had managed to speak to Rod Stewart in Germany.

Gladys related the story of Stewart's brief, mysterious message and his rapid decline into a drunken stupor. Elton laughed, and told Gladys that she had just solved a puzzle that had worried him for a number of months. He told her that at the end of the previous season he had been approached by Watford to see if he would be interested in taking a place on the board. Elton had been flattered and excited by the invitation, but had felt that he would need someone with experience of the modern game and the respect of both the football establishment and the media if he was to succeed.

Gladys offered her visitor a digestive biscuit and asked him to continue. The singer told her that if he was to be taken seriously in football, it was vital he had someone at his side who would give him the credibility that he needed. His plans and ideas were sincere, but the public and the media had been used to a football club director looking and working in a certain way, and they would have to be convinced that this move was no cheap publicity stunt. Elton was as depressed by Watford's current position as any other loyal supporter – but where he was different was that he was actually in a position to do something about it.

Financially, Elton was one of the wealthiest young men of his generation. Since their last meeting his career had gone from strength to strength. During 1973 and 1974 Elton had sold millions of records all over the civilised World, earning him a fortune. Hit albums such as *Tumbleweed Connection, Honky Chateau* and *Caribou* had been bought by the truckload by teenage music fans in over forty countries, and he had only just completed another record breaking tour of the USA. But, despite all that success, Elton felt that he was somehow missing out. As a youngster he had followed Watford from the terraces, and although he was a little too young to have seen Gladys in action for the first team, he was well aware of her links with the club. In the crazy world that is Rock 'n' Roll it was very easy for performers to lose the links with their past, and ultimately forget who they really were. Elton had seen it happen to some of his peers, and he was determined it would never happen to him. To him Watford Football Club represented more than just a struggling football team. Watford was a vital part of Elton's life. When he was living it up in Los Angeles, staying up late and drinking too much, he was able to bring himself back down to earth remembering the young Reg Dwight standing on the Red Lion terrace cheering his favourite team.

Gladys listened attentively as Elton told her that he had great plans for Watford. He wanted the club to rise up the League, ultimately to the First Division, and to be known and respected throughout the country. He was prepared to put his money where his mouth was and finance a huge investment scheme to improve both the stadium and the team. The two friends were on their sixth cup of tea, and Gladys' carriage clock showed that it was well past three o'clock in the morning before Elton came to the most important part of his speech. He told Gladys that he had mentioned to Rod Stewart that he was planning to buy Watford, and on hearing that Gladys would be with the Scotland squad had asked if Rod would quietly mention to Gladys that there was a possibility of such a deal.

Elton had been disappointed not to have heard from her, and assumed that she had not taken such news seriously. Now that he had discovered that Stewart had been unable to carry out the duty, he understood why he had not heard from the lady in Croxley Green.

At last Elton came to the point. He wanted Gladys join him in his attempt to take Watford out of obscurity and into the limelight. Gladys stood up and walked to her window. She took a sip of her tea and looked out. The street lights shone brightly in the dark winter morning and she noticed a few rain drops bounce off the shiny bonnet of Elton's white Rolls Royce parked outside her little house. Then she looked down at Elton sitting in her comfortable armchair with an empty pack of digestive biscuits beside him. The look in Elton's eyes convinced her that he was serious. She had come to know the pop singer quite well over the years and although they had at times clashed over his dress sense and choice of material on some of his albums, she had never doubted his sincerity. Gladys asked Elton to stand up, took his slightly pudgy right hand in both of hers and shook. She told him he had a deal.

The takeover soon became national news. The idea of a pop singer and an elderly woman buying control of a football club grabbed the imagination of the press, and within days Gladys and Elton agreed to hold a press-conference.

The current Chairman of Watford FC was a crusty old businessman named Jim Bonsor. His family had run the club for over sixty years, and he had always strenuously fought off any attempts to buy his controlling interest. However, Mr Bonsor was now nearly eighty years of age and had come to realise that the daily requirements of running a professional football club were becoming too much for him.

There had been speculation that Elton's flamboyant style would rub some of the older members of the board up the wrong way, but Gladys' diplomatic manner plus a healthy dose of good old fashioned flirting soon won them over.

Elton arranged for the press conference to take place in Gladys' garden, and during the morning a large marquee was erected on the lawn completely covering every inch of grass. Throughout the day electricians, carpenters and other workmen trudged through the house carrying arc lights, cables and plastic seats for the World's press. The conference was due to begin at 3 p.m., and by noon the nearby pub, the Fox & Hounds, was packed with thirsty journalists from all over he World. Both ITV and BBC had film crews covering the story, and as well as three TV networks from the USA there were nearly eighty reporters and cameramen from Italy, France, Germany, Holland and Japan. The Watford takeover was truly World news.

Half an hour before the press conference the two new owners of Watford F.C. stood in Gladys' spare bedroom sipping cups of milky tea. Surprisingly, it was Elton who was the more nervous. Despite having toured the globe and played his music in front of hundreds of thousands of fans, he felt rather uneasy at having to face a tent full of journalists. Gladys sensed her partner's nerves, and as Elton's manager, John Reid, gave them the thumbs up to take the small stage, she put her arm around the singer's shoulder and gave him a light peck on the cheek.

Elton was decked out in a yellow and black baseball cap over a green and black check suit while Gladys wore a brand new royal blue Adidas track suit with the letters 'GP' emblazoned in two inch white letters on her left breast. The questions were soon flying thick and fast across the marquee. Elton would rather nervously mumble a few words in answer to a question, then move on to the next. He seemed rather taken aback by the whole affair, and it was left to Gladys to draw on her vast experience of such gatherings, and she soon settled down and took control.

Obviously, the press wanted to know how a pop singer and an elderly woman could seriously expect to succeed running a small, down at heel club. One reporter in particular, a rather dishevelled individual from *The Daily Telegraph* continued to ask Gladys what made her think she had the qualities needed for such an ambitious enterprise. Gladys looked the reporter straight in the eye and asked him to come back in ten years and ask the same question then. Gladys did seem to get more and more annoyed at the patronising nature of many of the questions. Most of the reporters had next to no knowledge of the game, and simply assumed that Elton's involvement with Watford was nothing more than a passing fad. Gladys was looked on as merely an addition to the freak show.

Eventually, an American journalist from the *Boston Globe* overstepped the mark. He raised his hand and asked Gladys if, at her stage of life, it was a good idea to become involved with a fly by night crooner whose sexuality had been the centre of some debate in the U.S., and a decrepit, decaying football team who hadn't won a game for years.

Gladys took a sip of her mineral water, stood up, and made a short speech that has since gone down in football history. She told the reporter that she and Elton would find a bright young manager, and she promised that Watford would be a First Division club in less than ten years.

There was silence in the tent, then a few snorts of laughter. Soon the laughter grew to a crescendo, and within seconds the assembled pressmen were almost rolling in the aisles. Even the Japanese contingent, who hadn't really understood the gist of the statement were in fits.

Gladys stood silently, nodding to herself. Elton stood on the podium beside her and they waited for the mirth to subside. Eventually, the laughter stopped and the two friends stood in front of the now embarrassed band of journalists. Gladys politely thanked them for their time, then she and Elton swept from the tent back to Gladys' kitchen, leaving the pressmen to their cold buffet.

As the reporters stood together consuming white wine, vol au vents and sandwiches and gossipping over Gladys' amazing 'Ten Year' speech, Elton and Gladys discussed their next move. She apologised to Elton for losing her temper and making such a rash promise. After all, they had not even started to look for a manager, and now in the cold light of day, the promise to take Watford into the First Division seemed an impossible dream.

Perhaps the reporters had been right – maybe they had bitten off more than they could chew. Watford needed a manager to pull the players together, and they needed a manager soon. The new season was only a few weeks away, and time was not on their side. Elton and Gladys had inherited a team made up of bits and pieces players, men who had not made the grade elsewhere and had ended up at Vicarage Road because there was nowhere else to go. Gladys told Elton that the first thing they must do was to meet the players and find out just how much work needed to be done.

The next morning Elton picked Gladys up at eight and they drove the mile or so from Croxley Green to Vicarage Road. The stadium looked depressing in the early morning light. The stands had obviously not been painted for years and the wind blew litter over the almost bald pitch. The offices were empty, and many of the windows were broken. Some of the turnstiles were so rusty they would not turn. The two new owners found their way to the directors' offices and then to the Boardroom. The trophy cabinet was covered in thick dust, and apart from a small plastic cup engraved with the words 'Watford F.C. Runners-Up Pontins Five-a-Side, Bexhill 1970' it was empty. Suddenly the two friends realised just what they had let themselves in for.

Gladys and Elton sat in the boardroom and read the morning papers. The back pages were full of reports from the previous day's press conference. 'Elton's Folly' screamed *The Sun*, 'Ten Year Pipe Dream' read the *Daily Mirror*, while the serious press reported that even with Elton's millions and Gladys' knowledge of the game, the plan to have Watford in the First Division in thirty, never mind ten, years was surely not feasible.

Eventually, at around ten O'clock, the first of the office staff arrived for work. Some of the phones had been ringing, but no-one was at the club to answer them. A long haired youth walked into the boardroom carrying a bottle of milk and a box of teabags. He looked startled when he saw the room was occupied, and almost dropped his milk when he saw who the visitors were. He introduced himself as Ian Narrowhead and said that he was employed as Assistant Clerk in the club's ticket office. Ian was 16 years old, and had been working at the club since leaving school at Easter. Gladys asked if he would mind showing them around after he had done his duties in the ticket office. She presumed that there would be season ticket applications to deal with, but Ian laughed when she mentioned season tickets. He told her that he had sold just nine for the forthcoming season, and didn't expect to sell any more.

The dressing rooms were cold and damp with cracked tiles and a leaking roof, while the terraces were crumbling and beginning to be taken over by weeds. Many of the seats in the stands were broken, and there was litter from the final home game of the previous season – over eight weeks before – still scattered around the main stand. All in all, the ground was a complete shambles. Elton and Gladys had thought they would have to channel some money into maintenance of the ground, but neither of them had any idea quite how neglected the stadium had become.

Gladys asked Ian when the rest of the office staff started work, and he replied that the two other clerks usually turned in around noon, went off for lunch at 12.30, returned at about 4p.m. and left the ground at 4.30. Elton and Gladys were amazed that such a young lad should be left in charge of a football club. Ian went on to say that as he was the only one around, he had to deal with the transfer of a player, and actually managed to get £5,000 more for him than the manager had agreed!

When the two lead swinging office workers did eventually roll in, Gladys fired them on the spot.

That evening at a small Italian restaurant just a stone's throw from the ground Elton and Gladys, over a meal of whitebait, veal and spaghetti and a bottle of chilled Frascati, planned their next move.

The incumbent Watford manager was Mike Keen. He was an ex-player who had taken charge of the team by more chance than anything. The previous man had resigned, and with funds at the club running at such a low ebb there had been little possibility of tempting a new manager with new ideas to Watford. So Keen, who was one of the senior professionals on the books, had been given the job. His enthusiasm and dedication could not be questioned, but he had been unable to motivate a squad of players used to losing. The team were content to let things slide just as long as they could continue to pick up their pay packets at the end of the week. This attitude seemed to be rife throughout the whole club, from the tea-ladies and programme sellers right up to the older players.

With no money to spend, Keen had been unable to shuffle the pack, and couldn't even threaten to drop players who did not perform as they were all aware that there was no-one capable of replacing them. And so, with this situation, the club had slipped into the Fourth Division. As Gladys tucked into her veal she asked Elton who was going to tell Keen he was no longer required to manage the team. Elton thought long and hard, then told her that he felt it was up to him to break the news. It was never easy dismissing someone from their position, but Elton felt that it was best for all concerned if the sacking was carried out as soon as possible.

The team were due to start training for the new season in a week's time, and it was vital that they should find the new man by then. As they drank their Irish Coffees, a few names were mentioned. Elton thought that Bobby Moore or perhaps Geoff Hurst held the necessary credentials; they had experience and were sure to have the respect of the players, but Gladys disagreed. She told Elton that just because a player had had an illustrious career on the pitch didn't automatically mean they would be able to do the business from the manager's chair. The two tasks were totally different, in fact more often than not a player who had achieved great success found it difficult to deal with men who possessed less than their share of talent – they found it frustrating working with players who were unable to carry out their instructions.

A few more players who were coming to the end of their playing days were mentioned, then Gladys asked Elton if he was interested in going to watch a pre-season game the following night. Elton asked who they were going to watch play, and Gladys told him it was Lincoln City.

CHAPTER FOURTEEN: 'GET TAYLOR!'

The next morning, Elton rang Gladys to tell her he had heard there were severe traffic problems on the A1, so a drive up to Lincoln would be out of the question. Instead of travelling up to Sincil Bank in Elton's Rolls Royce, they would fly by helicopter.

The curtains in Gladys' road certainly twitched that afternoon as a bright yellow helicopter made a perfect landing in her back garden, and Elton dressed from head to foot in green tweed and wearing a huge orange Cossack hat and sunglasses made from red perspex dashed out from under the spinning blades to knock on her back door.

Gladys had never flown in such a craft before and was initially a little nervous, but after a few minutes in flight, the pilot, a tall moustached Texan named Hank, had made her feel totally at ease. Elton cracked open a bottle of Dom Perignon, and as they flew over the English countryside towards Lincoln, Gladys explained to Elton why they were travelling to watch Lincoln City play Boston United on a Tuesday evening in early August.

Gladys had been watching BBC Television's *Sportsnight With Coleman* a few weeks earlier when they had run a short feature on Lincoln's young manager. He had taken over in the hot seat at Sincil Bank at the surprisingly early age of 30 after having to retire from the game due to injuries. In a short time he had moulded Lincoln into one of the most entertaining and successful teams outside the First Division. There had been rumours of a number of top clubs approaching Lincoln in the hope of luring him away, but so far The Imps had been able to hang onto him. Something about the man's attitude and straight forward talking had made Gladys sit up and take notice, and she was keen for Elton to meet him and hear his views.

The name of that young manager was Graham Taylor.

Hank landed the helicopter on a patch of waste ground close to Lincoln's ground, and Gladys and Elton scurried over to the turnstiles with the other supporters. Although the game was only a pre-season friendly, around four thousand had turned out to watch the local derby. Under Taylor in his first season, Lincoln had won the Fourth Division Championship in impressive style, and last term had consolidated their position in Division Three.

As Gladys watched the Lincoln players go through their warm up routine she wondered whether an ambitious man like Taylor would really be interested in dropping down a division. The two Watford officials stood with the Lincoln fans behind one of the goals and watched with interest as the home side attacked incessantly throughout the first half. Lincoln had a tall centre-forward named Percy Freeman and his aerial power continually had the Boston defence in a panic. Gladys noted a number of the Lincoln moves down in a small exercise book, and was impressed with the work rate and high level of fitness of the players. The Imps scored twice in the first half, and in truth were a class above their non-league opponents.

During the interval Gladys treated Elton to a pie and a cup of Bovril, but they were unable to discuss the match in any detail as Elton was surrounded by local youths demanding autographs. In retrospect, Gladys thought that perhaps standing on the terrace in such an eye catching outfit was a mistake. The plan had been to attend the game in a more low key manner, but the helicopter landing and Elton's outlandish suit and hat had put paid to that.

News of Elton's presence at the game soon reached the ears of the Sincil Bank disc jockey and as the teams re-appeared for the second half he played *Daniel* at full volume.

Lincoln managed to score three more times to win 5-0, and as the players were applauded from the pitch *Saturday Nights Alright For Fighting* blared from the public address system.

As Elton and Gladys were leaving the terrace for their helicopter, a small ball-boy in a bright red tracksuit ran over to them and said that Lincoln's Chairman, Mr Dove, would like to have a word with them. The two Watford visitors were ushered into the oak panelled boardroom where an impromptu buffet was already in progress. Mr Dove had made a fortune in the meat pie trade and taken control of Lincoln City three years earlier. He had pumped money into the club, and been rewarded by Graham Taylor's astute management skills taking them to the verge of Division Two. He had a no-nonense attitude that appealed to Gladys, and she took an immediate liking to the man. Two paper plates piled high with chicken drumsticks and slices of cold meat were handed to the guests, and once again Elton was surrounded, this time by Directors' wives, all wanting autographs.

As Elton dealt with the pressures of being a world wide superstar, Mr Dove sidled up to Gladys and asked her how she thought Lincoln had played. She replied that the team looked a useful bet for promotion, and that she had also been impressed by the facilities as Sincil Bank. Gladys and Mr. Dove continued their small talk, discussing the weather, the price of meat pies and whether or not Boston United would ever gain League status. Eventually the Lincoln chairman asked Gladys if they could get down to business. He asked her if Elton wanted to speak to Graham Taylor. Gladys told him that if it was acceptable to him, yes they would.

They had come to Lincoln purely to see what kind of team Taylor had built, and had been impressed by what they saw. Elton was anxious that Watford should follow the correct procedures, and obviously that meant that they had to ask Mr Dove for permission to approach Taylor for the Watford job.

The Lincoln chairman told Gladys that Taylor was still under contract, and that he was tied to The Imps for another two years. With a glint in his eye he told Gladys that, obviously, Lincoln would do everything in their power to keep their manager, but if Watford were prepared to come up with an acceptable compensation package, then he would not stand in his way. Whether Taylor could be tempted to drop down a division – well, that remained to be seen. Mr Dove moved off to the other side of the boardroom to mingle with his other guests, and Gladys was joined by Elton who had now completed his autograph chores. Gladys related her conversation with the Lincoln chairman to him, and they were just about to tuck into a delicious looking lemon merinque pie when Taylor entered the room.

Graham Taylor had black collar length hair and an earnest, thoughtful face. He was dressed in the same tan leather jacket he had worn on the BBC Sportsnight programme that had first brought him to Gladys' attention. His busy, almost ferret like eyes scanned the Boardroom, and he immediately recognised the two visitors.

Taylor and Mr Dove were soon locked into a private conversation, and Gladys studied the other boardroom visitors, directors and their friends apart from one man who stood alone in a corner, quietly sipping a glass of white wine. Gladys had noticed the stranger watching her talk with Mr. Dove. He was a short stocky man in a dark blue suit, and was wearing a blue and white striped tie with a club crest. Gladys strained her eyes to try and make out the emblem, but from a distance she was unable to recognise it. The badge looked like a bird of some kind, but she could not be certain.

After ten minutes Mr. Dove and Graham Taylor walked over to Elton and Gladys and the four were formally introduced. Taylor had a firm, steady handshake and didn't seem the least bit uneasy meeting a household name like Elton John. Within a few minutes they were all talking football, and Gladys was flattered that Taylor was well versed on her feats in the game.

The Lincoln manager asked her what it had been like being in control of a World famous club like Real Madrid, and he was enthralled with her tales of the 1966 and 1970 World Cups. Elton told Taylor of his plans to build not just a team, but a *club* at Watford. He went on to say, that with his finances, Gladys' knowledge of the game and a bright young manager he was certain that Watford could make it into the First Division. Gladys was pleased that Taylor seemed to take the hopes of the Watford chairman seriously. On hearing that Elton wanted First Division football at Vicarage Road, Taylor had eagerly nodded in agreement, and not once questioned the wisdom of such a dream.

After twenty minutes of the conversation, Taylor told them that he must leave as he had promised to speak to another visitor. They all shook hands, and Elton asked Taylor if he would like to be a dinner guest at his house in Windsor one evening next week. Taylor agreed, and they made a date for the Tuesday.

Gladys was intrigued to see that the visitor Taylor was ushered over to meet by Mr. Dove, was in fact the man she had noticed earlier. Pretending to take a piece of Battenburg cake from the sweet trolley, she was able to get close enough tomake out the emblem on the mysterious strangers tie. The bird on the badge was a Throstle, the emblem of West Bromich Albion.

On the flight back to Watford, Gladys and Elton discussed their meeting with Graham Taylor. Elton said that he had a gut feeling that Taylor was their man, and Gladys agreed. She liked what she had seen, not only in the man himself, but in Lincoln's style of play.

Clearly, Mr. Dove was prepared to let Taylor go to the club who came up with the best offer of compensation. The only blot on the horizon was West Bromich Albion. West Brom were a First Division club, and were on the lookout for a new manager as their previous boss, Johnny Giles, had resigned claiming he had become disillusioned by the pressures of the present day game. Albion's Chairman was Bert Millichip, known in football circles as a man who got what he wanted.

Gladys wondered whether Taylor would be tempted by the salary on offer at The Hawthorns and the possibilities of working with such talented players as Cunningham, Brown, Robson and Regis. She felt that they had presented Watford's case as best they could and now they could do no more.

As the helicopter landed back in Gladys' garden, Elton asked her if she could arrange the menu for Tuesday night's dinner. If that went well, perhaps they could get Taylor to sign on the dotted line there and then and it would be all systems go. If Taylor turned them down, there was the possibility that Gladys would have to take charge of the first team until an alternative could be found.

Elton rang Gladys on Tuesday morning to say that Taylor had confirmed the dinner date, and would be arriving by train from Lincoln. He had not mentioned anything about his meeting with West Bromich Albion to Elton, so Gladys thought it was unlikely that Taylor would agree to the dinner if he had already pledged himself to The Hawthorns. Elton had arranged for a car to pick Gladys up at three in the afternoon to give her plenty of time to oversee the arrangements for dinner.

All seemed to be ready for a successful evening until Gladys opened her daily papers. The headline on the back page of *The Sun* read 'Taylor to be Albion Boss'. The story went on to say that the paper had 'exclusively' learnt that Graham Taylor was set to be officially named as the new manager of West Brom that evening. The Albion board had announced they were '99%' certain that Taylor would be their man. There was a small paragraph at the end of the article reporting that an attempt by a Fourth Division club to tempt Taylor was certain to fail, the paper noting that it was ridiculous to think of Taylor turning down a glamorous outfit like West Brom to manage a club in the Fourth Division.

Gladys arrived at Elton's imposing country house in Windsor and immediately began preparations for the evening's meal. Elton had given his cook, Maurice, the night off to leave Gladys in complete control. His butler, Chalmers, was on hand to deal with the tasks at table, while Betty the kitchen maid would help Gladys with the cooking. Gladys had decided on a traditional steak and kidney pudding with plenty of mashed potatoes, cabbage and gravy, followed by apple strudel and cream. Elton had wanted French cuisine with rich sauces, but Gladys had decided on a more homely English meal.

On Gladys' advice Elton wore a dark suit, a white shirt and his Watford FC tie while Gladys herself favoured her comfortable Watford tracksuit with a diamante brooch picturing the twin towers of Wembley Stadium to add a touch of glamour to the outfit. The two friends were understandably nervous as they waited for Stanley, Elton's chauffeur, to bring Taylor from Windsor station. The preparations were complete, the dining room was beautifully decorated with red, yellow and black silk flowers, and Elton's stereo played a Nina Simone L.P. to give the room an informal, cosy atmosphere.

Elton and Gladys had already discussed their tactics. Both felt it was important not to come over as too eager, but on the other hand to be as honest with Taylor as possible.

The Lincoln manager was aware that he was very much in demand. He had met with the West Bromwich board at the Birmingham Hilton the night before, and, according to the press reports, had been wined and dined until the small hours. There had also been speculation regarding the salary on offer to him at The Hawthorns. As a First Division club with average gates of 20,000 plus, Albion were able to put together a very attractive financial package, while Watford, despite Elton's considerable wealth, were still a Fourth Division outfit struggling with attendances of around 5,000.

Gladys had stressed that it was vital Watford were run on a solid financial basis. Just because Elton was able to pump millions of pounds into the club, it did not mean that he should do. Certainly, it was important for Elton to back the club with his resources, but for Watford to survive on a long term basis it was important that the club was able to generate as much money on its own as an ongoing business as soon as possible.

While Elton was changing the record on the stereo, there was a gentle knock on the door and Chalmers announced that their guest, Mr Taylor of Lincoln had arrived.

Taylor was all smiles as the three footballing colleagues warmly shook hands and politely discussed the news of the day. Chalmers was on hand to offer pre-dinner gin & tonics then left the diners to talk. Taylor thanked Elton for sending such a comfortable car to meet him, then he gallantly flattered Gladys on her lovely brooch.

Elton showed Taylor around his collection of souvenirs acquired from his many World tours, and his vast array of Gold and Silver discs. Taylor was particularly interested in Elton's huge yellow boots that he had worn in the film *Tommy*, and all three of them were in near hysterics as the man from Lincoln wobbled around the room in them. He confided to them that *Pinball Wizard* was in fact one of his favourite songs, and he often sang it to himself as he sat on the team bench.

Chalmers topped up their aperitifs, then mentioned to Elton that dinner was ready. They all followed the butler into the dining room, and Gladys was delighted to hear Taylor say that the meal smelt delicious. She was even more pleased when their guest confided that home made steak and kidney pudding was his favourite. On hearing this Gladys caught Elton's eye and gave him a playful wink, as if to say "We're on our way". Betty and Chalmers were quick, discreet and polite, and the steaming hot pudding was just as Gladys had planned it. Elton had brought up a couple of bottles of 1955 Chablis from his cellar to accompany the feast, and with a never ending supply of fresh crusty bread and butter, the meal was shaping up to be a great success.

Taylor accepted the offer a second helping of the pudding, and then asked Gladys if she would be offended if he unbuckled his belt to make room for the delicious fare. Gladys laughed and told him just to be himself, he was among friends. Eventually, there was an ominous silence at the table, and Gladys took the opportunity to raise he subject of the Watford vacancy. They had been immersed deep in small-talk for nearly two hours, and she felt it was the right time to bring the reason for the dinner out into the open.

Looking at Elton for approval she asked Taylor if he had enjoyed his night out with the West Bromwich directors. Taylor replied that he had, although not as half as much as he had tonight. Gladys took a deep breath and told him that she and Elton would like to offer him the job at Vicarage Road. She was about to go into details of the plans and schemes that had for the club when Taylor stopped her. She expected him to tell her that she had been wasting her breath, and that he had already signed a contract at The Hawthorns but instead he said one word. He said yes.

Elton immediately called for Chalmers, and sent him down to the cellar for Champagne, whereupon the three new partners drank a toast to the future.

Later in the evening, after yet another portion of steak and kidney pudding and the apple strudel, Taylor, Gladys and Elton sat in deep leather arm chairs in Elton's dimly lit study and sipped glasses of port while the two men puffed on huge Havanas. Taylor told them how he had made his decision to join a Fourth Division club. He said it was a gut feeling, then he burst into laughter as he told Gladys that, thanks to her, his gut was now twice as big as it was when he arrived!

Elton insisted that Taylor stay the night, so the next morning they could discuss the formalities of the contract. After the new Watford manager had telephoned his wife with the instruction to put their Lincoln home in the hands of an estate agent, Chalmers led him to the guest room.

Elton and Gladys had a last glass of port, and as they sat in front of a roaring fire, with Graham Taylor asleep upstairs, the two friends sensed that their dream to make Watford a great football club was really beginning to take shape. Gladys stayed in the guest room next to Graham Taylor's and slept like a log. She was awake at six, and after slipping into her tracksuit, set off on a three mile jog around Elton's estate.

The air was sweet, and the morning dew bright and cool as she covered the ground easily. From a distance, an onlooker would have guessed the runner to be in her late twenties rather than her twilight years. The developments of the previous night had made her brain buzz with activity, and as she ran she planned the next few years, her impressive pace quickening even more. By the time she arrived back at the house Elton was in the kitchen drinking fresh orange juice. He was dressed in a green and blue polka dot silk dressing gown and wore a purple top hat with the words 'Keep Rocking' written on it. He told Gladys that Taylor was still sound asleep upstairs, and he wanted confirmation that he hadn't dreamed that their visitor had indeed agreed to their offer. As Gladys walked to the shower room she told Elton not to worry. Taylor was a man of his word – once he had said he would do something, it was as good as done.

After Gladys had showered down and slipped into a clean tracksuit, she joined Elton for a light breakfast. Eventually, at nine o'clock, Graham Taylor came into the kitchen and asked for a paracetamol. Elton passed him a bottle of pain killers and a glass of orange juice. Gladys suddenly became a little concerned that perhaps Elton had been right. In the cold light of day Taylor would deny accepting their offer, and they would be back to where they started.

Taylor took two of the pills and drained his glass. He explained that he didn't normally drink so much, but as it had been a special occasion, he had felt it churlish not to enter into the spirit of things. He then walked up to Elton and shook his hand. Taylor had not shaken on the deal the previous night, and felt it was important that he did now. Gladys asked if they could get the formalities of signing over with immediately, and Taylor agreed. Gladys had drawn up a draft contract, and after a brief discussion over salary and bonuses Graham Taylor put pen to paper and consented to Gladys contacting Reuters to announce the news just as soon as he had telephoned West Bromich Albion to inform them of his decision. The call lasted under a minute. The West Brom chairman was obviously furious, but Taylor was diplomatic, polite but firm. He informed the Hawthorns' supremo that he had made his mind up – Watford were the club for him.

Within half an hour Elton's home was surrounded by press men eagerly awaiting more news of Graham Taylor's appointment as Watford manager. Chalmers informed Elton that the reporters were becoming impatient for an interview. The tabloids splashed the shock news across their back pages. *The Sun* ran the headline 'Taylor Chooses Elton's No-Hopers' while the *Daily Mirror* informed their readers that 'Taylor Stuns Albion'.

The overall opinion from the football experts was that Taylor had taken a great gamble by agreeing to take over at Vicarage Road. It was well known in football circles that Gladys Protheroe was a headstrong woman who did not suffer fools gladly, and despite Taylor's relative youth and inexperience, he had already gained a reputation for being his own man. The expectation was that the two would clash, leaving Elton to pick up the pieces. The truth of the matter was that Gladys had given her word to Elton that she would not attempt to meddle in team matters.

She was only too aware that if Taylor thought that she was continually looking over his shoulder, then he would react. She told Elton that she was always available if the new manager needed advice, but as far as she was concerned – Taylor was the boss.

CHAPTER FIFTEEN: 'ELTON JOHN'S TAYLOR MADE ARMY'

Graham Taylor's first task as the new manager of Watford was to take a look at the players he had inherited. Gladys arranged for the squad to assemble at Vicarage Road at 11a.m. on the Friday after Taylor's appointment. The meeting was to be an eye opener to Gladys as well as Taylor.

As the takeover and the change of management had taken place in the close season, Elton and Gladys had not had the opportunity to meet the Watford players. They had read the reports made by the previous manager, Mike Keen, and listened intently to young Ian Narrowhead's unbiased, objective views. Ian had told Gladys that as far as he was concerned the whole squad should be set free on a raft in the Atlantic Ocean, and Gladys was intrigued to see that he was only half joking.

Elton and Taylor arrived at Gladys' house at nine for a light working breakfast of orange juice and toast, and the three got down to the business of the day. Gladys had a Watford tracksuit ready for the newly appointed manager, and she had spent the previous evening sewing 'GT' in large white letters on the top. The three colleagues spent over an hour discussing the training techniques Taylor had used to great effect at Lincoln, and Gladys suggested trying out a libero instead of a flat back four.

Elton then drove them all down to Vicarage Road and parked in the directors' car park. Taylor and Gladys were surprised not to find any other cars at the ground, but assumed that the players had already arrived, and were changed and ready for their first day's training. Ian Narrowhead emerged from the players' tunnel, warmly greeted Graham Taylor and welcomed him to Watford.

Gladys asked Ian where the players were, and he replied that they never trained in the morning, and even then, the majority of them had to be pulled out of the public bar of the nearby Red Lion pub. The incredulous Taylor asked Ian if the letters informing the players that their new manager was to take the session had been posted, Ian replied that they had. Gladys was rightly furious. The squad had quite obviously cocked a snook at the new regime by their refusal to comply with simple instructions. Taylor was staggered that he should be met with such a rebellion, and asked Gladys what his next move should be.

Gladys suggested that Elton and Ian spend some time showing Taylor around Vicarage Road, while she would see what she could do regarding the playing staff.

Finding a pair of yellow and black Watford socks in the dressing room, she filled one of them with nuts and bolts that were spares for the club lawnmower, and put the heavy sock into the pocket of her tracksuit. Gladys strolled up to the Red Lion pub, from where, despite being over fifty yards away, she could hear *Radar Love* by Golden Earring blaring out from the juke-box. Even though it was barely half past eleven, the bar was packed with long haired denim clad young men, drinking heavily, and many smoking.

Gladys pushed the door open, and made her way to the bar where a skimpily dressed full-bosomed girl was French kissing the first team captain. The player broke off from the kiss, took a pull on a large reefer, downed a pint of Guinness in one gulp, let out a large belch, scratched his groin, and returned to his romantic duties.

Surveying the bar, Gladys recognised nearly all the drinkers as Watford players. There were a couple of small time drug pushers and a smartly dressed pimp haggling over a game of cards in the corner, but the rest of the clientele all seemed to be footballers and their assorted women-folk. Eventually a fat bearded Hells Angel in a once white string vest served Gladys with a Coke. The juke-box continued its distorted racket with a scratched copy of Deep Purple's *Smoke On The Water*. The noise was deafening, the smell of marijuana was overpowering, and still the Watford players continued to try and drink the pub dry.

Gladys sidled over to the jukebox, popped a ten pence piece into the machine and selected T5, *Your Song* by Elton John.

There was an immediate uproar from the drunken players as they searched for the intruder who had put the record on. There were cat-calls, boos and animal noises from the mob and Gladys had to nimbly duck as half a dozen empty bottles were thrown at the juke-box. She then pulled the plug from the machine, and there was complete silence in the bar. One by one the players began to recognise Gladys. Their dazed, drunken eyes managed to focus on her as she stood defiantly on a bar stool and demanded that they report for pre-season training immediately.

In court the following day, there were conflicting reports on how the melee started. The police arrived ten minutes after Gladys had made her demand to find every window in the pub smashed, seven Watford players needing hospital treatment and the juke-box smouldering. The barman had one of his ear lobes bitten clean off, a passing milk float had been completely destroyed and nine cars in the Red Lion car park had been severely damaged. Gladys herself had a deep cut over her left eye and her tracksuit bottoms had been badly torn, but she had been released from the casualty department of Watford General after having six stitches inserted.

The newspapers had a field day. *The Sun* printed a photograph of the wrecked Red Lion pub on their front page with the headline 'What A Start

For Taylor' and the *Mirror* had a picture of the burning milk float and the headline 'Elton's Mob On The Rampage'. Fortunately for Watford, the magistrates were as embarrassed as the club about the whole affair, and with the interests of the town at heart handed Gladys and the players only token fines for the incident. Elton John had already pledged to play a benefit concert for the community to make amends.

Elton made a statement to the press explaining that various outside influences had inflamed the situation, and although Watford accepted that their players and Gladys had indeed caused a great deal of damage, he hoped that the incident would soon be forgotten, and that the new management and officials at Watford F.C. would be allowed to get on with their work.

Privately, Elton and Taylor were pleased that Gladys had been able to sort out the trouble makers on the playing staff, and the day after the Magistrates Court appearances, Taylor announced that he was placing the entire first team squad on the transfer list.

With the season just a fortnight away the move was a bold one. Watford had already been contracted to play a friendly game at Vicarage Road against the Scottish side Falkirk, so Taylor and Gladys had just four days to get a team together to start the new era.

Fortunately, the inaugural meeting of the youth team was a calmer affair. Only the noise of a fracas in the corridor between Elton and a drunken first team player disturbed the discussions. Taylor and Gladys (who wore a bandage over her facial cut and sported a black eye) told the youngsters that they were the future of the club. They had been set a terrible example by their elders. Alcohol and soft drugs were not for athletes. They had seen what had happened to the previous first team, now it was up to them, if they were prepared to work hard and listen to advice, there was no reason why they could not become professional players.

After the meeting Elton, Taylor and Gladys discussed their plans. Whilst accepting that the Youth players were as keen as mustard, there was no way Taylor was prepared to pitch them in for the opening League game against Stockport County.

The friendly against Falkirk was the following Tuesday evening, and Taylor asked Gladys if she would be prepared to look after the management duties that night as he was planning to go on a scouting mission in an attempt to sign a few new players before the big kick-off. Gladys of course agreed.

So, for the first game of the Elton John era, it was Gladys Protheroe who sat on the bench directing tactics. The tough, wily Scotsmen were too much for the youthful Hornets however, and Falkirk ran out 3-1 winners. Young Luther Blissett picked up a nasty knee strain and limped off with ten minutes of the game still left. The biggest cheer of the night from the 5,000 crowd was for Gladys Protheroe as she ran onto the Vicarage Road turf once again wearing the No. 14 shirt. Watford had already used their two substitutes, but Falkirk boss Gordon Russell agreed to the extra player. In injury time Gladys had the Scots' goalkeeper scrambling to keep out a wicked, dipping volley that flew only inches wide.

Graham Taylor's spying mission had been a success, and during the next week he managed to cobble together a team made up of journeymen and youngsters to start the season with.

As the campaign got underway, it became obvious to Elton and Gladys that their decision to appoint Graham Taylor had been the right one. In a matter of months Taylor built a solid, professional squad and Gladys was delighted to be of help where and when she could. Occasionally, Taylor's lack of experience showed, and he would make the short journey to Gladys' office and ask advice on a particular team selection, a possible transfer or simply which tie to wear to an F.A. dinner.

Watford started to gain a reputation as an attacking, entertaining team. Attendances improved dramatically and a definite feeling of optimism prevailed at Vicarage Road. With this run of good results came more attention from the media.

The rather unorthodox set-up of Elton John the pop star millionaire chairman, Gladys Protheroe the elderly sportswoman and Graham Taylor a young, earnest, raw manager caught the public's imagination. The three were often featured on both ITV's *On The Ball* and BBC's *Football Focus*. Gladys accepted the offer of a weekly column in the *Daily Express* in which she examined the football topics of the day in detail, every Tuesday. There were a number of sketches on *The Two Ronnies, Morecambe and Wise* and *The Mike Yarwood Show* that made reference to the Vicarage Road hierarchy, and a record entitled *Watford's Three Wise Men* was made by a group called The Hornets and released for the Christmas market in 1978 although it did not make the charts. The game manufacturers, Waddingtons, unveiled plans for a board game based on the situation at Watford, but due to copyright difficulties regarding the Football League fixtures, the idea was eventually scrapped.

Graham Taylor became more and more confident dealing with the press and media, and Gladys was pleased to be able to stay in the shadows, dealing more and more with the administrative side of things at the club. By the end of Taylor's first season, Watford were on the verge of the championship race, but faltered in the run in, and missed out on promotion to Division Three.

But, in that extra twelve months, Taylor put things right, and the following season Watford took the Fourth Division Championship.

Young players like Luther Bissett made the breakthrough from the youth team. Taylor proved to be a shrewd dealer on the transfer market, plucking players from other clubs for small fees, and turning them into important members of his team. Success followed success, and Watford gained promotion for the second season running to make it back into Division Two for the first time in eight years. The added bonus of long lucrative runs in both the League and F.A. Cups meant that Elton was able to keep the bank manager happy as well as pumping more funds into the club to bolster the playing staff.

After a couple more seasons of consolidation in the Second Division, the unthinkable happened. In May 1982, Watford defeated Wrexham at Vicarage Road to gain promotion to Division One for the first time in their history. That night, long after the ecstatic Watford supporters had made their way home, Gladys, Elton and Graham Taylor sat on the empty Vicarage Road terrace with a bottle of Napoleon Brandy, and talked of their dreams and hopes for the future. Gladys reminded them of that press conference held in her garden when Watford were looked on as the laughing stock – but here they were, on the threshold of another chapter – the most exciting and ambitious yet, Division One, here we come!

The photographs in the press the following day showed Gladys being carried around Vicarage Road on Elton's shoulders, and one headline read 'Glad All Over'.

As Watford established themselves as a First Division force, Gladys spent more and more time seeking out young players from the local leagues who she thought one day could make a career in professional football. The list of players she unearthed is almost endless, but there was one youngster whose name stands out. He was a gawky, shy boy from Jamaica. His father was an Army Colonel, and the family had moved to the Watford area from the West Indies. The boy could do things with a football that Gladys had never seen before.

The name of that boy was John Barnes.

Gladys had been contacted by a Watford supporter who regularly watched sunday league football, and she was told that the boy Barnes was already creating an interest from a number of the big London clubs, and that unless Watford acted quickly, he would slip away. As it happened, Gladys was already aware of Barnes, as Ian Narrowhead, who had now risen through the ranks at Vicarage Road to become Gladys' personal assistant, had noticed the young Jamaican too. Ian's loyalty throughout the early days had been rewarded, and he had grown up to be an articulate, well-dressed businessman – a far cry from the long haired youth who had welcomed Gladys and Elton to Vicarage Road a few years before.

On a cold, wet Sunday morning in February 1981, Gladys, Ian and Elton set off to watch Barnes' team Sudbury Park play Askett Nurseries, a local works' side. Elton had taken Gladys' advice and worn a disguise that comprised a long, dark beard, a monocle a bobble hat and a huge brown duffle coat. The last thing they wanted was for other spectators to recognise them and tip off other club scouts that Watford were interested in the young star.

The three Watford colleagues took up their position behind one of the goals, and their attendance boosted the crowd to nearly twenty people. As Gladys opened her Thermos flask and passed Ian and Elton cups of steaming, sweet tea, the two teams trotted out onto the pitch.

Gladys immediately recognised the young Barnes. He was a strapping lad, obviously an athlete. As his team mates ran around to keep warm, Barnes – who Gladys noticed was wearing a pair of blue woollen gloves – performed breathtaking ball tricks, balancing the ball on the nape of his neck, then juggling it on his knees.

Elton remarked to Gladys that Barnes certainly seemed to have the skill to make it as a professional, but Gladys was more experienced in these matters, and told Elton to hold his horses. She told him that it was one thing to be able to perform party pieces on the training ground or in a pre-match warm up, but the test of real talent was whether or not Barnes could perform to such a level when there were a couple of beefy defenders snapping at his heels.

In later years, when Gladys recounted the opening minutes of that game, it is obvious that she felt that she witnessed the beginning of a great player's career. It took only a couple of minutes for Gladys to be convinced that there on the park pitch, was one of the most talented players of the era. Gladys nudged Elton, and whispered that it was time to get back to Vicarage Road. Elton and Ian assumed that she had seen enough, and therefore that they were all wasting their time. In truth, Gladys wanted to get back as soon as possible to obtain a signing-on form from Graham Taylor.

Gladys had noticed a couple of scouts from Arsenal and Tottenham amongst the sparse crowd, and she was keen to get Barnes' name on paper before the day was out.

Gladys drove Elton's Rolls Royce at breakneck speed through the Sunday morning traffic back to Vicarage Road. Fortunately, Graham Taylor was at his desk catching up on some paperwork. Gladys, Elton and Ian dashed into the office and breathlessly told Taylor that they needed a signing-on form, and quick.

Taylor was somewhat taken aback, not immediately recognising Elton in his disguise. He said later that he had feared he was the victim of a bloodthirsty gang of robbers – perhaps wanting to get hold of some season-tickets.

Taylor gave Gladys the form, and the three friends roared out of Vicarage Road with Elton's tyres squealing, and Graham Taylor scratching his head wondering what his assistant was up to now. Gladys sounded the horn and flashed the headlights to warn other drivers as they sped back to

Sudbury Court's ground.

Elton and Ian were in fits of laughter as Gladys threw the Rolls all over the road, weaving through cyclists and slow traffic and occasionally even mounting the pavement.

Unfortunately, Gladys' Grand Prix style driving was noticed by a police motorcyclist, and just as the three Watford officials rocketed through Harrow at 75mph Gladys noticed a blue light flashing in her rear view mirror. For a split second she was in two minds whether to put her foot down and try to shake the policeman off or to stop the car and try to explain their predicament. Thankfully she chose the latter.

It turned out that the policeman was P.C. Brian Seymour, a life long Watford supporter and a season ticket holder in the Rookery Terrace. P.C. Seymour recognised the driver and passengers of the Rolls Royce immediately, and although a little annoyed by Gladys' reckless driving, was keen to be of any help he could.

He explained to Gladys that due to an accident there was a monumental traffic jam between Harrow and Sudbury Park, and if they continued their journey in Elton's car, it could take up to an hour for the remainder of the trip. On hearing this news Elton, now without his beard, explained to the helpful officer just how important their mission was. Every minute was vital if they were to be successful in their attempt to sign a future star. P.C. Seymour's police training had taught him that in a situation like this, a quick decision was needed. He pulled out his spare crash helmet and lobbed it to Gladys. Elton pulled off his duffle coat and helped her slip into it while Gladys made certain she had the all important signing-on form with her. As P.C. Seymour gunned his huge motorcycle into life Ian pressed Elton's diamond studded Mont-Blanc fountain pen into her hand and wrapped an 'Up The Hornets' scarf around her neck. Gladys leapt onto the back of the machine, P.C. Seymour gave a thumbs up sign to Elton and Ian, and with a throaty roar and the siren wailing, he and his illustrious pillion passenger zoomed off down the Harrow Road.

P.C. Seymour expertly weaved through stationary traffic and jumped red lights, often running up onto the pavement and startling pedestrians on their Sunday morning strolls. Gladys hung on for dear life, her scarf trailing in the breeze and the crash helmet – a good few sizes too big – falling down over her eyes. The police patrolman looked at his watch and realised that unless he took a shortcut they would miss the end of the game, and with it the possibility of Watford signing a new player. He turned on his blue light, and shouted at Gladys to hold on tight.

The Harrow & District Allotment Society still talk about the Sunday morning a police motorcycle sped through their members' vegetable patches. Being winter, the allotments were not as busy as they would have been in Spring; however, the membership being a keen bunch, there were still nearly a dozen hardy gardeners digging and hoeing. They looked up from their toil to see P.C. Seymour and Gladys roar through at just under l00mph scattering canes, bean netting and potting compost in their wake. One of the gardeners, a sour old fellow and an Arsenal supporter, recognised Gladys as the passenger and immediately telephoned Graham Taylor to complain of his assistant's outrageous behaviour.

Three days later a lorry load of gardening equipment was delivered to the allotments courtesy of Watford Football Club as an apology for any inconvenience caused. There is also a yellow and black plaque in the Association's clubhouse celebrating their part in the career of one of the most skilful footballers of modern times. It is ironic that now nearly all the members of the Allotment Association claim to have been busy on their plots that morning.

If that had been the case, there would have been nearly 500 gardeners there. P.C. Seymour shot through the allotments, continuing his crosscountry course through a churchyard and a school playing field, then roaring across a rugby pitch as a match was taking place. Soon Gladys realised they were nearing Sudbury Park's tiny ground. She fumbled inside Elton's dufflecoat, and prepared the pen and signing-on form. At last the motorcycle overtook a milk float and a rag and bone cart, arriving at the ground as the players stood in the centre-circle enjoying their half-time oranges. Heads turned as the players and spectators heard the engine roar through the otherwise quiet Sunday morning. Gladys recognised Barnes and she tapped P.C. Seymour on the shoulder and pointed to their quarry. The Policeman slammed on his brakes and the bike skidded to a halt on the muddy pitch just as the young Barnes was about to treat himself to a third slice of orange.

Gladys still tells the story of the look on Barnes' face as she pulled off her crash helmet and handed him the form. She was obviously breathless from the breakneck ride, and at first Barnes thought she was a plain clothed officer handing him a summons. Eventually Gladys got her breath back, and was able to officially ask the player to sign for Watford. Barnes didn't need asking twice; he took Elton's pen, and using P.C. Seymour's back as a flat surface, he signed on the dotted line.

The new Watford player, Gladys and the Policeman started up a conversation, and were getting on like a house on fire until the referee blew his whistle and ordered the motorcycle to be removed from the pitch so the game could restart. Askett Nurseries, who incidentally went on to lose the game 2-0, actually reported Sudbury Park to the Middlesex Sunday League as they claimed the tracks made by P.C. Seymour's motorcycle made a part of the pitch totally unplayable, which was directly responsible for their defeat. Sudbury Park were fined £15 by the League for allowing unauthorised motor vehicles onto the playing area during the half-time interval. Gladys made certain that Watford settled the debt.

After the game, Gladys thanked P.C. Seymour for his invaluable assistance, and promised a VIP day out for him and his family as a reward. Elton and Ian eventually arrived after the final whistle and were of course delighted to hear that their mission had been a success, and that John Barnes was now officially a Watford player.

In just a few months as a professional, Barnes justified Gladys' faith in him, and convinced Graham Taylor that his assistant was still a very shrewd judge of young talent.

Gladys became Barnes' mentor at Vicarage Road, often taking him for one to one training sessions long after the other players had gone home. With her help Barnes learnt how to bend a free kick, how to make the best of his height and how to keep his hands really warm on cold afternoons. Being born and raised in the hot climate of Jamaica, plus the fact that he had poor blood circulation, meant that during the winter months his hands and feet froze, leaving them almost useless. Gladys knitted him a number of thermal socks and special heat retaining mittens that enabled Barnes to remain reasonably warm, and therefore perform to his usual high standards even when the temperature dipped below freezing. Barnes still wears his 'lucky' mittens in cold weather, and although he has had to take a lot of ribbing from supporters and fellow players alike, his performances in the snow and ice have justified his decision to continue wearing them.

Barnes' superb form for Watford soon attracted the attention of England manager Bobby Robson, and Gladys wasn't at all surprised when one evening the telephone rang, and Robson asked her for a dossier on the new Watford star. Gladys sent a factual report listing Barnes' attributes and his weaknesses, also suggesting to Robson that he should make the time to visit Vicarage Road and take a look at a couple of other Hornets who were taking the First Division by storm.

It took Bobby Robson only a few days before he contacted Gladys again and asked for a ticket to the next Watford home game. The match Robson attended was the visit of Sunderland, the Hornets stunning the football World by winning 8-0. Ironically, it was not Barnes, but Luther Blissett who caught the England manager's eye by scoring four goals. After the game, as Gladys, Graham Taylor, Elton John and Bobby Robson enjoyed a glass of wine in the directors' lounge, he confided to Gladys that he had decided to pick both Barnes and Blissett for the England squad.

Barnes soon established himself in the England set-up, but it was one particular goal that catapulted the young Jamaican into the role of a superstar. The F.A. had arranged for England to take part in a three match tour of South America, and Bobby Robson was concerned that some of the younger players would be intimidated by the vast, partisan crowds of Rio, Montevideo and Santiago. Robson was of course aware of Gladys' experience of international football and the respect in which she was held by the South Americans. So at Christmas 1983, Watford were officially approached by the FA for permission to invite Gladys to join the England tour in the capacity of Assistant Manager.

Watford were delighted to have not only John Barnes on the playing side, but Gladys Protheroe on the management team. As 1983 turned to 1984, Gladys could have no idea what the next few months held in store. Watford were by now established in the First Division, and Graham Taylor had been confident enough to accept a bid of £1,000,000 from A.C. Milan for Luther Blissett. The Watford manager had then stepped in to snap up a flame haired goalscorer from Partick Thistle, Maurice Johnston.

As Watford set off on the FA Cup trail with a tricky looking tie against local rivals Luton Town, Gladys received a telegram from Elton John. The Watford chairman had been away from Vicarage Road for a number of months, and had missed much of the 1983/84 season due to recording and performing commitments in Australia. The telegram was brief and mysterious. It simply read "Get to Sydney A.S.A.P. You're in team for big match stop. Elton stop".

Elton's manager John Reid telephoned her to say that a First Class British Airways ticket was ready and waiting at the VIP desk at Heathrow, and that the flight left in three hours. Gladys hurriedly packed a holdall, still in the dark about the reason for her mission.

The long flight to Australia gave Gladys an opportunity to catch up with some paperwork, and she enjoyed the in-flight film shows. As she travelled towards Sydney, Gladys wondered why Elton was so keen to have her with him. He must have been only too aware that it was mid-season back in England and although Graham Taylor had been very good in giving her permission to fly to Australia, she did feel awful leaving him at such a busy time.

When the Jumbo eventually touched down after a flight of nearly 24 hours, Gladys slipped on her Watford tracksuit top and walked with the other passengers to collect her luggage from the customs hall. As she queued at the passport desk, a baggage handler noticed her Watford badge, and shouted out across the crowded hall that she must be as surprised as a 'Wombat In A Joey's Pouch'. Gladys didn't understand the Aussie greeting, but waved and smiled, moving on to collect her bag.

Elton had sent a car for her, and the driver immediately recognised his passenger, carrying her luggage to a huge yellow Bentley. The driver's name was Mal, and after making sure Gladys was comfortable in the back seat, drove her through the Sydney rush hour traffic to Elton's hotel. As they drove along, Mal asked Gladys what the reaction to Renata had been back in England. Gladys didn't have a clue what the man was talking about, but presumed that 'Renata' was a new record by Elton, and not wanting to seem rude replied that everyone thought it was very nice. Mal burst out laughing, saying he suspected that was an under-statement. Gladys supposed this 'Renata' record must be quite a disc.

At The Sydney Hilton, John Reid was on hand to welcome Gladys, and tell her that they only had an hour and a half before the ceremony. Gladys grabbed Elton's manager by the arm, and asked him what the hell was going on. Reid was shocked to realise that Gladys knew nothing, and asked her to sit down. He then explained that Elton was getting married to his sound engineer Renata later that day and had been determined that Gladys was to be the The Matron of Honour. Gladys was staggered, and asked Reid if he would get her a large brandy.

Reid then told Gladys that the news had been released to the media while she was in the air from London to Sydney, and when she had eventually arrived, everyone had automatically assumed she knew. When Gladys recovered from the shock she asked Reid just what she was supposed to wear. Her Watford tracksuit was smart, but surely not the choice for the wedding of the year. Reid told her not to worry, Elton had picked a number of outfits for her, and they were ready and waiting in her suite.

After freshening up, Gladys took a look at the clothes Elton had selected for her, and was delighted to find that his taste was as impeccable as ever. Eventually she decided on a Chanel primrose yellow two piece suit over a white silk blouse and a red David Schilling hat. As Gladys was applying her make-up there was a gentle knock on the door, and in stepped Elton decked out in white from head to foot. The two old friends embraced, and there were a few tears as Elton told her of his whirlwind romance.

Gladys proudly walked to the limousines with Elton on her arm. There was a barrage of flashbulbs as the two Watford officials stood on the steps of the Sydney Hilton and waved to the assembled pressmen, then Mal signalled to them that it was time to get to the church.

The pavements were three and four deep with fans screaming and waving as the car pulled up outside St. Agnes' Church, and half a dozen burly Sydney cops had to help Elton and Gladys up the steps away from the happy throng. Once inside the Church, Gladys gave Elton's hand a little squeeze and pecked his cheek before taking her pew in the second row. After a few minutes, Elton's bride Renata arrived, and Gladys gave the dusky German sound engineer a warm smile as she walked up the aisle to join her husband-to-be.

The ceremony itself was beautiful, and Gladys had to reach for her handerkerchief more than once. On the steps afterwards, Gladys stood with Mr and Mrs Elton John and posed for the wedding photographs which were on the front pages of newspapers and magazines throughout the World within a matter of hours. The Spanish magazine *Hola!* featured a ten page spread of the wedding in its March 1984 edition under the headline 'Elton's Valentine Day Big Match'. The copy of the magazine holds a special place in Gladys' souvenirs, and she often flicks through the beautiful colour photographs, especially proud of the number that feature her smiling face. For most people, the name Gladys Protheroe conjures up an image of a track-suited sportswoman, and although that is how she would like to be seen, it is important to remember that at the end of the day, Gladys is a woman. And like any woman, there are times when she wants to be more than a hardworking athlete. The photographs from Elton's wedding really let the World see just why Ernest had lost his heart to that beautiful young girl all those years before.

Indeed, Gladys looked so glamorous at the wedding that a number of Australian gossip-journalists published articles in their tabloid papers claiming that it was in fact Gladys and not Renata who stole the show.

At the magnificent reception, Gladys was able to have ten minutes with Elton to discuss business matters before jetting back to Heathrow and Watford. Gladys embraced the newly-weds, and gave them their wedding gift of her Wembley Twin Towers brooch, leaving Elton to wonder if he would ever get the opportunity to wear it at the Stadium itself. On returning to Watford, Gladys passed on Elton's best wishes to all the players and backroom staff, and after her first training session on returning she brought out a huge box of Elton's wedding cake to go with the tea.

In her absence, Graham Taylor had started to worry about new signing Maurice Johnston. The player had the manner of a little boy lost, and Taylor had noticed that he seemed confused by the move from Scotland, so he asked Gladys if she would be kind enough to let Johnston lodge with her until he found his feet. Gladys agreed immediately.

To make Johnston feel at home Gladys brought out her old Rod Stewart LPs that the tartan singer had given her in Germany back in 1974, and for his first meal with her she cooked him a huge dish of Aberdeen Smokies and 'nips with a couple of cans of McEwans beer to wash it all down.

Gladys found Johnston to be shy, polite and God fearing. He had been at Gladys' house for just a few days before he asked where the nearest Roman Catholic church was. He told Gladys that he had not been to confession since his transfer to Watford, and he was keen to speak to a man of the cloth before his next appearance in Watford colours, so on the Friday evening before the home game with West Bromwich Albion Gladys gave him directions to St. Patrick's Church, with express instructions to be back home by 9pm as Graham Taylor was a strict believer in all players being in their beds by 10pm the night before a matchday.

Just after Johnston left for church Gladys telephoned Taylor to tell him that Johnston seemed to have settled in well, and that he had gone to cleanse his soul before facing the Baggies. Taylor was pleased with his new signing's religious beliefs, and mentioned to Gladys that perhaps it would rub off on some of the more ungodly members of the first team squad.

Gladys first started to become concerned at 9.30 when there was still no sign of Johnston. She pulled on her overcoat, popped on a Watford FC bobble hat and set off down to the Church to see if perhaps the confessions had gone into 'extra time'. But when Gladys arrived at St. Patrick's she found the church in darkness with all the doors locked. Fortunately she bumped into Father O'Malley who was out taking his dog for a walk. Gladys asked the priest if a young red haired Scotsman had arrived at the evening service, and the father confirmed that indeed he had, given his confession, then left at 8pm – nearly two hours earlier. Gladys set off home expecting Johnston to be waiting on her doorstep.

However, as she neared the Fox & Hounds pub Gladys clearly heard a Scots voice booming out rebel songs. She was certain that the singer was Watford's new inside forward, and on entering the saloon bar saw Johnston bellowing out a drunken chorus while surrounded by two young women who were likewise engaged in attempting to drink the pub dry. Gladys caught the eye of the barman and asked him how long this sing-song had been in progress. The barman replied that Johnston had come in around 8.30, had quickly downed four large malt whiskies and four pints of what the player called 'heavy'. Within half an hour he had become maudlin' and sentimental, and had bored many of the regulars with tales of his early days in Glasgow. As he was obviously carrying a full wallet, two local 'ladies of the night' had quickly befriended him, and Johnston had been buying them drinks for the last hour.

Gladys marched over to the drunken player, and in a school madamly way demanded that he left with her immediately. The player, through blurred eyes, recognised his landlady, and feebly attempted to make excuses as to why he was in the pub.

Gladys told him to be quiet and pick up his coat so they could walk home together. Johnston attempted to wrestle free from the grip of his escorts, but the two girls refused to let him go. They were both horribly drunk, and screamed that Johnston had promised them a Chinese takeaway, and then a night's dancing 'Up West'. The girls, Trudy and Tina, became abusive when they saw their meal ticket being taken from them, and they began wailing and screaming as Johnston was manhandled from the pub by Gladys and the barman.

Eventually, Gladys got the Scotsman onto the pavement, but Trudy and Tina were not giving up. The barman who was only too pleased to make sure the incident took place away from his premises ran back inside, bolted the door and left Gladys to it. Johnston tottered a few steps away from Gladys and was violently sick over a hedge into someone's garden. The girls, on seeing that there was no way Johnston was fit to continue the night's entertainment, vented their spite on Gladys accusing her of wanting the player for herself. They screamed that Gladys should be ashamed of herself, because she was old enough to be his grandmother. Gladys kept her self discipline and refused to be intimidated by the girls' vulgar goading. She simply picked the by now passed out Johnston up in a fireman's lift, brushed past Trudy and Tina, leaving them turning the night air blue with their curses and oaths, and walked as fast as she could back to her house.

On the way back home she heard and then felt Johnston continuing to be ill, and mentally pictured the disgusting state the back of her overcoat would be in. On arriving home, she threw Johnston on his bed, ran a cold bath, stripped the player naked, then after brewing up a huge pot of rich, black coffee, she lowered the drunken Scotsman into the bath. After ten minutes or so in the cold bath, Johnston opened his eyes and his teeth began to chatter. He was still unable to move, so Gladys picked him up, towel dried him then slipped him into his pyjamas before laying him on his bed. After three cups of coffee, Johnston began to mutter an apology, but Gladys cut him short, telling him to get some sleep. They would sort the matter out in the morning.

Gladys was woken at 7am by a gentle knocking on her bedroom door. She told the early riser to enter, and in came Maurice Johnston carrying a tray piled high with a delicious looking full English breakfast. He had showered and shaved, and in his Watford tracksuit looked every bit the young successful professional footballer – a far cry from the drunken reveller who had caused such a commotion the night before.

Johnston placed the tray on Gladys' bed then explained that he had made breakfast, washed Gladys' coat and posted a letter of apology through the letterbox of the Fox & Hounds, and all of this before 7a.m. He had also tried to find the garden in which he had been sick so he could clear up the vomit. On hearing this Gladys held her hand up and asked him to stop. The smell of the eggs and bacon was not doing anything to make his story any the more acceptable.

Gladys ate her breakfast while Johnston went on a short jog around Croxley Green to run off the previous night's excesses. She was in two minds what to do. Hopefully the player would have learned from his experience, and having got such a night out of his system, would be ready to buckle down. After a long think, she decided not to tell Graham Taylor about the player's outrageous behaviour. Her one worry was that news of the events in the pub would reach the Watford manager through the local grapevine.

After showering down and slipping into her matchday tracksuit, Gladys sat Maurice Johnston down in her kitchen and asked him for an explanation of his unruly behaviour. The player explained that he had gone to church, given his confession, then set off to return home, but had somehow taken the wrong turning and had ended up outside the Fox & Hounds. He had heard an old Glasgow song being sung, and decided it would be nice to nip in for a quick half to remind himself of his home city. Before he knew what was happening he had been joined by Trudy and Tina. The rest of the evening was just an alcoholic blur.

Gladys told him that she had decided not to take the matter any further, and she would not involve Graham Taylor. Gladys told Johnston that the Watford manager was a strict disciplinarian, and if he even heard a rumour that a player had been out drinking before a match day, then he would be on his way out of Vicarage Road in no time.

She recounted her experiences with George Best and the terrible situation with the players at Watford before Taylor took over. Johnston listened with an ashen face, staring at the floor. Finally, she told him that in her vast experience, football and drink simply didn't mix. It was up to the player. Johnston had the potential to go all the way to the top, but this was his one and only chance. If Gladys found that he was going to ignore her advice and continue with his merry-making, then she would have no alternative but to inform Graham Taylor. Johnston accepted her point of view, thanked Gladys for her frankness and for having faith in him. He apologised once more, and promised that it would never happen again.

Maurice Johnston stayed with Gladys for another three months, during which time his goalscoring exploits for Watford brought him to the attention of the Scotland management, and by the end of the season he had won his first full international caps. Eventually, Johnston bought himself a bachelor apartment in North London, and soon his wild nightlife became common knowledge. Gladys realised that there was very little she could do about the situation. The Watford management attempted to keep the young star away from the various parasitic elements that always surround young, wealthy sportsmen. Unfortunately, Johnston's head was turned, and although he served Watford well in the eighteen brief months he was at Vicarage Road, Gladys was left with a feeling of 'What Might Have Been'.

Eventually, Gladys and Graham Taylor realised that Johnston's off the pitch activities were having a detrimental effect on the other players in the team, so it was with great regret that Watford accepted a bid of £400,000 from Celtic in October 1984. But before Johnston headed back North to Scotland, he was instrumental in Watford achieving yet another first.

For on May 19th 1984, Graham Taylor led his Watford team out onto the Wembley pitch for the F.A. Cup final against Everton. Gladys, Taylor, Elton and Renata had a pre-match dinner on the Friday before the final at a small restaurant near to Wembley Stadium, and Gladys was delighted to see that Elton wore the Twin Towers brooch she had given him as a wedding present. As they toasted their players, and wished each other the best of luck for the following day, Elton reminded Gladys of how he wondered if he would ever get the chance to wear the brooch at the great old stadium. And tomorrow, only three months after receiving the gift – he would!

One of the most moving images of the afternoon, and a great reminder of just how amazing it was that little Watford were actually taking part in an F.A. Cup Final, was the sight of Elton John crying like a baby as the crowd sang *Abide With Me* before the kick-off. Gladys stood beside him for the singing of the traditional Cup Final hymn before taking her place with the players to be introduced to the Duchess of Kent after which she sat beside Graham Taylor on the Watford bench, the very same bench she sat on with Sir Alf Ramsey some 18 years before. Unfortunately, the Watford players were unable to do either themselves or Gladys, Elton and Taylor justice that afternoon. Gladys was up off the bench complaining to the referee when Everton's Andy Gray seemed to head the ball out of Hornets' goalkeeper Steve Sherwood's hands for the Toffeemen's first goal. But the goal stood, and when Graeme Sharp made it 2-0, Gladys knew deep down that there was to be no repeat of her success at Wembley back in July 1966.

Who can forget the scene when Graham Taylor sent Gladys up those famous 39 steps to collect her Runners-Up medal? Then she was with the Watford players as they ran to the end the Hornets supporters stood at, and as one they burst into a rousing chorus of *We're Gladys' Boys*.

Despite the defeat, the Watford officials were determined to commemorate the day with an after match dinner at The Savoy. Gladys sat on the top table flanked by Elton and Renata, and they discussed the events of the greatest day in Watford's history. The dancing went on until the small hours, and as the band finally packed up their instruments, Gladys and Elton sat alone at a table with a bottle of cognac as waiters stacked up chairs and swept the dance floor. Elton was contentedly puffing on a huge Havana cigar as they chatted about the old days, when Elton was a struggling pianist, of their days in America, their battles to establish Watford as a force in English football and of course their feelings and emotions on the amazing day that had just passed.

Suddenly Elton stood up and made his way over to the piano. He had a quick word with the band's pianist, then sat at the stool, flexed his fingers and played a beautiful, soulful version of *We're Gladys' Boys*. Instead of the raucous, sometimes beery version of the song that was known on the terraces the World over, Elton turned the piece into a tender, gentle ballad. By the end of the last chorus, tears were spilling down Gladys' cheeks. The staff and guests alike stopped in their tracks to hear a true superstar play a chilling tribute to one of the major influences in his life.

For a moment after Elton finished his performance you could hear a pin drop, then the dining room was filled with applause. Elton stood, took a bow, emptied his glass of cognac and gestured to Gladys to join him in his car home.

Gladys slept well that night, her head full of memories from such a special day. The Sunday papers published photographs of Taylor sending Gladys up the Wembley steps to receive her medal, and the reporters agreed that the gesture was certainly appreciated by football supporters the World over.

But as usual, Gladys didn't have long to rest on her laurels. The England squad were set to leave for their South American tour at the end of the week, and on the Sunday afternoon following the Cup Final Bobby Robson was on the telephone to confirm travel arrangements.

CHAPTER SIXTEEN: 'A PERIOD OF TRANSITION'

England's first game on their 1984 South American tour was a tough fixture against the powerful Brazilians at the World famous Maracana Stadium in Rio.

The reason for the trip was to acclimatise both players and management to the climate, facilities and playing styles of South America prior to the 1986 World Cup which was to be held in Mexico. As a veteran of the 1970 tournament, Gladys' presence on the tour was looked on as a trump card by the F.A. Gladys' last visit to South America had ended in despair and misery, but she had won a place in the Brazilians' hearts for her no-nonsense, sincere views on football, 'The Beautiful Game'. They had evidently not forgotten her, despite it being fourteen years since she had left Mexico branded as the scapegoat for England's defeat by West Germany. But all that seemed long, long ago as the flashguns once again popped for Gladys Protheroe. Due to injuries and club commitments, Robson had been unable to select a full strength squad, so there was an opportunity for some lesser known players to make an impression, and stake their claim for a place in the 1986 World Cup squad. Duxbury of Manchester United, Fenwick of Q.P.R. and Chamberlain of Stoke City along with Watford's John Barnes were all picked to play against Brazil for a game in which few experts gave England any chance.

The Brazilians, although in something of a transitional period, were unbeaten on home soil for nearly six years, and their manager, the wily Zito, had announced to the press that his team were ready to prove how insular and poor the English game had become. Robson had appeared for England in the 1962 World Cup in Chile, and had visited South America a few months before the tour to arrange hotels for the squad, so he was well aware of the pressures the media could place on the young, mainly inexperienced England team. Peter Shilton had been through the mill a few times, and he and Gladys enjoyed a pleasant supper one night while they reminisced over the extraordinary goings on in Bogota some fourteen years before when Shilton, then a young, raw goalkeeper went undercover to try to get to the bottom of the Bobby Moore bracelet affair. Now Shilton was the senior professional on the tour, and he was responsible for keeping a close eye on the younger players.

Once again Gladys' linguistic skills were invaluable as she calmly answered the scores of questions the Rio journalists fired at the England management at their first press conference. One question was particularly interesting: a writer from the daily football paper *Rio Gola* asked if it was true that England did not possess any star players these days. Gladys thought for a moment then replied that she felt young John Barnes would one day be a world class player, and who knows – perhaps he would show the crowd at the Maracana his skills.

The night before the game against Brazil, Bobby Robson and Gladys took charge of a training session under lights at the magnificent stadium in downtown Rio. The ground could hold up to 200,000 people, although the Brazilian officials had warned the England management that ticket sales for the game had been slow, and they expected a crowd of around 60,000 at the match.

That night, as often happens when a European team plays in Brazil, the England hotel was surrounded by a whole array of motor vehicles blowing their horns, with supporters letting off fireworks and blowing whistles from midnight until 5a.m. As she had done before on her trips to South America, Gladys handed out ear plugs to all the players before bedtime, and they slept peacefully, oblivious to the fact that the Rio supporters were determined to make the English feel as uncomfortable as possible.

Bobby Robson had decided to play an attacking formation with Woodcock of Arsenal, Hateley of Portsmouth, Chamberlain and Barnes in the forward line, the hope being that Hateley's aerial power would knock the Brazilians out of their stride, and his heading ability would bring the other forwards into the game.

Gladys walked around the dressing room before the kick-off ruffling heads, patting backsides and handing out chewing gum as the players waited for the buzzer to sound that would call them to mount the steep steps leading from the underground dressing rooms out into the white hot atmosphere of the playing area.

Gladys noted that Brazil were playing the skilful Roberto in midfield, and she had a quiet word with Ray Wilkins on the best way to shackle the Brazilians' forceful runs from the centre of the field. Then it was time for the players to take to the pitch, and Bobby Robson and Gladys knew they could do no more.

Brazil started the game as Robson had expected, piling on the pressure and forcing six corners within the first ten minutes. Shilton was in superb form, tipping over a wicked volley from Tato, then diving at the feet of the oncoming Milacaz as he was poised to shoot. Slowly though, England started to gain superiority in mid-field with Bryan Robson and Terry Fenwick in commanding form.

After about half an hours play, John Barnes picked up a pass from Ray Wilkins inside his own half, just in front of the England bench, but at first seemed to be uncertain what to do with the ball. When one watches the video tape, one can plainly see Gladys get up from her seat and shout

188

encouragement. Barnes skipped past a lunging tackle then continued his run out to the left wing. Gladys jumped from the dug-out and ran along the line urging her young prodigy to keep going. The England winger beat two more Brazilians, sweetly dropped one shoulder and sprinted into the penalty area. By now Gladys was almost on the pitch, screaming at Barnes to keep going, Barnes heeded Gladys' words and drew the Brazilian goalkeeper Costa off his line. The video shows Gladys bellowing at Barnes to shoot, which he eventually does, his effort skidding into the empty net. Gladys could not control herself, and ran onto the pitch to join in the celebrations of one of the finest goals ever scored by an England player. Her incursion onto the pitch did earn her a rebuke from the Mexican Referee, but as the game was a friendly, he did not resort to his yellow card.

The goal was shown all over the World, and on the strength of it Barnes suddenly became a very hot property. The video has been shown in bars and pubs from Rio to Ruislip, from Santiago to Southampton, and many fans agree that the solo effort was perhaps the most exhilarating piece of skill they had ever seen. Mark Hateley added a second goal for England early in the second half, and the team played magnificently to hang on for a marvellous victory. Then the fanatical Brazilian supporters stood to applaud the England team off the pitch at the final whistle. Bobby Robson and Gladys, both obviously delighted by the result, ran on the pitch to embrace their triumphant players. The two other games on the tour were, in all honesty, an anti-climax after the tension and glamour of Rio. England lost 2-0 to a muscular Uruguyan team in Montevideo, and were then held to a goalless draw with Chile in front of only 4,000 spectators in Santiago.

At the end of June England returned to Heathrow where the waiting reporters were keen to interview England's new star, John Barnes, to ask him about the rumour that he was set to leave homely Watford to join Italian giants Juventus. The Fiat backed club had been impressed by the now famous Rio goal, and were now ready to put a bid of £2,000,000 on the table. Barnes told the journalists that as far as he was concerned, his immediate future lay at Vicarage Road, and if they didn't believe him – then they should ask Gladys Protheroe. Gladys was wearing a Chile shirt given to her by their striker Venegas, who had seen her on stage with Bruce Springsteen in New York all those years ago when he was a teenage runaway living on the streets of that cruel city. Gladys simply told the press that Barnes was under contract at Vicarage Road for another two years at least, so Senor Annielli would have to wait.

After a brief holiday in a gite in the Dordogne, Gladys returned to Vicarage Road to begin preparations for the 1984/85 season. She assisted Graham Taylor in the re-signing of Luther Blissett from A.C. Milan after the player's unhappy season in Italy, then Gladys dealt with Maurice Johnston's transfer back to Scotland with Celtic. She has said since that arranging the Johnston deal was one of the saddest moments in her football career.

For the first time under Taylor's management Watford struggled, and it took 10 league games before the Hornets registered their first win, a 3-2 victory at Chelsea. There were even a number of letters in the local press calling for Taylor to be sacked, and for Gladys to take control of team affairs as Watford slumped to the foot of the table. However, Taylor did turn the team's fortunes around, and at the end of the season Watford finished a comfortable 11th.

The 1985/86 season found Watford continuing to establish themselves, but by the end of the campaign, Gladys couldn't help but notice that something at Vicarage Road seemed to be wrong. Due to his recording schedules, Elton John had been conspicuous by his absence, and it seemed that Graham Taylor was becoming frustrated by the lack of progress on and off the pitch.

There had been an orchestrated attempt by *The Sun* newspaper to discredit Elton by publishing outrageous stories about his private life. On top of that Gladys was aware that all was not well between Elton and Renata, and it seemed that the Watford Chairman was finding it difficult to find either the time or the energy for his football club.

Gladys flew out to Florida on Christmas Eve 1985 to spend the Festive season with Elton, and found her old friend in a very low frame of mind. The scandalous accusations made by *The Sun* had hurt Elton, and one night after dinner he broke down in Gladys' arms as they talked about the possibility of signing Tony Woodcock from Arsenal. Gladys held the sobbing pianist in her arms, and gently rocked him as one would do with an unhappy infant. The newspaper articles, marriage problems and the threat to his career posed by a possible malignant growth on his vocal chords had become almost too much for him, and Gladys was only too aware that Elton was 'on the edge'.

It was Christmas Eve, and Gladys was determined that Elton would be able to spend Christmas Day in a tranquil, loving atmosphere. She packed Elton's suitcases, rang to book two tickets on the next flight to Heathrow and called a taxi to take them to the airport. Twelve hours later Gladys and Elton sat in her little kitchen, considering what to eat for their Christmas lunch. The shops were shut, and all Gladys' freezer contained was a rather ancient Spotted Dick and half a loaf of bread. Fortunately, in the cupboard were a couple of tins of baked beans and a few eggs, so Gladys was able to whip up beans on toast a la Croxley Green. Gladys dug out a bottle of Cahors wine she had brought back from her holiday in the Dordogne, and the two friends enjoyed a hilarious Christmas lunch.

In later days, when Elton had successfully sued *The Sun* and settled his problems with Renata, he cited his Christmas with Gladys as the turning point in his personal crisis.

However, Gladys was still concerned about Graham Taylor's apparent frustration. Elton had given the go-ahead for a new stand to be built at Vicarage Road, a project that was to cost the club well over £2,000,000, but attendances had fallen off, and there seemed to be an air of complacency amongst supporters.

Despite Watford continuing to hold their own in the First Division, South West Hertfordshire was no hot bed of football support, and it seemed that the initial thrill of playing the big names was beginning to wear off. Gladys knew that Graham Taylor was an ambitious man, and she was concerned that perhaps he would see Elton's apparent lack of interest as a sign that it was time for him to move on.

In February 1986 Gladys arranged a clear-the-air meeting between the three main forces behind Watford's climb from Division Four to the pinnacle of English football. The meeting was to be held at Graham Taylor's house in Watford on a Sunday lunchtime. Gladys was the first to arrive on her newly acquired mountain bike. She took the opportunity to have a long chat with Taylor away from the pressures of Vicarage Road. She asked him if he was happy. He took a long time to reply, but eventually told Gladys that he needed to be needed. He had started to feel that Elton was taking him for granted, and, despite all the help and advice he got from Gladys, he felt that he couldn't continue to run both the team and the club without some input from Elton. Almost on cue, Elton rang the doorbell, and Taylor's loyal and dedicated wife Rita, let the bespectacled pop star in. After a little small talk, Rita informed the visitors that lunch was ready, and the three footballing friends strolled into the Taylor's dining room.

As Elton sat down for his starter, Taylor stood up and went to a cupboard, pulled out a bottle of Napoleon brandy, and plonked the bottle down in front of the startled Chairman. Taylor told the embarrassed Elton that drink was all he really wanted wasn't it? So why didn't he have a good old fashioned drink instead of the delicious meal Rita had cooked for them all.

Gladys didn't know where to look. She had been aware that Elton, like many creative types, enjoyed a drink – but she had no idea that alcohol had been a problem. She coughed, and excused herself saying that she needed to powder her nose, leaving the menfolk to sort out their disagreement. Gladys sat with Rita Taylor in the Taylor's kitchen as the chairman and manager of Watford Football Club almost came to blows. She could hear every word of the argument as the pair ranted and raved. At one stage Rita Taylor wanted to go in and calm them down as the sound of broken crockery was heard, but Gladys told her to sit down and let them get on with it.

Eventually, Elton walked out of the dining room, his shirt unbuttoned to the waist, his Panama hat askew. He thanked Rita for lunch, then told Gladys that he'd see her at Vicarage Road the next morning, before walking out of the front-door and into his Rolls-Royce. Gladys went in to see Graham Taylor, and asked him what had gone on between the two friends. Taylor replied that he felt the pressure of his recent problems was getting to Elton. The chairman had obviously put Watford to the back of his mind while he sorted out his personal problems, which was all well and good, but Taylor needed to know where he stood.

As Gladys cycled home after lunch, she realised that nothing lasted for ever, and wondered how much longer Graham Taylor would stay at Vicarage Road.

In fact, the Watford 'Dream Ticket' of Elton, Taylor and Protheroe were to stay together for just one more season.

In May 1987, Aston Villa's chairman, Doug Ellis approached Elton to ask permission to speak to Graham Taylor regarding the Villa Park job. Ellis later told the press that he expected to be turned down flat, but Elton told the Villa chairman to go-ahead.

This he did, and when Taylor asked Elton if he wanted him to stay at Vicarage Road, the Watford chairman replied that if he felt it was time to move on, then move on he must. On the 18th May 1987 Graham Taylor was appointed manager of Aston Villa.

Much of the business regarding Taylor's departure from Watford was dealt with by Elton John, and Gladys has often said that if the Watford Chairman had confided in her then Taylor would still be at Vicarage Road today.

24 hours after Taylor left for Aston Villa, Elton rang Gladys to tell her that he had appointed David Bassett as Watford's new manager. Gladys did not know a great deal about Bassett, only being aware that he had led Wimbledon from the depths of Division Four to the top six of the First Division. Gladys told Elton that she was pleased he had found a successor to Taylor so quickly, was there anything else he wanted to tell her. Elton fell silent, then in a melancholy, hoarse voice told her that one of Bassett's conditions of taking the job was to be able to bring in his own backroom staff.

Gladys stopped Elton there and then, and told him that she had some news for him. She had decided it was time for her to hang up her tracksuit; it had been a decision she had given a lot of thought to and perhaps this was the right time.

Once again Elton fell silent, then he thanked Gladys for all her help over the seasons, and told her he'd be in touch soon. There was no doubt in Gladys' mind that Elton had telephoned her to tell her she no longer had a future at Vicarage Road. In football, when a new man takes the helm at a club, it is not unusual for him to want to bring in his own regime. At Watford, it was clear that the shadows of Taylor and Protheroe would always fall on the man in the manager's chair, the same way as Busby, Revie and Shankly will forever haunt the men who follow them. David Bassett was his own man, and Gladys respected his wish to be able to do the job without any ties to the past.

So, on 1st June 1987 Watford F.C. issued the following press release; "Gladys Protheroe has announced that as from to-day she will no longer be associated with Watford Football Club on an official basis. She feels, at this time of her life, that she has contributed as much as one can reasonably expect from a petite woman. Gladys will of course, continue to support the club from the terraces, and sincerely hopes that new manager David Bassett will carry on the good work. Elton John and all at Vicarage Road would like to take this opportunity to thank Gladys Protheroe for all her hard work over the past years, and to inform her that there will always be a welcome for her at Watford Football Club."

There followed uproar in the local press with the letters page of the *Watford Observer* being swamped by irate fans demanding Gladys' reinstatement, and calls for her to be appointed manager and for Bassett to be given his cards. The national press picked up on the story, *The Sun* ran the headline 'Glad Quits Watford', while the *Daily Mirror's* back page shouted 'Elton Dumps Proth'.

There was talk of Watford supporters starting a petition and a sit down protest at the opening League game of the 1987/88 season, but fortunately Gladys appeared on Thames TV's *Sport At Six*, and in an in-depth interview with their football correspondent Graham Miller, Gladys told the Watford fans that she had indeed resigned, not been sacked, and she urged the supporters to get behind the new regime. This defused the volatile situation, and Watford calmed the whole affair by announcing that they would play a Testimonial game for Gladys at Vicarage Road, a game that eventually took place in September 1987 when a Watford Select XI beat Gladys' International XI 4-3 in front of nearly 18,000 supporters. Gladys amazed and delighted the fans by playing 20 minutes as a 'Libero'. The one major disappointment of the Testimonial game was George Best's failure to turn-up for the fixture. He had faithfully promised to play in the match, and indeed his thoughtlessness caused Gladys a great deal of embarrassment, although the star studded line up that included such World famous names as 'Bobby Moore, Peter Shilton, Osvaldo Ardiles, Denis Law, Bobby Charlton and many others delighted the huge crowd.

After the pulsating match Gladys was carried shoulder high by some of the most famous players in the modern game, and the packed terraces burst into *We're Gladys' Boys*.

To cap the evening, Michael Aspel, a film crew from ITV and that famous big red book turned up in the dressing room just as Gladys walked from the showers, and the First Lady of English Football, her team-mates and many hundreds of close friends and colleagues were whisked to ITV's studios on the South Bank to record a star spangled edition of *This Is Your Life*.

There were tributes from players, managers and officials from all four corners of the globe, as well as messages on video tape from Rod Stewart, Bruce Springsteen and Margaret Thatcher. At the dinner afterwards at Claridges, the tributes kept on until the wee small hours. Elton John took this opportunity to have a quiet talk with Gladys. The two old friends had not seen a great deal of each other since Elton appointed David Bassett as manager, and Elton felt it was the right time to set the record straight. He told Gladys that the pressure he had been under meant that he had been unable to give enough of his time to Watford and this had caused Graham Taylor to look elsewhere for a job. When the approach from Villa Park had been received, Elton had been in two minds but he felt that perhaps the time had come for a parting of the ways, and now Taylor had gone. He had hoped that David Bassett would want Gladys on his staff, but the new manager was adamant – he would only take the job if he could bring in his own men.

By now, Elton was in tears, and Gladys held him comfortingly and told him not to worry – she was no longer a young woman and the time had indeed come for her to take it easy.

To commemorate Gladys' Testimonial match, the *London Evening Standard* published a four page colour supplement tracing her career back to the days with the England Ladies team, right up to the present, and the day after her big match Gladys reported to Madame Tussauds where her wax work model was unveiled. To this day Gladys' model is one of the top ten attractions in the sports section.

So, in the Autumn of 1987, Gladys was away from the day to day rigours of professional football, and in an exclusive interview she gave to Steve Ryder on BBC's *Sportsnight* programme, she told the watching millions that it was unlikely that she would again be involved at the top level. Despite this statement, there had been numerous offers of management jobs from clubs at home and abroad – there had even been an inquiry from Greek club AEK Athens to see whether Gladys would be interested in a one year playing contract – and she was now 80 years of age!

Through Elton John's manager John Reid, Gladys was invited on a speaking tour of U.S. Universities, and in February 1988 she returned to the States for the first time since the Elton John tours, and addressed keen young students on how football had become so popular throughout the World, and why in her opinion, it would not be too long before the U.S.A. were chosen as hosts for the World Cup. Her manner was easy and cheerful, and Gladys' no-nonsense talks were an instant hit with the college graduates. Another plus point of the fifteen stop tour was that Gladys earned more in that month than she had done over the previous ten years with Watford!

While in the States, Gladys took the opportunity to meet up again with Bruce Springsteen and he persuaded her to contribute backing vocals on a number of tracks that later surfaced on the *Tunnel of Love* LP. Bruce did ask Gladys if she would consider going back on the road with him and The E Street Band for their 1989 World Tour, but after giving the matter some thought, she declined the offer.

By the time Gladys returned to Croxley Green in the Spring of 1988 David Bassett had resigned from the managers chair at Vicarage Road, and Watford were fighting a losing battle against relegation to Division Two.

Elton John had accepted responsibility for the rash decision in appointing Bassett as manager, and there was talk in the press that Gladys was set to be named as the new Watford boss. In fact, she was officially approached by Elton and the Watford board, but she declined the club's advances, telling them that her time had gone – now it was time for younger men.

CHAPTER SEVENTEEN: 'THE AUTUMN YEARS'

In quiet, reflective moments Gladys had planned the 90s to be the decade of rest and retirement. The First Lady of English Football, with perhaps only the Queen Mother and the late Brian Johnston as peers, has won a place in the nation's heart. Gladys has the ability to appeal to all generations, classes, colours and creeds. Two separate polls published in very different magazines prove the point perfectly. The November 1993 edition of *Tatler* carried a six page questionnaire asking its readers their thoughts on politics, health, sexual preferences and sporting matters. Only Princess Diana, Margaret Thatcher and Mother Theresa made more appearances in the poll. Gladys was voted 8th in the 'Next Prime Minister' category, 12th 'Best Dressed Woman in UK', 10th in 'Person You'd Most Like To Have Dinner With', and predictably was runaway winner of the 'Sporting Celebrity' section. The other side of the coin is that football fanzine *When saturday Comes*' 1993 Readers Poll voted Gladys Protheroe as England's Number One Soccer Personality. Her influence on younger supporters is clear when one browses through the latest fanzines. Watford's *Glad All Over* and Liverpool's *When Protheroe Played* are but two of the titles that take inspiration from her achievements.

Like millions of other supporters, Gladys watched the Italia '90 World Cup from the comfort of her armchair. One incident from that tournament brought home to the world's football fans how dearly Gladys is held in the hearts of everyone connected with the game. In the semi-final between England and West Germany in Turin on 4th July 1990, one moment caught by the television cameras and pressmen of the world proved this beyond doubt.

The young, talented English midfielder Paul Gascoigne was becoming more and more influential, and was on the verge of winning the game for England, so putting them just 90 minutes away from the title of World Champions. A sly piece of gamesmanship by the German, Brehme, stopped Gascoigne in his tracks and probably cost England the chance of victory. The videotape clearly shows Brehme walk up to Gascoigne and whisper something in his ear. Within seconds the England midfielder is in tears, in near uncontrollable hysterics. Gary Lineker and his other colleagues attempt to console the distraught Geordie, but he appears beyond help. Gascoigne's contribution to the game waned, England were unable to score that vital second goal and were, of course, eliminated from the tournament on penalties.

The question the English public asked was exactly what did Brehme say to cause such distress? The answer is that Brehme had told the naive Gascoigne that Gladys Protheroe had been knocked down and killed by a milkfloat in Watford. A cynical, scurrilous lie of course, but how was the 22 year old playmaker to know that?

When the truth became known England lodged an official complaint with FIFA, but by then the Germans were on their way to the final. The English press were up in arms at such a diabolical piece of skulduggery, and the unsavoury episode led to a boycott of German lagers at many English pubs, a move that severely hit the profits of many brewing companies including Holsten who, ironically, are sponsors of Gascoigne's then club, Tottenham.

So once again Gladys was involved in World Cup controversy, and this time all she was doing was sitting with her feet up and a warm drink watching the match on television two thousand miles away. Many pundits have since asked whether Pearce and Waddle would have missed those penalties if Gladys had been with the England squad in Italy. Her prowess from the spot is well known in soccer circles, and back home in the BBC studios Jimmy Hill and Terry Venables concurred that perhaps Bobby Robson had made an error by not including Protheroe in his squad.

With England out of the World Cup, Bobby Robson resigned as national manager. As always happens on such occasions, the media were constantly coming up with names of a successor. Gladys was delighted at the way her old partner Graham Taylor had revitalised Aston Villa and she was not at all surprised to see his name top of most lists. Taylor had kept in touch since his move to Villa Park, and Gladys had ventured up the M1 on a number of occasions to oversee training sessions or have a calming word with a troublesome player that Taylor felt unable to discipline.

On the evening of 13th July 1990 Gladys received a telephone call from Taylor. He excitedly told her that he had been offered the England job, and though he had decided to appoint Lawrie McMenemy as his full time assistant he would like Gladys to assist with training sessions and on match days.

Consequently on 12th September 1990 Gladys took her place once again on the team bench at Wembley stadium as England opened the Taylor era with a 1-0 win over her old adversaries from Hungary. As Gladys stood for the Hungarian anthem her mind drifted back some 37 years to the day her football management career was nearly ended by the nimble footed Magyars.

Gladys has frequently admitted that she was not the best footballer of her generation, nor the best manager or coach, but she was a trier. She persevered. She would not give up, and without those qualities there is little doubt that Gladys would not have stayed the pace. Then the band struck up *God Save The Queen* and out of the corner of her eye Gladys noticed Graham Taylor, his chest puffed out with pride, ready to start a new chapter in English football. As the new England manager roared out the words to the national anthem he turned to Gladys and gave her a boyish wink, acknowledging the fact that if it hadn't been for a crazy helicopter trip thirteen years earlier he might still be trying to make ends meet at Sincil Bank.

It seemed to Gladys that Taylor was a little too keen to stamp his own personality on the England team. Every manager wants to make sure that the players in the squad are *his* players, but Gladys has found that evolution, rather than revolution, is the way forward. She was disturbed to see that the once decisive Taylor would one day champion a particular player, then the next rubbish him. One such example was the unknown winger Kevin Booth, called up for the game against the Republic of Ireland in Dublin on 14th November 1990. The match was a vital European Championship qualifier; an England defeat might mean missing out on the finals in Sweden. Consequently many observers were staggered when Taylor named the 24 year old Booth in the squad, telling the press conference that he was an up and down winger who would test the Irish full-backs and he was 99% certain to play. Journalists scoured the Football League for background information on the promising winger, a number certain he played for Arsenal, others equally sure he turned out for Everton. In fact Kevin Booth was Graham Taylor's postman, and the new England manager had decided to pick him for the Irish match on the way he was able to outstrip his two nippy Jack Russell terriers on the daily dash down the Taylors' garden path. Gladys was all for innovative ideas, but she was perturbed that Taylor was prepared to throw in a complete novice like Booth at such a vital moment. Likewise Taylor's insistence on calling up Eric Cantona and Jean-Pierre Papin for the game against Turkey in Izmir.

However, Gladys was prepared to give her old ally the benefit of the doubt, believing that in time Taylor would decide once and for all on the players who would fly the flag in the European Championships and, more importantly, the World Cup. England managed to grind out the results to qualify for Sweden, though not without coming under heavy fire from the press. Many experts felt Jack Charlton's Republic of Ireland side were desperately unlucky not to win the group and qualify.

Before travelling to Sweden Gladys went into the recording studio to cut a version of *Mona Lisa And Mad Hatters* for the Elton John tribute album *Separate Rooms*. The idea for the album came from Elton's manager, John Reid, and featured Gladys along with stars such as Kate Bush, The Beach

Boys and Rod Stewart. Gladys recorded her song with Mike Joyce, Andy Rourke and Johnny Marr of The Smiths, a group who had been heavily influenced by Gladys' early recordings. *Q* magazine reported in their March 1992 issue, '*Separate Rooms* is a competent affair, but it is only when Gladys Protheroe breaks loose to give *Mona Lisa* a whole new interpretation does the project gain credibility. With Morrissey now embarked on a solo career I see no reason why The Smiths should not re-form with Protheroe at the helm.' The reviewer gave the album three stars.

The England party arrived in Sweden five days before the opening game against outsiders Denmark, who had only made it to the finals as a late replacement for war-torn Yugoslavia. Gladys had left selection of the squad to Taylor and McMenemy while she concentrated on helping Gary Lineker get his confidence back in front of goal. Lineker was to start the championships just one behind Bobby Charlton's record of 49 England goals, and with England due to play at least the three group matches the prolific Tottenham striker was odds-on to set a new benchmark while in Sweden.

Once again Gladys had to bite her lip when Taylor notified her of the squad. She was only too aware that injury had robbed England of Barnes, Gascoigne and Wright, but she did raise an eyebrow at the inclusion of such journeymen as Batty and Curle and Taylor's rather over-enthusiastic methods of selection had again proved troublesome: a provisional squad presented to the media had included the names of Ally McCoist and the Middlesex spinner Phil Tufnell.

It was during a light one-to-one training session with Lineker that Gladys first realised all was not well between England's premier goalscorer and the national manager. The once chirpy striker had become sullen and moody, and Gladys was astonished to see him, in a fit of anger, hurl a complete smorgasbord into the team hotel's swimming pool and punch an elderly cleaning woman in the stomach. Alone on the training pitch, Gladys broached the subject of Taylor's tactics and team selection. On hearing the manager's name Lineker flared his nostrils and his eyes began to swivel in their sockets. Gladys was terrified. Lineker ran wildly from the pitch towards nearby scrubland ranting that Taylor was Beelzebub the cloven-hoofed one. Gladys followed, shouting at him to calm down. When she caught up he was hiding under a bush, his head had turned through 180 degrees and his voice had become a throaty raw growl. Lineker told Gladys that Taylor had been sent by "Stan" to destroy him. When Gladys asked if he meant "Satan" Lineker told her that was what he had said.

It took half an hour for Lineker to recover sufficiently to return to the hotel. With Gladys' physiotherapy experience she was able to swivel the amiable striker's head round to the correct and his voice slowly returned to its normal, friendly Midlands burr. Gladys said nothing of the incident to

Taylor or McMenemy but decided to keep a close watch on developments.

England went into the Denmark game full of optimism. Taylor had told the English public to sit at home, open a beer and enjoy the game, and while Gladys was all for confidence in the team camp she was a little dismayed to hear the England manager tell the press that "Denmark are so full of bacon and piss-poor beer that we're going to kick their blond asses all over Malmo." The result was 0-0.

Three days later England lined up against the French, but again a patternless, indecisive display meant another goalless draw. The two major incidents from the game were Boli's unprovoked headbutt that felled Stuart Pearce and Gladys' left hook as the teams left the pitch which left the giant centre half needing five stitches in a head wound. Video clearly shows some kind of scuffle taking place in the players' tunnel and Boli falling to the ground holding his head. The press made more of Gladys' retribution than England's sterile performance. *The Sun's* back page headline read "Glad To Be English", while the *Daily Star* went with "Protheroe Hits Back."

After gaining just two points and failing to score, the final group game against host nation Sweden in Stockholm became an all or nothing affair. Taylor, McMenemy and Gladys sat at the back of the England coach on the trip from Malmo to Stockholm and discussed tactics. Once again, Taylor's indecision was obvious. He showed Gladys the team he felt would 'do the business' against Sweden, but she was dismayed to see 60s pop singer Billy J. kramer pencilled in as sweeper and Big Ted from Playschool on the left side of midfield. Gladys also began to doubt McMenemy's input. On the few occasions she had attempted to discuss forthcoming games with the giant ex-guardsman she had always found conversation turning to the 1976 FA Cup Final. It seemed obvious to Gladys that McMenemy resented her presence at the tournament.

In the dressing room before the game Gladys was able to have a few minutes alone with Gary Lineker. He seemed calmer now, but she was still concerned that the player was not himself. She was more worried when he showed her the contents of his kitbag. There was a bottle of holy water, a dozen crucifixes, six Gideon bibles - presumably taken from the hotel in Malmo - and a small voodoo doll dressed in a blue England tracksuit and sporting a pair of black framed spectacles. Gladys realised that as long as Lineker believed Taylor was the Anti-Christ he would not do himself justice on the pitch.

But after just three minutes of the game it did look as if everything was going to plan. David Platt scored England's first goal of the tournament, settling the players and management, and for the opening 45 minutes qualification for the semi-finals looked well within their grasp. However, within six minutes of the restart Sweden were level, and suddenly the tables were turned. The English defence was under siege as Brolin, Limpar and

Dahlin seemed to break through at will. Gladys noted Lineker getting more involved; he had two shots well saved by Ravelli and she felt it was only a matter of time before he got the vital goal. When Taylor shouted to substitute Alan Smith to start warming up Gladys presumed Tony Daley, the out of touch Aston Villa flyer, was the man to be replaced, but she was staggered when Taylor and McMenemy called Lineker off. Instead of joining the England party on the bench Lineker ran straight to the dressing room. England were now under the cosh, desperately keeping the Swedes out. The stadium was a cauldron of noise, the crowd aware that the game was there for the taking. Then, with eight minutes left, Brolin broke through England's static defence and slotted the ball past Woods for the winning goal. England were out.

Gladys reached the dressing room first, to be greeted by a scene which looked like something from an abbatoir. There was a slaughtered goat on the physio's table, headless chickens scattered among the tracksuits, a horse's head in the players' bath and Lineker's voodoo doll nailed to the wall with the legend, "666 Is The Number Of The Beast" scrawled in blood underneath. Lineker was nowhere to be seen.

Taylor told the disappointed players that a drunken local butcher had broken into the dressing room during the latter stages of the game, so they were all to get changed and showered at the hotel. On the journey back Gladys asked Taylor if he had been aware of the player's state of mind. The England manager told Gladys that he was not the devil, and that as far as he was concerned Lineker needed his backside kicking. The incident meant that Lineker ended his England career on a low note. Not only did he miss out on Bobby Charlton's goalscoring record, he was also presented with a cleaning bill of over 10,000 Swedish Kroner. Many cleaning experts felt that the sum was outrageous for merely clearing away a few animal carcasses and it was widely rumoured that Lineker's decision to take the Yen trail to Grampus Eight in the newly formed Japanese J League was directly connected to that Swedish cleaning fee.

The English press tore into Taylor, *The Sun* depicting him as a turnip, Gladys as a parsnip and McMenemy, oddly, as a slice of Black Forest gateau. Back home it was open season with not only the tabloids but *The Times* and *The Independent* calling for Taylor's head. Even *The Warcry* ran the headline "Bugger Off Taylor" across the front page of its September 1992 edition. But Taylor told Gladys he was determined to lead England to the 1994 World Cup in the United States. He was certain that a new crop of players such as Geoff Thomas, Dennis Wise, Andy gray and Vic Reeves would help England qualify, and within a few months the failure in Sweden would be forgotten.

In World Cup Qualifying Group Two England were drawn with Norway, Holland, Poland, Turkey and San Marino. The top two would go on to the USA, and during a light lunch at the Fox and Hounds Taylor, Gladys and McMenemy set about planning their tactics. In the aftermath of the Swedish debacle Gladys had appeared on BBC TV's *On The Line* debating tactics with presenter Ray Stubbs; she also won many plaudits from critics for her easy going style hosting Radio 5's phone-in show *6:06*. An indication of her influence on the younger age group was the news that Sega were set to launch a mega-drive computer game called "Glad-i-ator", an exciting explosion of state-of-the-art graphics and remarkable stereo sound that portrayed her sporting life.

As with the qualifying matches for the European Championships, England's early performances were uninspired. Taylor had, unsurprisingly, dispensed with Gary Lineker's services, goalscoring now being the responsibility of Wright of Arsenal, Shearer of Blackburn and David Platt. A 1-1 draw with Norway at Wembley was hardly the start the press wanted, although the situation began to improve after decisive victories against Turkey and San Marino.

During the early part of 1993 Gladys was approached by disc jockey John Peel who, with ex-Beatle George Harrison, wanted to remaster the Protheroe back catalogue and release a CD entitled 'An Evening With Gladys Protheroe'. Gladys gave her blessing, and with the aid of modern technology recordings that had been made decades before were given new life. Gladys was delighted to see that dance group KLG featuring Ragga Ruffa Ron made the top ten with an electro-rap version of *We're Gladys Boys*, appearing on *Top Of The Pops* in January 1993.

As far as Gladys was concerned 1993 was the year of World Cup qualification. She was looking forward to returning to the States and taking part in the greatest football competition on Earth. The first game of the year was the visit to Wembley of minnows San Marino. The FA had give a Channel 4 film crew from the documentary series *Cutting Edge* permission to film from behind the scenes, so Gladys, Taylor and Lawrie McMenemy were wired for sound during the game. The press seized the opportunity to highlight the bad language used on the England bench; all in all there were over 100 uses of the 'F' word, many coming from Gladys' lips. On one occasion her voice can be heard screaming "Get f*****g forward, Gascoigne you fat f*****g w****r!" Gladys was not surprised by the public outcry but she reminded the press that football was a man's game and occasionally, in the heat of the moment, all coaches used industrial language.

One moment before the kick-off will stay with Gladys forever. Hurrying to her place on the England bench she bumped into her old friend and ally, Bobby Moore. Moore was at Wembley to commentate for BBC Radio, and the two friends only had seconds to speak. They embraced and promised to meet again soon. Twelve days later Gladys attended the great man's funeral.

England managed a convincing 6-0 win over San Marino, following that up with a no frills 2-0 victory in Turkey. Slowly but surely, without really firing on all cylinders, it did look as if England were on their way to the United States. The home game against the powerful Dutch was next, and most experts came to the conclusion that if England could win this one qualification would follow. The surprise package had been Norway, who had set off, as Gladys put it, "like a rat up a drainpipe", winning four and drawing one of their opening five matches. Even at this early stage it looked as if the Norwegians had won the group, leaving just the runners-up spot to play for. After thirty minutes of the Dutch game the England supporters were checking the dollar exchange rate as goals by Barnes and Platt put the home side into a commanding position. But then the game turned sour: Gascoigne was carried off after a vicious challenge, then Bergkamp and Van Vossen scoring to give the Dutch a point.

Immediately after the rigorous domestic season ended England were to play two vital away games in the space of just four days, a situation Gladys found ludicrous. Many of the England squad were shattered, most carried injuries and she was disturbed to notice that the Arsenal pair of Adams and Wright had been playing so many games they continually wore football boots, even with dinner jackets.

Taylor had tinkered with tactics once again, and for the match against Poland in Chorzow he had even suggested playing the Crystal Palace goalkeeper Martyn on the left side of midfield. A goal from substitute Ian Wright won England a very fortunate point and the party flew off to Oslo with the criticism of the English press ringing in their ears.

The pre-match press conference in Norway was a bad-tempered, spiteful affair with many of the tabloid journalists goading Graham Taylor. Some, Gladys noticed, sat at the back of the room yawning and making obscene hand gestures every time one of the England management team answered a question. At one point she had to pull Lawrie McMenemy away from the *Hello* football correspondent, who had inadvisedly called the ex-Guardsman 'a big mincing Geordie queen.'

Gladys had been all for Graham Taylor taking a special interest in Paul Gascoigne, but she did feel that the England manager had now gone overboard with his pampering. Normally, before an international, only members of the squad were allowed in the dressing room, but Gladys was disappointed to discover a round-faced Geordie lad rejoicing in the name of Five Bellies eating a huge doner kebab in the players' bath. When questioned, he told Gladys he was "with Gazza" and was in charge of the midfielder's 'refuelling'. As if on cue, another lad sporting an unwashed T-shirt with the slogan 'I've got huge gonads' burst into the room with a crate of Newcastle Brown Ale and a chicken vindaloo.

Over the stadium p.a. just before the kick-off, the Norwegians played the infamous after-match remarks made by the TV commentator when their side beat England twelve years previous: "Winston Churchill, Lady Diana, Gladys Protheroe, Maggie Thatcher - your boys took one hell of a beating".

Gladys could hardly bear to watch as England were out-manoeuvred, out-thought and out-fought. The Norwegians scored either side of half time, and to be truthful could have gone on to win by a bigger margin. The abiding image of that disastrous evening that will stay with Gladys forever was the sight of Paul Gascoigne wolfing down a steak and kidney pudding as Norway took a corner.

Luton Airport was like a battlefield as the England party returned in the early hours. Angry supporters overturned cars and set them alight on the runway, effigies of Taylor, McMenemy and Protheroe burned in the dark and the players and officials had to walk a gauntlet of abuse as they were guided to their coach. Gladys was hit on the back by a half-eaten pastie and Taylor struck full on the face with a bag of dirty nappies. Taylor attempted to boost everybody's spirits by reminding them that the next match was a friendly against the United States and McMenemy advised the press to bring their pocket calculators - they'd need them to tot up England's goal tally!

Gladys didn't travel to the United States in the summer of 1993, deciding to stay at home and prepare for the final qualifying games. She did, however, find time to appear as a guest panelist on BBC TV's *Have I Got News For You*, and show that despite her advancing years she could still win the respect of a younger audience when she was interviewed by Terry Christian from Channel 4's youth-oriented show *The Word*.

Her other appearances were on ITV commenting on England's matches in the USA. Gladys sat between Aston Villa boss Ron Atkinson and the newly appointed Chelsea manager Glenn hoddle on the 'experts panel'. England, Brazil and germany had been invited to take part in a pre-World Cup tournament. Gladys sipped white wine in the green room of ITV Sport discussing international football matters and Hoddle's religious beliefs before being introduced to the nation's armchair fans as 'England's Premiership Lady'. Gladys has since described the ensuing 90 minutes as perhaps the most embarrassing of her football career. England were never at the races as the USA stormed to a 2-0 win. Memories of Belo Horizonte 40 years earlier - a result that indirectly led Gladys into international football - came flooding back. After the final whistle the TV studio received thousands of obscene telephone calls demanding to know what the so-called 'Premiership Lady' was going to do about Graham Taylor. Within half an hour an angry mob had gathered outside and a number of Molotov cocktails exploded in the executive car park.

The videotape of the after-match analysis shows Gladys to be initially calm and reasonable as Ron Atkinson and ITV anchorman Elton Welsby heap criticism on the England manager. With heavy sarcasm

Atkinson told the viewers, "Maybe at the Darby & Joan Club a performance like that is acceptable but to everyone in the real world it's obvious that Taylor couldn't run a bath." The Villa boss, warming to his theme, then described Watford as a 'hell-hole', Elton John as a 'four-eyed bald crooner', and anyone connected with the England set-up 'a washed-up, dried-up weirdo'. In a split second Gladys had Atkinson by the throat, then threw him from his leather armchair across the designer coffee table into a large rubber plant. Welsby attempted to calm his lady guest, but was quickly felled by a rabbit punch and a blow to the kidneys. Atkinson, now on his feet again, lumbered over to Gladys carrying a chair; she dipped one shoulder and punched the burly soccer expert twice in the solar plexus, sending him spinning into a cameraman. During all this time Hoddle sat rigid in his chair stroking his rosary beads.

"England Crash And So Does Big Ron", screamed *The Sun* next day. A colour photo of Atkinson being revived by a St. Johns Ambulanceman covered the whole front page. All the tabloids carried news of the amazing TV studio punch-up on the front pages, while both the BBC's *Kilroy* and ITV's *The Time, The Place* discussed the previous night's fracas. News of Gladys' actions reached the England squad in the USA, and many observers believe that they inspired the players to produce much improved performances against Brazil and Germany.

In late August 1993 Gladys was able to spend an afternoon with Graham Taylor when he was her guest at the recording of *Gladys Protheroe - Unplugged*. The acoustic show was taped for American music channel MTV, with a band made up of friends and colleagues from both the music and football worlds: Nigel Olsson and Tommy Smith sharing drum and percussion duties; Johnny Marr, Bruce Springsteen, Kevin Keegan and Luther Blissett on guitar; Sting and George Best on bass, while John Barnes, Morrissey, Elton John, Maurice Johnston and Talking Heads' David Byrne and Tina Weymouth sang backing vocals. The fruit of the day's labour was a magnificent set including all the highlights of Gladys' musical career. She was pleased to see that Taylor and his wife Rita both enjoyed the day and hoped that getting away from a football environment would show him that there was more to life than kicking a bag of leather round a field.

The future of English football now rested on two games, the visit of Poland and a tough looking fixture against the Dutch in Rotterdam. With Norway having qualified, it was a three horse race for the second spot. On 8th September 1993 England took on Poland at Wembley. As Gladys walked to the bench she smiled to the supporters, occasionally stopping to ruffle the hair of a young fan or sign an autograph or two. She looked up at the twin towers and wondered if this would be her last visit to the great stadium. There were three games remaining and by Gladys' reckoning they needed at least seven points to make it to the USA. If that target wasn't achieved it did not take a genius to predict that Graham Taylor's position would be in jeopardy and she felt it unlikely any new regime would want her on the payroll.

For 90 minutes the Poles barely got a kick as goals from Ferdinand, Pearce and gascoigne earned England a comfortable win. Taylor was in his element, patting players' backs and cracking bawdy jokes. Next day Gladys was pleased to see even the most critical of the tabloids had given England credit for a job well done, with Taylor, McMenemy and Protheroe earning some hard-won praise from Fleet Street. The one negative point from the game was that Gascoigne received a yellow card, his second of the series, rendering him ineligible for the trip to Rotterdam. But with spirits so high Gladys was convinced that England could overcome such a handicap.

Gladys was able to briefly escape the pressures of World Cup football by overseeing the editing of *Protheroe, A Footballer's Life - The Director's Cut.* Francis Ford Coppola and Martin Scorcese had been working on a film of Gladys' life in the game, and using Pathé newsreels, archive TV footage and a mountain of press cuttings put together a seven hour epic. With the help of a soundtrack by Ry Cooder and cameo roles by such international stars as Lauren Bacall, Marlon Brando, Al Pacino and 'Bobby' de Niro the feature film was acclaimed by critic Barry Norman, among others, who described it as, "Up there with Citizen Kane". Cooder reached number 6 in the US charts and the top ten in the UK with *Glad's Theme*, a haunting instrumental that closed the movie.

Gladys and the England squad arrived at Bisham Abbey in leafy Buckinghamshire during the first week of October 1993. All Premiership matches had been postponed so Graham Taylor was able to have his players together for nearly ten days. Gladys figured that a draw in Rotterdam might just be enough. The Dutch had to play their final game in Poland, while England's last match was against the group's whipping boys San Marino in Bologna. In training the players looked fit and confident, eager for the day of the game to arrive. Gladys was able to gauge the squad's enthusiasm when she took part in a practice match. She was marked by Arsenal's Tony Adams, who left her on her backside a couple of times with robust tackles. Gladys was pleased to see Graham Taylor relaxed and at ease with his players, joining in the horseplay and even allowing everyone a night out at the local pub.

England flew from Luton Airport on Monday 11th October. A hundred or so well-wishers were there to see them off, and Gladys particularly noticed a couple of fans holding up a huge banner which read 'Graham & Glad - It's Shit Or Bust'. Gladys whispered to midfielder Carlton Palmer that that about summed it up.

After two training sessions in the Rotterdam stadium Gladys and Taylor attended the obligatory press conference. Having been in the game for such a long time Gladys was sensitive to the 'vibe' of such gatherings, and as they took their seats on the podium Gladys held her hand over the microphone and confided to Taylor that she didn't like the mood of the media. The England manager told her to relax and assured her he could handle it. But like Christians in a Roman amphitheatre the two friends were ambushed by volley after volley of sarcastic, intimidating questions. The man from *The Sun* asked Taylor if it was true that he liked to wear women's clothing. *The Mirror* wanted to know when Gladys had last seen a man naked, and even the correspondent from *The Independent* stood on a table and shrieked that he thought Taylor and Protheroe were just "a pair of silly Watford poofdahs". Gladys told Taylor to take it in his stride but she could tell he was becoming more and more irate. Then a big-chinned hack from *Today* shouted out that he was worried about England's performance. Taylor told him not to worry, but instead of sitting down, egged on by his colleagues, the journalist turned on Gladys, asking if it wasn't about time a "silly old lady" retired from football and got on with pressing flowers. Wasn't she aware she was holding England back, she had lost the respect of the players and supporters and was turning the England team into a freak circus?

As he turned to milk the applause from his braying associates Gladys launched herself from the podium, leaping over three rows of seats onto the tubby media man's back. In a second he was in a headlock, pinned to a table, his shirt ripped, eyes blacked, after which Gladys hurled him through a plate glass window. The entire incident was captured by the filmcrew for *Cutting Edge*. The room went silent, except for the groaning of the beaten writer. Gladys strode back to the podium and asked if there were any more questions. There weren't.

Reports of Gladys' attack on the reporter made the front pages of all the major European newspapers. Back in the UK, *Today* ran a telephone poll inviting readers to think of a suitable punishment for Gladys. Three days later 'Being horse-whipped in the centre circle before the cup final' had been chosen by 68%. *The Sun*, however, took a different view. 'Glad Duffs Up Dreary Drip' screamed the front page, while in their editorial, '*The Sun Says*', the leader writer ranted that Gladys had shown that the English will always fight their corner. 'What do the Dutch know about battling?' *The Sun* asked, 'in the war, they fought for a Wednesday afternoon before packing it in.'

On the evening after the fateful press conference Gladys and Graham Taylor was ordered to appear before a kangaroo court held in FA Chief Executive Graham Kelly's hotel room. Kelly and fellow FA Committee member Peter Swales read Gladys the riot act, warning her that any more violent outbursts would result in her being sent home. Gladys responded by telling Swales to 'keep his hair on'. The Manchester City chairman glared at Gladys and asked her to explain this last remark, to which Gladys, with a straight face, replied that it was just a figure of speech.

Feyenoord's Rotterdam stadium was full to bursting, a sea of orange as the Dutch fans, inflamed by soft drugs and Grolsch beer, roared out their national anthem. Taylor, Gladys and McMenemy had given the England lads a thirty minute team talk, telling them to go out there and grasp the nettle. As Gladys took her place on the England bench she put her arm round Taylor and told him not to worry. She was ready to do the same to McMenemy, but he cut a solitary, strangely distant figure in a dark blue blazer and strangely coiffured hairstyle, so she gave him a thumbs-up sign instead.

The game kicked off in a cloud of orange smoke and the ear-splitting noise from hundreds of firecrackers. England settled quickly and were able to carve out a number of early chances. David Platt and Paul Merson looked lively, and the England bench were on their feet when an early strike hit the Dutch upright. That incident seemed to bring the home side to their senses and after half an hour Frank Rijkaard was unmarked as he apparently headed the Dutch ahead from a free kick. But England were given a reprieve as the linesman flagged that the Milan player was marginally offside. The half time whistle blew with the sides level, and in the dressing room Gladys and the suspended Paul Gascoigne made sure all the players had plenty of hot sweet tea and at least one slice of Gladys' home-made Dundee cake.

The Dutch piled on the pressure straight from the re-start, with Bergkamp looking particularly dangerous. But then, on the hour, a long ball from the England defence found Platt in space. The ex-Crewe man controlled the ball and set off towards the home goal. Just as he was about to fire in a shot Koeman, the Dutch defender, pulled the England player down and the German referee immediately pointed to the penalty spot. The England management and substitutes were on their feet. Gladys grabbed McMenemy by the waist and kissed him on both cheeks. "Off! Off! Off!" chanted the England supporters. Gladys ran to the section that housed the visiting supporters and punched the air. Not only were England to have a penalty but the fact that Koeman had clearly pulled Platt down in a goalscoring position meant the blond from Barcelona had to go.

Gladys remembers the next few moments as in slow motion. Herr Assenmacher signalled for a free kick and pulled out a yellow card. She had always prided herself on her reactions, but this time Taylor was simply too quick for her. Before she knew it the England manager was on the touchline brandishing a revolver. He fired three shots into the dark sky and was lining up Herr Assenmacher in his sights when a FIFA observer threw himself in front of the enraged boss. Gladys tried to wrestle the smoking pistol from him but he was still able to fire off five further rounds, one winging the Dutch striker Roy, another ricocheting off an advertising hoarding and hitting the photographer from *The Daily Telegraph* in the arm. Gladys and

McMenemy were eventually able to take the gun from Taylor and hand it to the linesman. She hoped that due to the pressure of the evening the referee would turn a blind eye to he incident, but he called Taylor over and lectured him for a full minute before showing a yellow card. The Dutch crowd behind the England bench felt that Taylor's actions should have earned him at least a red card, but as ITV's Brian Moore commented, "FIFA directives with regard to handguns are a little unclear... the referee has obviously given Taylor the benefit of the doubt."

Gladys and McMenemy led Taylor back to the bench, his right hand clearly scorched by gunpowder burns. In an attempt to relax the England manager physio Fred Street massaged Taylor's neck and fed him ginseng tablets and camomile tea. As Taylor lay flat on his back in the dugout Gladys assumed control of the team. She shouted to Merson and Shearer to step it up. On the video of the game she can be seen out near the touchline, fists clenched, teeth bared, urging on her boys in white shirts.

But the Dutch were on a high. Bergkamp, Overmars and Roy were finding more and more space and after a long period of pressure they won a free kick just outside the England penalty box. Gladys screamed at the England players to form a wall, and when she saw that it was the hard-hitting Ronald Koeman to take the kick she instructed her players to place their hands over their private parts. She was aware that most of the squad were keen on having more children, and the damage a thundering strike from the Barcelona player could do didn't bear thinking about.

Gladys was relieved to see the free kick strike the English wall and the ball cleared, but the referee blew to signal for the kick to be retaken. Herr Assenmacher made it clear that the England wall had encroached, a decision that enraged the visitors' bench. As Gladys stood in the dugout warning the defenders to keep their concentration Koeman stepped up and, instead of blasting it, chipped the ball over the wall, beyond Seaman and into the net.

The stadium erupted as firecrackers and smoke bombs exploded on the packed terraces. Graham Taylor was back on his feet. Gladys had never seen him in such a state. Suddenly the England manager ran from the dugout and disappeared down the players' tunnel. Gladys was anxious to know where Taylor had gone, but realised it was now up to her to inspire the England players.

Gladys was constantly up on her feet, urging the team on, trying vainly to be heard over the crowd. England were now fighting for their World Cup lives. Merson struck a free kick inches wide, and for a few moments it did look as if the Dutch defence was vulnerable. But against the run of play Bergkamp broke free and beat Seaman with a low, swerving shot. Gladys had been in the game long enough to know it was 'Goodnight Vienna'. The Dutch crowd were in ecstasy, singing, chanting and igniting all manner of pyrotechnics. Gladys was telling substitute Ian Wright where she wanted him to play when all of a sudden the stadium fell silent. Out of the tunnel had walked Graham Taylor. But instead of an England tracksuit Taylor wore a camouflaged flak jacket, leather trousers and mirror sunglasses. Most astonishing, however, was his hair. Taylor now sported a mohawk cut, and looked the spitting image of the character Travis Bickle from the film *Taxidriver*. Then, from under his jacket, Taylor pulled a .44 Magnum and began blasting off rounds in the general direction of the German referee. "You know we've been f*****g cheated, don't you?" he screamed. The referee, following FIFA rules, kept the game flowing as a tracksuited FIFA observer attempted to wrest the gigantic pistol from Taylor's grip. "Are you talking to me? Are you talking to me?" shouted Taylor as he was led to the England dugout by Lawrie McMenemy and Fred Street. The England players, obviously distracted by their manager's touchline gun play, were on their last legs. With a few minutes of the match remaining Taylor broke free and ran to the linesman. Gladys had given the pistol to reserve goalkeeper Chris Woods to look after, but she was still concerned that Taylor might exercise some kind of unarmed combat technique on the official. "F*****g well tell your f*****g mate he's f*****g well got me the f*****g sack you f*****", shouted the pressurised England boss.

Gladys has since said that after all her years in the game she had never looked forward to hearing a final whistle as much as that night in Rotterdam.

As expected, the English press erupted. 'Turnip Tries To Top Cheating Kraut', read *The Sun*'s front page, with a full colour photograph of Taylor, his face blackened with burnt cork and boot dubbin, firing into the ink black Dutch sky. *The Daily Mirror* lead with 'Night Of The Gun'. Both BBC TV's *Good Morning With Anne & Nick* and ITV's *This Morning With Richard and Judy* devoted their entire programmes to the previous night's events in Rotterdam. England's defeat meant that the chance of World Cup qualification had all but disappeared. On the flight home Gladys had, on the back of her boarding card, worked out that if Poland beat Holland and England won 8-0 or more against San Marino in the final games, England could still make it.

During the weeks between the Rotterdam debacle and the San Marino game Gladys tried to keep a low profile. The press had gone overboard with their attacks on the England management. On a trip to Croxley Green library she was dismayed to see the front page of *Gardening News* which, apart from a free plastic trowel, read 'Taylor and Protheroe - Why Don't You Piss Off!' It did seem as if only the most patriotic and optimistic supporters gave England a chance.

A week before the trip to Bologna Gladys invited Graham Taylor to her house for supper. She told the England manager she wanted to talk tactics, but in reality she wanted to boost his spirits. Unknown to Taylor she had contacted Elton John, who agreed to make it a threesome; and with her thoughts going back to the night Taylor agreed to manage Watford, Gladys cooked one of her famous steak and kidney puddings. As the three old friends sat in their armchairs contentedly puffing on Havana cigars and sipping vintage Port Gladys saw that, for the first time in many months, Graham Taylor looked at ease. As Gladys passed the Port Elton rose to his feet and asked permission to say a few words. The bespectacled pop star cleared his throat and began. He told his colleagues that, no matter what old Shanks had said, football was not more important than life and death. It was a game. Yes, a great game, but a game nonetheless. He went on: one of the reasons this old game is so great is that it brings together all sorts of people, from every walk of life, every colour and creed, from the back streets of Naples to the busy dual carriageways of Watford. He then asked Gladys and Taylor to raise their glasses. The toast was 'friendship'.

On the Saturday night before the San Marino game Gladys appeared on the BBC TV show *Tonight With Danny Baker*. Dressed in a Vivienne Westwood designed England tracksuit, Gladys confidently dealt with the chat-show host's digs at the England team and tied the bubbly media guru in knots with her witty ad-libs. At the end of the show Gladys joined fellow guest Robert Plant to perform a rocking version of *Trampled Underfoot* followed by a high octane rendition of *We're Gladys' Boys*, accompanied by the house band. After the programme Gladys, Plant, Baker and some of the production crew took a taxi to the Hard Rock Café, where they partied until the small hours.

On the flight out to Bologna Gladys sat next to the now fully fit Stuart Pearce. Pearce was a man of few words, but Gladys was able to strike up a conversation with the England captain. They spoke about Pearce's first club, Wealdstone, who had briefly shared Vicarage Road with Watford. As the England jet soared over the snow-capped Alps Pearce confided to Gladys that he had forgotten his boots. He told her that he didn't want to look a fool in front of his team-mates so he had decided to keep quiet and try to buy a new pair in Bologna. He asked if Gladys would accompany him on his shopping trip, and seeing the player was in a predicament she agreed.

At the pre-match press conference, as in Rotterdam, the English journalists set about Taylor and Gladys with relish. An exception was the man from *Today*, who took a seat at the back of the room, not asking a single question throughout. Just out of hospital, he was swathed in bandages and entered on crutches.

Self-styled football thinker Brian Glanville, a long-time anti-Taylor lobbyist, stood up, quoted Jean-Paul Sartre, Bertrand Russell, Kafka, Zola and, rather surprisingly, ex-Burnley favourite Peter Noble before performing a Dadaist free form mime. He told the assembled journalists that Taylor and

Protheroe were football infidels, soccer Philistines who had probably never even heard of Gunter Grass. After Glanville had finished his monologue Gladys took the microphone and replied by suggesting he should stick his head up his arse. An earnest youth in a U2 T-shirt claiming to be from *When Saturday Comes* asked if Gladys was aware that in a recent readers poll she and Taylor had been second only to Cilla Black in the 'Guy or Chick You'd Most Like To Give A Piece Of Your Mind To'. She replied that she was unaware of this honour but if he wanted some advice on how to get rid of his spots he should just ask. The young writer, realising he was way out of his depth, flushed deep red, stammered something incoherent and ran from the room.

Gladys had not forgotten her promise to Pearce, and as arranged they met in the lobby of the team hotel. She had made enquiries at the training ground, and discovered there was a small sports outfitters just ten minutes stroll from the hotel. The shop was run by a tubby, shifty-looking ex-AC Milan reserve by the name of Betiscolla. Gladys and Pearce inspected the footwear on offer, and after trying on a couple they plumped for a pair of size 9 Bazdas, not a brand Gladys had previously heard of. With Pearce's mind at rest Gladys was able to spend the afternoon before the match with the rest of the team. The theme of the training session was goals. Taylor had asked Gladys to work one-to-one with Arsenal's Ian Wright, a prolific scorer with the Gunners but yet to really settle at international level. Gladys asked Wright who he disliked more than anyone else on Earth. The Arsenal man thought for a moment, then mentioned that he had always despised the Belgian surrealist René Magritte. Within half an hour Gladys had obtained a number of Magritte prints from a nearby poster shop. One by one she placed them on an easel in the goalmouth and, with the help of Blackburn's Stuart Ripley, crossed balls for Wright to rifle into the paintings. Fired up by his hatred of Magritte Wright volleyed, bicycle kicked and headed goal after goal. After half an hour Wright was exhausted and the prints were a pummelled mass of bowler hats and clocks.

In the dressing room before the game Gladys flicked through the match programme. The San Marino team were made up of bus drivers, clerks, plumbers, computer hackers and rodeo riders,the usual mix of part-timers. But one name did catch her eye. Playing at no.7 was Betiscolla. That name rang a bell. She looked at the team picture and her blood ran cold. Just then the buzzer rang and Graham Taylor ushered his team out onto the pitch. As the teams stood stock still for the anthems Gladys tried to catch Stuart Pearce's eye. She had a dreadful feeling that his boots were not all they seemed.

San Marino kicked off and knocked a long ball into the England box. Pearce collected it easily, turned and attempted to play the ball back to David Seaman. Then suddenly his right boot burst into flames. The San

Marino striker Gallaterri nipped in and knocked the ball past the amazed Seaman to put San Marino one up.

The England bench fell silent as Betiscolla ran to the touchline, called Gladys' name and made a revolting hand gesture before collapsing with laughter. England had to win this game by eight clear goals and here they were, seventeen seconds in and a goal down. Taylor asked Gladys what the San Marino player had meant by his lewd actions and Gladys felt obliged to explain that she feared Pearce's boot had been sabotaged. Taylor went quiet, then suddenly stood up shrieking, "Do I not like that!" Pearce's boot was inspected by Fred Street, who promptly confirmed that some kind of incendiary device had been inserted into the toe-cap. The England captain's foot was placed in a fire bucket and a replacement pair of boots found from the kit bag. England eventually got over the shock of conceding a goal in such circumstances, finally winning the match 7-1, but in reality it was a hollow victory. The news of a Dutch win in Poland had reached the stadium, and as the final whistle blew, England were out.

A subdued squad flew back to Luton, Graham Taylor ashen faced and tight-lipped, the players aware that for many of them the opportunity of playing in a World Cup finals had gone for ever. Gladys had experienced the ultimate success, but for some of the squad USA 1994 was their one and only shot. Her heart went out to men like Ian Wright and Carlton Palmer, already in their late twenties. France 1998 was going to be too late.

Predictably the arrival lounge was a media circus. A band of anti-Taylor activists had painted 'Taylor Out' on the runway, and Gladys noticed a number of effigies burning in the night air as they left the plane. As Gladys, Taylor and McMenemy walked through a police cordon to the car park where Rita Taylor was waiting, a man, completely naked and painted green, ran towards them firing a starting pistol with one hand and spraying an aerosol with the other, getting to within a yard of the England management team before being manhandled away by security men. As he was dragged off he shouted, "Oi, Taylor, Lineker was right about you."

The incident with the naked demonstrator had obviously shaken Taylor. For him, in a career that had gone from success to success, this was the first taste of defeat, and he found it hard to accept. Strangely, the experience brought Gladys and McMenemy closer together. As two hardened professionals they had seen the other side of the coin, Gladys with her time as England manager in the 1950s, and the big ex-Guardsman while in charge at Roker Park, Sunderland. As Rita Taylor dropped McMenemy off at his Hampshire home Gladys helped with the luggage, then shook hands with the former Southampton boss. McMenemy looked down at Gladys and suddenly embraced her, lifting her off her feet with his power. He told her that they both knew, deep down, this was the end. With a tear in his eye he said that he had never been 100% convinced by some of her more radical tactics, but at the end of the day he took his busby off to her. Then, quietly, he made her promise one thing: that she would look after Graham Taylor. Gladys told him not to worry. She'd make sure the England manager kept his head. After another embrace McMenemy turned and made his way up the garden path. Just as he reached the front door Gladys shouted out that maybe, just maybe, McMenemy would find himself back at The Dell.

On the journey home with Rita at the wheel Gladys and Taylor talked about the future. The England boss was all for carrying on. He made a gung-ho speech saying that with the European Championships being held in England in 1996, the national team could win it. He went on to mention Keane, Kharine and Giggs, three youngsters who were already pencilled in for his next squad, not forgetting Eddie Izzard and Alan Partridge. Gladys saw a neon sign for a Happy Eater ahead and asked Rita to pull in and if she minded waiting for ten minutes while the two footballing colleagues had a private chat over coffee. At their table Taylor, his brow furrowed, looked at Gladys and asked her if it really was over. She took a sip of coffee, looked out of the window and whispered "Yes". It was. They had come to the end of the Yellow Brick Road.

One week later the FA had received the official resignations of Taylor, Protheroe and McMenemy.

In January 1994 Channel 4 screened their *Cutting Edge* programme *An Impossible Job* that documented the last weeks of Taylor's reign as England manager. The press made a great deal of the language used by Taylor and Protheroe, and a short time after the broadcast Gladys appeared on Channel 4's *A Right To Reply* where she faced a number of offended viewers including veteran campaigner Mary Whitehouse. At the end of the forty minute debate the two parties agreed to disagree, but not before Gladys had goaded Mrs. Whitehouse into using a number of oaths. After the recording Gladys shook hands with her adversaries, adding that, in the heat of the moment, it was easy for even the most righteous of folk to lose their cool.

On 16th January 1994 Gladys celebrated her 87th birthday. She had planned a quiet supper with her loyal housekeeper Mrs. Cornes. Cauliflower cheese had been mentioned. Now out of the limelight once more, Gladys spent the morning jogging around Croxley Green. After a shower and a sandwich she spent the afternoon in front of the television, enjoying *Today's The Day* hosted by Martin Lewis followed by Channel 4's *Countdown*. Gladys was especially interested in the latter as she had been approached to appear as a celebrity guest in the show's 'Dictionary Corner'.

As Gladys began thinking about the evening meal there was a knock on the door. She called Mrs. Cornes, but there was no reply. After popping the last Rich Tea biscuit into her mouth, she rose from the settee. Through the frosted glass she could just about make out a man in a hat and she hoped it wasn't that silly Jamiroquai. The man at the door was Elton John. At the end of the garden path was Elton's Daimler. Behind that was a silver double decker bus with 'Happy Birthday Gladys' glowing in neon lights. Elton told Gladys she had ten minutes to get on her glad rags - not a second more.

An hour later Gladys was sitting at a table in the Ritz with Elton at her right hand, Graham Taylor on her left. The bus had been packed with friends and colleagues from over the years. The seating plan at the Ritz looked like a Who's Who of world football and contemporary music: Astle, Best, Costello, Dury, Eusebio, Finney, Glass, Hall & Oates, Ince, Jordan, Knopfler, Lydon, Muller, Neeskens, Oakey, Prince, Quinn, Rivelino, Springsteen, Tiny Tim, Ure, Violet, Wright, X-Ray Spex, Yello and Zico to name just a few.

Gladys was delighted to see that Graham Taylor was in attendance, and after the two old friends had wowed the other guests with a gutsy display of jiving to a number of Buddy Holly tracks Gladys confided to Taylor that she thought he looked years younger since resigning from the England post. Melvyn Bragg and a film crew from *The South Bank Show* wandered from table to table asking each guest how Gladys had influenced their life.

When the diners had finished their port and cheese and waiters were making sure every table had at least one bottle of Napoleon brandy Elton John got up to say a few words. He told the guests that they all knew why they were there: to honour one of football's greats. He went on to say how delighted he was that so many household names had made it to the dinner, some travelling many thousands of miles. Then, with a hushed voice, he mentioned that, unfortunately, some of Gladys' great friends were absent. On cue, a curtain behind him opened and a giant video screen flickered into life. The diners were suddenly transported back to 1966. There, hoisted onto his team-mates' shoulders, was Bobby Moore. Held proudly in his right hand, the Jules Rimet Trophy. In slow motion Moore jumped down and ran to embrace Gladys. The dining room was filled with the sound of grown men weeping.

Then in true *This Is Your Life* style a burst of flamenco erupted from the p.a. and from behind the screen strode ex-Real Madrid chairman Senor Juan Gomez. Now an old man himself, he had sold his stake in Real and operated the Spanish Fantasy Football League. After him came Bernie Crabtree and the Hospital team led by Jimmy Wilson, no longer the boy football fan but a wealthy scrap metal dealer. Gladys hugged and kissed each friend from the past. Still they came, Puskas, Di Stefano, Pele, Bernie Taupin and the others. Ian Narrowhead, now a Watford director, bounced out from behind the screen and threw Gladys in the air. The parade continued for nearly an hour, each surprise guest being greeted by raucous applause from the now well-refreshed diners. Eventually Elton came to the last guest. Out stepped Sir Alf Ramsey. He walked up to Gladys, looked into her eyes, then took her into his arms. The flashbulbs popped and TV cameras whirred as for the first time since July 1970 the two people responsible for the greatest days in English football were re-united. Sir Alf whispered to Gladys that it was all he could do to stop Elton forcing him to appear out of a huge pink cake!

After dabbing her eyes, catching her breath and taking a sip of mineral water Gladys took the microphone. She thanked Elton for arranging such a fantastic night and giving her the opportunity to meet up again with so many friends. Then in a quieter voice she read a telemessage from Old Trafford. It was short and to the point: 'Enjoy the night. Sorry, can't make it. Matt'.

When the full English breakfast was served at 7 a.m. not one guest had left and the manager of the Ritz had to send out for extra cognac, port, Budweiser and pork scratchings. Gladys had spent the night catching up with news from former colleagues; laughing uncontrollably with old Bernie Crabtree as they talked of the Hospital's great cup run all those years ago, talking with Bruce Springsteen on how much modern rock music owed to the recently departed Frank Zappa and chatting knowledgeably with Premiership boss Rick Parry. As Gladys strolled from table to table, shaking hands here, signing menus there, she came upon a group she had yet to meet. A tall latin gentleman stood and clicked his feet before introducing himself and his party. His name was Gianluca Picca, and he was from Verona.

Over 60 years earlier, Gianluca's grandfather had been the chairman of Verona. The 1930s had been the club's greatest era, however, and these days Verona were a mid-table Serie B side. The club was still controlled by the Picca family, and as Gladys was introduced to the other Italian guests Gianluca confided that these days he would pay many millions of lira for a modern day 'Whippet'. Gladys met the club coach, the three directors and the club captain before being introduced to a frail gentleman resplendent in club blazer and light grey trousers. Gianluca named him as Luigi Baggiani, the only member of the 1931 side still alive. Senor Baggiani held Gladys' hand between his, then kissed her passionately on both cheeks. He told her that although Ernest had only played briefly the supporters still remembered him. The Verona fanzine was called *Il Whippetto* and the more excitable fans were known as 'Ernie's Ultras'. Gladys sat with the men from Verona for nearly an hour, and before they left for Heathrow she promised to visit Italy later in 1994 to open the club's new family terrace. As Gianluca walked to the door he turned and pressed a small gift into Gladys' hand. It was a silver medal, engraved 'Verona 1932 - Ernest Protheroe' and set into the centre, a tiny photograph of Gladys' husband nutmegging a Napoli defender.

At noon the party began to break up and Gladys stood at the door to thank everyone for attending. Elton, Graham Taylor, Bernie Taupin and Keith Floyd accompanied Gladys back to her home in Croxley Green where over sweet tea and biscuits the old friends chatted about the future. Elton and Bernie were set to fly to Los Angeles to take part in an AIDS benefit concert. Floyd was preparing a new BBC TV show, *Floyd On Football*, in which he would travel the world examining the various hot snacks on offer to supporters. Graham Taylor had taken Gladys' advice and not rushed back into football. But, her guests wanted to know, what of Gladys? She had been linked to the vacancies at Everton and Liverpool, rumoured to be involved with Francis Lee's takeover at Manchester City and even to be 'Madame La Grande' to buy out Bernard Tapie at Olympique Marseille. The newspapers had been full of speculation regarding who would assist the newly appointed England coach, Terry Venables, although on BBC TV's *Grandstand* transmitted on 12th January 1994 Gladys told viewers that she thought Venables managed teams the same way he wrote books and to her mind *They Used To Play On Grass* was a crock of shit.

Eventually, after all promising to meet up again soon, Gladys was left in her house alone. She was tired, suddenly, very tired. After a mug of hot chocolate and a glance at the evening paper she decided to have an early night. As she lay in bed listening to Radio 4 a shiver ran down her spine. The news bulletin reported that Sir Matt Busby had passed away. The game had lost another great. Five minutes later the telephone rang. It was George Best. Arrangements had to be made for Sir Matt's funeral. Throughout the night Gladys was in demand from the world's media, all wanting a few memories to publish.

At 3 a.m., her duties fulfiled, Gladys took the phone off the hook. as she lay in bed she placed her hand under her pillow and brought out the silver medal Gianluca Picca had given her. She looked at the handsome winger with the ball at his feet. A tear filled her eye. "Goodnight, Ernest my love", and in the dark she clearly heard, "Sleep tight my pet, sleep tight."

THE END

Football Appearances

Gladys Protheroe

Hertfordshire Ladies	184 appearances	12 goals
England Ladies	64 bonnets	6 goals
War-Time Combined Services XI	6 appearances	1 goal
Watford	28 appearances	1 goal
Liverpool	1 appearance	0 goals

Alf Simpson

Burslem Port Vale	90 appearances	3 goals
Leicester Fosse	33 appearances	1 goal
Watford	84 appearances	1 goal

Ernest Protheroe

Charlton Athletic	74 appearances	22 goals
Watford	38 appearances	17 goals
Verona	2 appearances	1 goal

Discography

We Can Do It (Pye) - Released March 1965. Highest chart placing:16

Back Home (Pye)   with England World Cup Squad- Released June 1970. Highest chart placing: 1

Honky Cat Live Version (DJM) with Elton John - Released July 1974. Highest chart placing:18

Born To Run Live Version (UA) with Bruce Springsteen - Released September 1978. Unreleased in UK. USA Highest chart placing: 3

You're Gladys' Boy (YYY) Bobby Moore tribute - Released March 1993. Highest chart placing: 9

Compilation: *An Evening With Gladys Protheroe.* CD boxed set containing all recorded material 1966-1994. To be released Autumn 1994.

Records by other artists

We're Gladys' Boys (Decca) - The Terrace Boys, June 1970. Highest chart placing: 18
Watford's 3 Wise Men (ALB) - The Hornets, December 1978. No chart placing.
We're Gladys Boys '90 (Factory) - New Order, July 1990. Highest chart placing: 4
We're Gladys' Boys Techno Mix (Rave Rekordz) - KLG featuring Ragga Ruffian

Ron, December 1993. Highest chart placing: 8

Glad's Theme (Warners) - Ry Cooder, November 1993. Highest chart placing 10; USA placing: 6